The Accessible Pet, Equine and Livestock Herbal

Choosing Abundant Wellness for Your Creatures

By Katherine A. Drovdahl MH CR DipHIr CEIT

Published by Katherine A. Drovdahl

Stacy MacGregor ♡

may you + yours
always be
abundantly
Blessed ♡
♡ Katherine +
turtle ♡

Disclaimer

Please note that the information in this book has not been evaluated or approved by the FDA. Nor do I or this book attempt to diagnose, treat, cure, or prevent any disease. The information contained within is simply an offering of historical and traditional approaches on the time honored use of herbs and other alternative methods with creatures in order to help them feel and look better. At no time does the author, the publisher, Fir Meadow LLC, The School of Natural Healing, Dr. Christopher's or any heirs, family members or agents take any responsibility for your or others use of any information in this book. This book does not replace the care or supervision of a veterinarian or other medical practitioner. Please do not hesitate to contact a veterinarian or other medical practitioner if you would like their assistance for any health care need, emergency, or to make use of their diagnosing skills.

Dedication

This book is first dedicated to my Lord Jesus Christ, who is THE Master Herbalist, having created these wonderful plants with their properties and these creatures for our use and enjoyment. I also want to dedicate this book to my loving husband, Jerry, without whose continual love and support this book or way of life would have not been made possible. To my mom, Margarethe, who has always been a delightful encourager, a wonderful mom, and wonderful friend- even though she, as does my husband, knows all of my flaws! Also to my loving grandmother now residing in Heaven, Omi or Kaethe, whom I have been named after and in whose herbal steps I follow. I love all of you dearly.

A big huge thank-you to Kristie Miller for her editing work and to Taunya Molnar & Laurie Dodge for indexing.

A big huge thank-you to our friends and acquaintances who have prayed for us and this book project. We feel extremely blessed!

"Be diligent to know the state of your flocks, and attend to your herds; for riches are not forever, nor does a crown endure to all generations. When the hay is removed, and the tender grass shows itself, and the herbs of the mountains are gathered in, the lambs will provide your clothing, and the goats the price of a field; you shall have enough goats' milk for your food, for the food of your household, and the nourishment of your maidservants."

Proverbs 27:23-27 NKJV

Forward

From my early days my fascination with both animals and plants has never ceased. One of my earlier memories, at three or four years old, is of me being intrigued by the rose kissed apple blossoms and asking my dad what they were. I used to spend hours pouring over books on animals of all types and especially farmstock and poultry. Hours and years spent exploring the woods and meadows and mountains on my sunlit palomino pony, and then later with my blood bay Arab gelding. Surveying and pondering trees, plants, and shrubs, and wondering what all of them were for. Beauty, of course. But there was more to it than that. There had to be. Planted deep within my soul there was a knowing that there was more.

My grandfather on my dad's side, a colorful character, was a trapper and hunter by trade. E. Boone knew his native plant identifications and animals, and he would quiz me on them often. I did not even realize how much I learned from him on gardening, until I started thinking back on his garden by the old chicken house.

My grandparents "Omi" and "Opa" came to visit for several summers during my childhood. Both speaking only German, I could not really converse with them much, but still I gleaned treasure from them. Watching them lovingly nurture the garden and our home orchard and observing my grandmother, who had been a nurse in the earlier 1900's in Germany. Her culture is still a world leader in herb and alternative use as they never left their herbs. She would gather herbs and dry them, make tinctures and teas all the while humming German folksongs and hymns. We used to think it was different, but now I do the same things!

From what I know now from holistic iridology; hobbies, passions and memory can go generational through DNA. You see it all the time- children with parents' or grandparents' talents or likes or habits. A person's keen heartfelt interest in the land of their ancestors even if they have not been there is another glimpse into this observation. Sometimes we say it's 'in the blood'. So here I am.

Really dabbling with herbs began in my 20's. In fact, my flower beds often contained more herbs than flowers (and they still do!) Over the years we also owned horses, chickens, ducks, a butcher lamb, a few pigs and steers, an iguana and other miscellaneous lizards, farm cats, and livestock guardian dogs. In my 30's I obtained dairy goats, and they temporarily displaced my 30 years of horse ownership. It's amazing how they can do that! We began breeding show and milking stock (LaManchas and Toggenburgs), having been blessed with nice milk records, linear appraisal scores and show records. In early 2011 we have added horses back in, going with my husband's Norwegian heritage with the 4000 year old breed of Norwegian Fjord Horses. You can always visit our website if you want to take a peek at the gents and ladies.

A few years back I was granted (by God I believe) an opportunity to fulfill a dream I have always had for formal herbal education. I am very thankful to have my M.H. (Master Herbalist) in conjunction with a master's degree in herbology, and love every day of its usefulness for us and others. International certification in aromatherapy (essential oils use), state certification in Reflexology, and Holistic Iridology for humans and iridology for creatures have further rounded out my alternative education and I really feel blessed to have each of these tools for the benefit of man and creature kind. Of course, one never stops learning when truly passionate about what they do, so additional reading, training, research and courses keep me on my toes.

My wish for you, the reader, is that this book would contain some nugget that will make a difference in your day, and that you will be truly blessed as I have been in the use of these God given plants. If that happens, then this project has fulfilled its purpose.

May you and yours be fully blessed,

Kat

Contents

9

Part One- Herbal Basics, Whys, and How To's

Welcome to the world of herbs! In this part I lay a foundation for you so that you will eventually become more comfortable with practical herbalism, not just theory and hopefully at some point you will be able to make many decisions on your own because you have some understanding of WHY you are doing what you are doing! I also walk us through some Life Cycle Herbalism and some special circumstances as you've seen from the chapter titles. Don't forget to glance through the appendix to learn about additional recommended reading and resources that may be of interest to you. Let our journey begin!

Chapter One- Herbal Foundations

Any of you that have listened to me at a speaking engagement know that you don't get to just learn about what one herb is and how I might use it. I really feel you will be much more adept in your usage of herbs if you have some "Herbal 101" under you.

Why One Ought to Consider Using Herbs

There are MANY reasons why I like to use herbs, and at the risk of missing some, I'm going to give you several on my list sprinkled in with more foundations. I do want to clarify here that when I am talking about herbs, I am talking about plants that are NOT: poisonous, toxic, or habit forming. There are so many herbs (thousands and thousands) that stay out of those categories. I lean pretty heavily on Hippocrates "Do no harm" clause. I wish more of our health care industry did the same.

Adverse effects

Should a creature experience an allergy or other reaction to the herb, once the herb clears the system (just hours) the reaction is GONE. Not to belittle an adverse effect. Synthetics/medications can cause adverse effects that cause serious permanent damage.   Because a person or creature, due to their personal toxicity levels and collection of synthetics within the body, could be allergic to any substance or plant found on this planet, one can play it safe with a very small dosage of an herb and monitor for two hours before increasing its use. This is especially true if you have recognized a reaction before in your herd, flock, kennel or in family members to your creatures. Always be absolutely sure of the identity and purity of your plant before using it if you are harvesting it yourself.

Alteratives

Alteratives are sometimes known by the term 'tonics', but I prefer to call them alteratives as it explains better what it is that they do.   Alteratives are herbs that want to nourish the body in a way that it will want to return it's out of balance organ, tissue, or structure back into balance over time, rather than control something in the body or block a symptom like synthetics (medications) do. For example, if a thyroid is overactive or underactive, it is not going to change the herbs I use as I'm not controlling the body, but nourishing it so it can make its own repair.   Watch for alteratives and work some into your creature's diet for supplements.   Dr. Christopher's Vitalerbs can be used, Fir Meadow's Better Daze herb blend, or use some of the herbs I'll list for you.   Barberry, bayberry, black cohosh, black walnut (not for equine/camelids), borage, carrot, cayenne, chaparral, chickweed, echinacea (always take a break after 10 days of use), hops, plantain, red clover, red raspberry, yarrow, and yellow (curly) dock are some choices that are usually easy to obtain or grow.

Availability

Many herbs can be very easily obtainable. For most people in the US and Canada and Europe, especially those that at least have a yard or access to a park or some countryside, finding a dandelion or some plantain is not all that difficult or time consuming the right times of the year.

I just did a quick herb walk here in the high desert of Central Oregon and found dandelion, couch (quack) grass, mullein, saint john's wort, juniper

The Accessible Pet, Equine and Livestock Herbal

(monospermum) berries, pine trees (not ponderosa), elderberry, roses with huge hips, and oregon grape. Not too bad for a 20 minute walk. I dare you, take a good herb book with good quality photos and a notebook and pen, and a basket. See what you can find in 20 minutes. If you don't know what something is, put on your gloves, pick it and take it home to identify it. Keep all unidentified plants out of the reach of children and pets/creatures in case they are poisonous. Do not smell them until you do have a positive identification of the non poisonous plants, as some of the toxins can be in the essential oils creating the aroma or odor of the plant.

Cleansing/Healing Crisis

As you work with <u>chronic</u> situations, you may find that they become worse before they become better. Don't let that shock you as long as your creature is stable. As cells begin to get healthier, they get the strength they need to start cleaning out the trash, and there are trillions of trash receptacles- one per cell. They will be dumping their accumulated waste faster than they acquired it, and that tends to make one feel like they have the flu. Hang in there and offer LOTS of warm or room temperature water to your animal so that they can flush quicker. Cleaning the liver and kidneys, is a very important consideration here- both as the creature improves, and again afterwards to reclean what the liver and kidneys had to sort through as cells body wide did their dumping. One example of this would be an old wound or dermal ulcer that refuses to heal. Adding herbal nutrition to the area and given orally, many times will cause these obstinate sores to ooze out pus for awhile, when previously they had been clean. The cells finally feel well enough to dump their toxins and waste. Once they have dumped enough to begin repairing, they will. It's an interesting process to observe. Horses and pets seem to be notorious for this due to the higher level of toxic exposure for these creatures.

Cleansing and Nourishing and Proper Diet

If there is a foundation or 'Chief Cornerstone' to herbalism, along with Vitalism (explained later in this chapter) this would be it. Most of herbalism centers around using x herb for x condition and then mixed results are received, even with efficacious herbs. If the cells are full of toxins, if the liver and kidneys are full of toxins, if the blood is full of toxins, they are not going to react as efficiently to the herbal nourishment that is being taken. For a cell to work at its peak performance and to replicate healthy cells it needs to be clean. We live in an unclean world. Our air has heavy metals from jet fuel, vehicle exhaust, and other particulate in it, which then gets rained down onto us and our land- even our organic foods. Our land- I won't even go there. You know what we have done to it, especially since World War II. Even organic land may have toxic residue deeper in the soil from arsenic or DDT from back in the days when those were allowed for pesticides and herbicides. Grooming products, medications, vaccines, fly sprays, tick and flea collars, feeds, naval dips, and more cause everything to be a potential source for contamination. Don't get overwhelmed worrying about it, as God has given us these wonderful herbs to help us clean those things back out of the systems of our creatures. Then we can have clean cells which will react faster and more efficiently to the herbal nutrition given.

Cleansing, for the most part, revolves around making sure the GI tract is clean, then the major cleansing organs of the liver and kidneys, and then the bloodstream and cells. Metals cleanses can be done afterwards and is something to seriously consider in an industrialized society. They SHOULD be done in this order. We make adjustments for pregnant animals, however. I do not like to cleanse beyond bowel work when something is pregnant, especially during first trimester unless it is absolutely necessary to save the dam in a crisis. The liver and kidneys can have some slower support during this time, but not a full blown cleanse. We will cover these cleanses more in depth in the related body section chapters. Just remember that everything we do involves cleansing and nourishing and also proper diet which will be discussed in the Supplements chapter. I like to consider cleansing as 1/3 of the program, nourishing with appropriate efficacious herbs as 1/3, and proper diet or food intake as the other 1/3. Leave one out and you are at 66% of the program. Leave two out (which is common) leaves us at 33% and shows why many people don't have good results with herbs. Who can take 33% of their medication and hope to see anything happen with what they are trying to control by doing that? How about a pilot having 33% accuracy landing at his expected location? I don't think he'd remain employed very long! No wonder many people "fire" herbs. I discuss cleansing in greater detail in Part II of this book.

Cost Effectiveness

Due to their ease of obtainability, many are very cost effective to use and they don't require a prescription either. If you are wild crafting, please be considerate and take no more than 10% of an herb from a location, and please plant any seeds of that herb you may find there, as well as taking a few seeds home, if allowed by your state or country, to get it propagated at your place. Carefully observe how it is situated for light, water, soil and duplicate the environment it would like as best as you can. In general seeds are planted at twice the depth of the seed size. Very fine seeds such as stinging nettle are just rested onto the ground and then gently pressed in with your hand but never covered. Some seeds will need to experience 'winter'. Those should be placed for at least four to six weeks in your refrigerator in a closed canning jar. If I don't know if they need a winter, since that is the norm for the climate in which I live, I give them a winter anyway.

Efficacy

There are thousands of years of anecdotal usage and results. Many years of studies too, but nearly all of the correctly done studies are outside of the USA. Let's look at some things to consider to know that the herbs you have in your hand actually are efficacious (effective).

You've hit one of my hot buttons here. Just like hay quality and food quality varies GREATLY from source to source, herbs definitely are subject to the same problems! The reason it is a hot button for me, is because sometimes the lives of my animals depend on the traditional therapeutic effect of an herb doing what I need it to do for body support, and to be used by the body to perform quickly. Sometimes I don't have time for playing with an herb to see if it will work well enough or not. For example, in a past year I had a dairy goat doe hemorrhaging during kidding and before we had all of her kids delivered. I needed effective herbs working in her in seconds, not minutes or hours. Wiese and I certainly had no use for mediocre herbs. We now have her daughters Aster and Enzian and she survived that incident.

<u>Your herbs should SMELL</u> like the herb. When I'm at events, people tell me that they can smell our herbs from across the room- even with them in their packaging!

<u>Your herbs should taste</u> like that particular herb should taste- and yes, I do taste them- even the icky tasting ones. Tinctures should still taste like herbs, even though they will be in a carrier that can have a strong taste. TASTE your herbs before you use them. Something's well being may depend on you knowing that you have the right herb at a strength that can nourish. Practice and exposure to many herbs will teach you.

<u>Some herbs are going to give you a reaction.</u> Quality cayenne is going to make you sneeze, and sneeze, and sneeze and start moving a lot of mucous out of your upper respiratory and get your salivary glands going- just from breathing some of it when airborne. Quality echinacea root is going to make your mouth numb (see all the fun I have checking out herbs). Learn what it is you are supposed to be tasting, feeling, observing. I cannot tell you the number of times people have brought to me what they have been taking. After gaining permission from them to break a capsule open to sample it, we often find lack of taste, correct color, and reaction. No wonder so many people say that herbs don't work.

<u>Your herbs should have vibrant coloring</u> correct for that herb and not have been dyed or altered to make bad herbs look better. This includes alfalfa pellets for feeding stock or pets.

Though you can pick and use herbs anytime you need them, obviously picking them at their <u>peak nutrient load</u> (usually, but not always, prior to bloom) is going to give you the best product. For herbs picked other times of the season or even day, you may have to use more herbs to compensate for lesser quality. Sometimes you won't have enough quality to work with if harvested at the wrong time. Again, taste and observe your herbs. You'll get it.

<u>Light</u> is a big enemy of herbs. See in the grocery store those beautiful clear glass bottles of spices that sit under fluorescent or other lights often 24/7 and maybe for years? Tsk tsk tsk… Keep them in a dark location and/or amber glass bottles.

The Accessible Pet, Equine and Livestock Herbal

Using amber glass does not give one the ability to leave the herb on a sunny shelf to let it cook.   Still keep it in an area where sun or heat will not damage them. I like them in the cabinets or cupboards in a climate controlled area.

<u>Moisture</u> is another foe of dried herbs. Keep them sealed and dry. If you live in a humid climate, get them in a dry canning jar, with a sealed lid.

<u>Aging</u> also reduces viability.   Ideally dried herbs should be used within a year of harvesting.   A few roots must be used much quicker due to deterioration once harvested. In general tree barks must be aged a year before use.   Do your research to know your plants.   Now having said that, high quality herbs harvested at peak and stored properly may last longer than that. Dry herbs not planning to be used within a year can be frozen in extra layers of bags/containers.   Some loss of vitamins will occur, but most minerals and many other phytochemicals will stay intact. Remember to put them in some kind of container that will not allow light to hit them when you open the freezer door, day after day or week after week. Putting your containers in a brown paper bag or cardboard box, labeled with date and herbs contained, is helpful. They can also be tinctured for long term storage, which is preferable to freezing.

<u>Purity is important</u>. Herbicides, pesticides, road contaminants, power lines all have negative impact on the quality of the herbs near them.   Never use plants that have been subjected to chemical fertilizers, herbicides, pesticides, or are within 50 feet of a roadway.   Even though leaded fuel is not used today in passenger vehicles, it will still be in the soil from years past.   I would stay even further away from busy roads and highways if not avoiding herbs in their vicinity at all.   Beware of old commercial orchard ground where arsenic and other nasty things used in the past still could be in the soil. Consider being cautious with fields that still may contain DDT in the soil from years gone by. Don't forget areas that may be affected by polluted water (does the neighbor upstream spray?), or by rain bringing air pollution down to the soil in areas that are noted for air quality problems.   And yes, avoid major power lines.   As they affect the energy in a person or creature (note we contain electrolytes in order to transmit electronic pulses via our nervous system), it also can negatively impact the energy within a plant. If you are raising your own plants and garden, and haven't had your water tested for awhile, consider

it. Often you can have tests run for the top 100 contaminants. If your place is older with old pipes beware of lead solder contamination as well.

Radiation should go without saying, but unfortunately needs to be addressed. Please under any circumstance do not use anything that has been irradiated, and that includes the use of a little reactor in many people's kitchens and barns called a microwave oven. Fat soluble nutrients (all plants contain them) may be altered into carcinogenics, and life in the plant is rendered dead. DNA changes may also occur from continual exposure to microwave activity. You cannot support life with death or with radiation. We haven't used one in about 20 years and I don't miss it at all. I just recently got a story in from a client whose baby was having appetite and digestive tract problems. Come to find out, the baby's breast pumped milk her mother would provide to feed the baby at daycare, was being microwave heated. The same day that was stopped, the baby's appetite returned to normal and GI problems disappeared- without herbs. Hmmmm.

Your herbs need to be used properly to get the desired effect. That means you need to use the proper dosage, the proper amount of times, be of good medicinal quality, and you NEED to keep in mind their therapeutic effects. Make sure you are using an herb that actually can be used for that situation, and be aware of all of its therapeutic effects to make sure that you don't create another problem. A good example of this would be herbs that would work well for a situation with your dairy goat, mare, pig or other that is lactating, but some of those same nice herbs are also galactaphygous which dry up the milk production. Probably not the therapeutic effect you are after. Also watch out for using parturient (birth promoting) or cathartic (can induce strong intestinal cramps and induce labor by accident), or emmenagogue (cycle promoting) herbs without trained herbalist supervision on a pregnant animal. At that point you need to be familiar with how to counter various therapeutic effects in various herbs, which will be beyond the scope of this book.

Organic does not mean efficacious. In this case I mean organic as in no added pesticides/herbicides. Many organic producers do a wonderful job of producing nice products and I highly commend them for that (thank-you!), but there are also many out there that produce shoddy quality. Know the integrity of your product provider, and please remember, organic does NOT mean efficacious or even something to use for that matter. Canola is a good example of that. You can buy it organic, but it's still toxic. Do some research on rapeseed and European studies. It was renamed canola merging the words Canada and oil for marketing to America to avoid the negative connotations associated with rapeseed. Organic also does not mean that something is whole food, whole herb, raw, or pure as in unadulterated. Again, we come back to labeling and exactly what the rules are within the organization that gave the approval for the organic label. Different organic companies have different standards. Know what they are if that matters to you.

I DO use organic products; however I do not shy away from responsible resources of wild crafted or naturally raised foods or herbs. Again, for those of you who are doing organic right- you are AWESOME! Thank-you!

Essential Oils and Their Use

Though this book is not intended to be a full teaching on essential oils, I will cover using them here and there through the text. Here are some key things to remember.

Please never use essential oils UNLESS you have been guided by someone that has some training. That can be via a QUALITY book, or via a person trained in aromatherapy, as the field is called. Please do note that at this time in the United States one cannot call themselves an Aromatherapist even with that training, and even if they could claim that title in another country.

Essential oils should always be used with RESPECT- they are powerful! There are many that are quite safe at REGULAR dosages, which are nearly always further diluted before use. They should never be used directly on skin unless it is one of the very few oils you can do that with. Different oils are safe at differing age groups. Some oils CANNOT be used by anything pregnant. Some other oils can be used during pregnancy, but with greater dilution. Some are not safe for infants or young ones. Very few essential oils are safe for cats; their livers tend to have fits with them. Stick to hydrosols (the water soluble by product of distilling essential oils- somewhat similar to an herbal tea/infusion) with cats, or the herbal suggestions in this book. Essential oils must never be left where children, creatures, or those of inadequate understanding may have access to them. Any accidental consumption of them is an IMMEDIATE MEDICAL emergency and poison control should be called without haste. Keep them put away out of reach.

Essential oils should be obtained from reputable sources. Learn to label read. If it says "oil of……" and not pure essential oil or 100% essential oil, it is likely adulterated. It is very rare I find one at a store that is quality oil. That's not the fault of the store; usually their purchasing agent is not trained in essential oils, so they just have all of the glossy marketing brochures and catalogs to make their purchasing decisions from. Also read the label to see if something like almond oil or sesame oil is also in the list indicating that it is really a blend and not a pure essential oil. That is fine, but you need to know what you are buying and what the actual essential oil strength will be if you choose to purchase them. That is not always labeled however. Often there will be solvents in them which also are not labeled. More on that follows.

Essential oils should smell correct for that oil. Recognizing that takes practice and more practice, some training, and exposure to good oils that were properly distilled. When you put some on a blotter paper (I use 3 x 5 cards and label my blotter squares with oil name and brand, then blot away), within 24 hours you should have nothing but a smell of the essential oil. There should be NO oily mark (except on resins like frankincense and myrrh or high oil plants like carrot). If there is an oily mark, the oil was diluted before purchase and is not a pure essential oil.

Your oils should ideally be packaged in amber glass bottles. They should be stored by you in a cupboard at room temperature. I prefer the amber bottles to the blue, as the blue bottles are not always consistent in quality and I don't want my oils interacting with the blue, which can happen in lower quality bottles. Also the amber bottles come in greater variety and are less expensive than the pretty blue ones.

Essential oils are obtained the BEST ways by steam, water and steam, and water distillation. Also low pressure steam distillation and CO2 extraction methods allow for quality oil production. This allows just the pure fat soluble parts of the plant to be extracted. It can literally take a dump truck load of herb just to make a few one ounce bottles of essential oil with some herbs, thus their price is affected by that and will fluctuate. Lower quality herbs, and some, like jasmine, are obtained with other methods, including the use of petrochemical solvents, and are not considered therapeutic grade or safe for medicinal use.

Most essential oils are produced from plants that don't grow in the United States, or that grow to a better quality in other countries, so expect to see a worldwide collection of them. Many of them actually have better phytochemical (plant chemical) profiles for medicinal use when under the stress and strain of their native environments.

This also brings up the topic of chemotype. Just because an essential oil may have thyme or eucalyptus or another name for the first part of their name, does NOT mean that you can use them interchangeably. Different distills of the herbs in different locations and climates will give a significantly different phytochemical profile, or chemotype. They are not all used the same way. Please do some research instead of just using them interchangeably to be sure you are still using the right oil for the application you want to use it for.

I like their long term penetrating effect when blended with olive oil, a sort of herbal time release use, and I use them to that advantage as part of a whole program. The general rule for use is two to three times per day, up to ten days in a row. Then at least a three day break to grant the liver additional time to clear any possibility of buildup. Another alternative to this is to use it 5 days on (weekdays) and weekends off. If a creature has a known compromised liver then I personally would limit essential oil use and rely heavier on whole herbs until I have time to support and help the liver clean itself for a few months. Usually I will use them for one or two days, occasionally three, to add emphasis to what it is I'm doing with herbs, and then I take a break from them.

Essential oils that were correctly processed and correctly stored can have a multiple year shelf life. Their worst enemies would be exposure to sun, heat and oxygen. That includes the oxygen that you decant into the container every time you use your oil. Buy the smallest amount feasible for what you do, or repour into smaller containers after purchasing so that only a little of your oils (the bottles you are currently working with) are being exposed to air at a time. I keep mine in cupboards under climate control, except my barn oils which are in a cupboard. I only keep small amounts in the barn for use there and refill from my house stock as needed.

Essential oils that should never be used due to toxicity problems. Please do not use them or oils that contain them unless you are educated CAREFULLY in their use. One mistake with them could be disastrous. This does not mean, however, to throw out the herbs they are from. Remember that these oils are highly concentrated fat soluble nutrients; the herbs will be much weaker and whole herb. Some of these oils would be: Bitter Almond, Boldo, Calamus, Camphor of the yellow and brown types (white is fine), Horseradish, Mugwort, Mustard, Pennyroyal (caution on the herb), Rue, Sassafras, Tansy (don't use the herb either it can poison some stock), Thuja, Verbena, and Wormwood. Remember that even getting one 'just for the smell' is not a good idea. I had a client that wanted me to order one just because he liked the scent in his room. I had to remind him that anything he smelled went into his lungs and consequently would be taken up by his bloodstream and circulated in his body. Is that really something you want to do with a toxic anything?

Photosensitivity can occur with some oils, the ones most commonly used would be the citrus types including those with a citrus name like lemongrass, so keep that in mind. Use them in the evening only or during low sunlight season or animals on indoor stall or kennel rest.

Skin irritations can occur if used straight on the skin, especially from the stimulant herbs such as thyme, peppermint, oregano, cloves, cinnamon, ginger and others like them. These tend to be hot to the taste if you touch the teeniest smear on a toothpick then onto your tongue. These same stimulant essential oils should not be used in pregnant stock without much more dilution than normal, if used at all, unless you know how to counter some of the effects in them.

Any allergic reactions, are rare, but can happen. Discontinue the oil use and switch to another plan. Any allergic effects should be gone in just hours as the liver metabolizes it out. Giving stinging nettle, lemon and or dandelion tea during this process can be supportive.

The Accessible Pet, Equine and Livestock Herbal

Herb Holidays

Yes, your herbs want a vacation! It has been found that when using herbs daily for a chronic situation, that the tendency is for the body to use them more efficiently if you take one day off a week. At our farm we do that on Sundays. However, I do not consider basic nutrition in that holiday. Those would be kelp and alfalfa with my dairy goats and any grain ration I have them on for body support. If I am working on a chronic situation that started out as acute, such as watching a broken bone repair, then I will herb at least 10 days in a row before I start working in a weekly herb holiday.

Herbs Always Work

That's a pretty strong statement, isn't it? But they do. They always nourish. Always. There are times, however, that despite all you do, it is time for your creature to go be with The Good Shepherd. No amount of herbing and prayers are going to keep them here in that circumstance. There are also times, when a situation is so advanced when you start to address it, that there is simply not enough time to turn it around before the damage wins. In addition there are scenarios when the wrong herbs are used, not necessarily harming, but not helping either. Using an aspirin to go after a toe nail fungus isn't going to work, and neither is the wrong herb in the wrong situation. Or efficacy is a problem. Or a complete assessment of issues needing to be addressed hasn't occurred. Remember that medications do not save 100% of its consumers either.

How do I know when to quit supporting an animal? Well, I don't. If the animal is still here, I'm going to keep trying to turn its situation around. I don't decide when they go, I let God do that. Really it's His anyways, He created it. I'm simply its loving caretaker and steward for Him. What a privilege. And yes, what a heartbreaker when we have to let them go. I remember I had a beloved 13 year old toggenburg dairy goat that had even kidded that year, but was starting to shut down over the course of a week. Early on she quit urinating, which would not have been a pain free or unnauseating situation for her. We were able to use one of our herbal products to nourish her body so it would start her functioning and peeing again. We still lost her at the end of the week peacefully in her sleep, but we didn't lose our beloved Faith from kidney failure and the associated toxemia. Did the herbs win? I think so.

Hering's Law of Cure

Constantine Hering, M.D. (1800-1880) noticed a healing pattern that an individual will expect. I have witnessed the same in animals & humans and likely so have you if you've been around traditional approaches for awhile. He said that a condition will heal, "from above downwards, from within outwards, from a more important organ to a less important one, and in reverse order of their (symptoms) coming." Paraphrased this would mean that healing starts from the mind (and I believe God) downwards, from within the body to the outside- generally starting with the digestive tract and moving outwards towards the skin. From more important organs to lesser ones- the body will always try to correct the health of the bowels, liver, lungs and kidneys first as these are essential for nutrition and detoxification. This also helps correct emotions as the liver is responsible for breaking down and eliminating those biochemicals. And healing in reverse order of the symptoms. This can take a day, a month, or 1 to 2 years depending on how long the condition has been allowed to develop. Remember, just because you are only now seeing symptoms, does not mean that this issue has not been developing for weeks, or even years! Therefore, one cannot expect to be 100% symptom free in a day. The herbs do not hide symptoms, as synthetics can do. The symptoms are also keys to help us gauge our progress. Holistic Iridology reveals this type of data in the irides (both irises) of the eyes, sometimes 20 years in advance to symptoms. Hering's law also brings more understanding to the healing or cleansing crisis which will be covered more. Remember that emotional and mental states are affected by this as well.

Heritage

God's farmacy was here first. They were given by our Creator, God, in Genesis 1:29 – 30 (remember the law of first mention) as food for us and for the animals and were reemphasized by Him again right after the flood. We've been using herbs for at least 6 millennia longer than we've been using synthetics (*pharmakeia* for you Bible students).

Label Reading

If you are buying an herbal supplement or even a bag of feed or dog food, here are a couple things I look for: Does it say the product is standardized for x percent of a plant chemical (phytochemical)? If it does, then that is telling me that some scientist in a lab somewhere, extracted an active ingredient, often an alkaloid, and put more of that alkaloid back in the product than the herb itself originally contained. That alkaloid may not even be from the same plant! That is moving out of the realm of herb safety and into drugs and can cause some serious problems, side effects, adverse effects, or cause system or nervous system imbalances. Ephedrine is one of those. The very useful plants in the Ephedra genus are blamed for whoever it was that decided they would extract out the alkaloid ephedrine. Caffeine is another one of those powerful alkaloids that is giving strokes to children (and I've heard of one documented adult death from heart attack) drinking the high powered energy drinks. Keep your plants whole.

Something else I look for is if there are individual vitamins or minerals listed as added ingredients. If they are we call these isolates. Again, this is not whole herb and can cause body imbalance. Also most of these products are obtained from synthetic (petrochemical) or rock mineral sources. How many calcium supplements can you find where the labeled source is carrots or shavegrass or oat straw? Way too few.

A vitamin and mineral product that lists only vitamins and minerals rather than the plant sources they are derived from. Besides often being synthetic and/or rock based, we are trusting science to know exactly what a creature's body needs and in what amounts every day of its life. Currently there are over 600 bioflavanoids that are known. Not even all of them are named, let alone do we even know what they do or at what balance they are needed with which other nutrients. What if tomorrow's larger microscope shows us there are really 6000 bioflavanoids, or even 60,000. I will trust God's whole herbs sooner than I will trust our limited human knowledge and information, as great and growing as it seems to be.

Another thing I look for is if magnesium stearate is on the label. That was put into the product for the manufacturer's benefit, certainly not for yours! Capsuling machinery operates much quicker when this is in the blend, making the company more money per hour. If the company's focus is on making more money and not on providing a quality <u>whole</u> food product without adulteration, please keep looking. Expect the companies that do it right to charge more for their products to cover their overhead.

You should also look for things like isolates, proteins, casein, spices, etcetera that can indicate that MSG will be in the product. Google MSG and see what you learn if you want to know more. It is AMAZING all of the things it will be in without it being required to be labeled for.

There are literally thousands of additives that are NOT required to be labeled by the FDA. Know the integrity of your provider.

Reading a label is much more involved than just glibly going over the contents list. You have to understand the FDA definition and source for each word listed, which often will not be the same as the Webster dictionary definition. Do some research if this concerns you. One of my 'favorites' to quote is "100% USA Honey". That means it is 100% USA, not necessarily 100% honey. How about "no sugar added" juice from concentrate. Concentrates typically contain about 20% sugar without any requirement to define the sugar type or content on the label. UGH! Have I made you crazy yet?

Living and Active

Herbs are living! Kirlian photography shows the energy that surrounds and sometimes bounces like mini lightning bolts off of living plants and creatures. This energy along with the plant nutrients, sustains our health and well being. Yet this same photography, on a piece of cooked meat, refined flour high heat cooked bread, processed foods or feeds, or microwaved food, will just render darkness. Choose life to sustain life. Look up an image of stone crushed olive oil done with Kirlian photography on the internet. You might be amazed.

Love

"And now abide faith, hope, love, these three; but the greatest of these is love."
1Corinthians 13:13 NKJV

Not enough can be said for love.   I expect you do love your critters; otherwise a book like this would never make it into your hands.   From what I've observed, from what I've learned in anatomy and physiology (no tests, please, there is so much more to learn!), and from what one can glean from the scriptures,   love is that all important ingredient that can make or break your effectiveness in helping your beloved creature.   We know it enhances the immune system and alkalinizes blood ph levels and   we know that love helps a child, parent, or pet relax.   I have many times,   seen and heard my goats and my horses sigh a sigh that sounds like relief and relaxation when I arrive to comfort one that is down or damaged for whatever reason. Even the iguana I had years ago settled down greatly once I had her held against me after she sustained an injury (beware of mean iguanas, mine was a sweetheart).   I have had a dairy goat doe drop her head in my lap as if to cry as I sat cross legged next to her, after she aborted a beautiful doe kid years ago.   I simply think they try harder to get well if they know they are loved by your actions and doted on.   I've been known (shhhh) to take naps with a doe that is down.   I put on my carhardt bib overalls, stuff on a winter hat to keep my head clean, grab a wool blanket if needed, toss down some more pretty straw or soft grass hay and crash out next to her. Besides, who has a farm that doesn't need an excuse for a nap???!   Our successes seem to exceed the normal statistics by people for animal loss due to differing health issues and injuries. Love is certainly something to think about in your care program.

Milk and Meat Withdrawals in Livestock

If you stay with the herbs discussed in this book, or other herbs that are not toxic, poisonous, or habit forming, then you don't have anything to worry about in the way of phytochemical residues that would be in milk, eggs, or meat in the creatures or products that are consumed.   The herbs NOURISH and CLEANSE. Any milk consumed or used for raising the baby animals will also contain some of the nutrients and benefit, at a reduced level than what the dam received.   Any milk used by humans will have the same effect (although for your long term cellular well being, please use raw milk only in low quantities and preferably goat, if at all).   As to milk flavors,   any herbs fed within 4 to 6 hours of milking can taint the milk. Many herbs don't, but some do.   When I feed herbs, I feed them at milking time or just after if I'm giving them garden and herb trimmings.   An unhealthy animal can take as long as 12 to 14 hours for the herbs to clear their system, but then you should not being using milk from a creature that is that ill anyways, if they are even producing milk while that sick. If you have an animal that is very toxic on a liver/kidney or cells cleansing program, you may choose to forgo products from that creature until they are further into their program which would be up to four months, depending on their toxic load. Goats do have a higher/faster metabolism than other creatures, so I expect that they would process the herbs even faster, perhaps as quickly as 2 to 3 hours in a very healthy individual.

Nourishment

Whole herbs provide nourishment for every cell of the body, packed with vitamins, minerals, protein, fats, sugars and other phytochemicals, many of which probably have not even been discovered yet. This is especially so when left in their whole herb form. We've discussed that some and I'll touch on it more as we go through this book together.

Organic Versus Inorganic

To an herbalist, organic does not mean 'without pesticides' although certainly we like our herbs and foods to be clean.   Organic means, "living or that which is able to sustain life".   That would be our raw plant foods, or carefully low heated (under 130 degrees) dried plants.   Inorganic means, "dead or that which is not supporting to life".   Rock minerals, cooked animal & plant products, processed and packaged products, and synthetics fall under this category. We believe that plants support us and creatures, and that rocks and soil support plants.   I don't, as a rule, recommend feeding synthetics or dirt (rock based minerals) to animals. Salt is about the only exception I can come up with to this.   I'll discuss salt in the supplements section. Carnivore animals do well with raw meat in their diet due to their much straighter intestinal tracts that can move out meat fast enough for it to not become toxic. That is rarely true for humans and grazers. But only raw meat without plants in their diet or only cooked meat or meat products grants them the diseases now plaguing our pets that once only plagued our humans.   They too need organic living foods. I will discuss more on feline and canine diets further into this book.   Don't just switch their diet overnight, wait until you have more information in the Supplementation and Feed chapter.

Organic nutrients are fully assimilable to the creature so their system can take what it needs, and is fully able to eliminate the rest.   Inorganic rock nutrients are partially assimilable at best and full elimination is difficult if even possible. Rock nutrients tend to store in joints, along veins and arteries, in body organs, in the placenta, and in the brain. I recently had a human client that told me that her doctor told her she had calcium deposits in her face and her breasts! Many human health and creature ailments are compounded or created by them.   Urinary calculi in the urethra, similar to kidney stones in humans, are one large consideration. Inorganic synthetic nutrients will fill the receptor sites or be taken up by villi in the digestive tract as the chemical shape meets their requirements for uptake,   BUT, over time malnourishment or other imbalances can occur if this is continued. Fortunately for them, most animals don't have the lifespan of a human to actually witness the result of many of these issues. We are seeing more of it more often though. I believe that is in part to generations with weaker constitutions. We can only throw synthetics at creatures for so many generations before we reap the consequences.

PH (Potential Hydrogen)

Herbs and plants keep the bloodstream and body at the alkaline ph that it needs to remain in a healthy condition, while at the same time providing nutrients for a healthy stomach/rumen to be at the acidic ph it needs to be at to start to break down proteins and minerals into usable forms.   All synthetics whether medications or supplements cause acidity that lowers the body's PH. Packaged and processed food, including highly processed pet and animal foods also have this problem. Stress and negative emotions additionally make a body more acidic. Acidic bodies provide an environment that is favorable to tumor, parasite, bacterial, fungal, and viral issues. Positive emotions such as love, peace, joy, gentleness, and kindness encourage alkalinity within body tissues. Interesting that our Creator knew that millennia before science discovered it. Favorable emotions also contribute to body PH that makes an internal environment that is less suitable for parasite, tumor, and microbe survival.

Plant Synergy

James Duke, PhD talks a lot about plant synergy and based on my own personal experience with herbs lean heavily on this concept. Synergy is the greater therapeutic effect of putting plants together than they would be individually, but added together. Or in another example, one herb plus one herb might equal the benefit of perhaps three or more plants when you start combining herbs, rather than just the two of the individual herbs taken singly at different times. Though using herbs singly can provide some amazing results, using several plants towards the same goal, all that work a bit differently, can get you there faster and further than just one or maybe two herbs will. Just be sure you are not adding in a group of herbs together that may cause a problem, such as using a number of cycle causing herbs (emmenagogue herbs) on a pregnant animal. You'll get a therapeutic effect alright, but certainly not the one you were looking for! Since each herb is a unique combination of nutrients and energy, you benefit from the combined effect of those nutrients, like you would eating a mixed salad versus just a romaine salad. You'll get some chances to play with synergy when you come to the chapters discussing conditions. There I will supply some herb choices, which you will be free to combine as you feel led. It is very rare that I will use only one or two herbs to support the body in a situation. The body part experiencing a problem is not an island to itself, but often there are multiple systems or areas involved. I am BIG on blends. I've seen far too many wonderful wellness stories working with them.

Pleomorphism

Pleo what? Pleomorphism, or 'many bodies' was a concept formed during the early 1800's.   I'm not going to discuss if it is valid or not as there are articles and controversy on that,   but I think it is something we must consider as a possibility. Pleomorphism, as applied to illness, is the theory that bacteria, virus, and fungi really are one base unit called a protit, and that these organisms can morph back and forth between themselves to the form they think is expedient to survival. There is much more to it than that and medical science wants to debunk it, but I think we need to keep this possibility in mind when supporting our creatures during illness.   When I formulate or give my farmstock herbs,   I consider that although what I'm battling may be a viral issue or you name it,   I need to consider that more forms could be involved or even unassessed secondary issues may be at work concurrently. So I include a plan for those possibilities as well.   This may be a partial additional explanation for those 'superbugs' that are out there.   I think you will find your herbing much more successful if you consider this concept.

Practical Synergy

You will be reading, later in the book, about herb choices you can make when working with different situations.   I want to mention a few special herbs that can be used to make your herbing even more effective.   These herbs, if added to your other herbs you are using, will make them more bioavailable to your creature and could allow the herbs to nourish at a quicker rate and may allow them to last longer in their system.

Cayenne is a favorite of mine. If you've seen me teach then you may have seen my cayenne pepper apron.   Whenever I am working with something cardiovascular, or want the herbs to hang around in the body for longer, then I use cayenne.   Cayenne's first location of interest is the heart, and it will lead other herbs that direction.

Ginger is another herb I really like, it will lead herbs as cayenne does, but favors the legs, arms, head, wings, brain and reproductive organs.

Prickly Ash bark (aged) or berries can also be used. Prickly Ash will not run the herbs around as fast as the first two, but will stay in the system longer.

Rosemary is one I like to use if I'm trying to nourish the brain faster, and also extremities or skin.

Lobelia inflata will take herbs to the area the body deems has the greatest need, but it doesn't hang around very long, so should be used in conjunction with one of the other herbs. Other stimulating herbs can be used, but these I have mentioned I consider the safest for using with pregnant, very young, or fragile creatures, so are the only ones I'm going to list here.

Prayer

You can know your herbs inside and out, and think you understand the situation you are facing, but without God's guidance, you may not choose the best herbal approach, dosage, timing, etcetera for this creature with this issue! There could be other issues as well that you aren't even considering. Often times I've thrown up a quick "help me Lord'" prayer and then have just known what it is I need to do. Sometimes that may involve using a plant or procedure or dosage or even a new application I wouldn't have normally used. God KNOWS the situation, I only think I do. I like to think "Father knows best".

For those people that have a practice of anointing those that are ill with olive oil or an herb infused olive oil certainly you can do that with your creatures. I will leave that up to each person's leading and comfort level. To me, if this practice gets you remembering Who really is the source of life and health and increases your focus on prayer and the Lord then it's always going to be beneficial. Certainly our Lord could choose to do a miraculous healing for your creature for His glory also. I say go for it if you are so led.

Quality

You can, in many cases, control the quality of the product you are using. That is dictated by when you harvest, where you harvest, age of plant or stage of the plants reproduction when harvested, how preserved, how stored and length of storage, etcetera. You'll pick up more tidbits on that as you read on. There are also several quality resources, some of which will be listed in appendix of this book for you.

Safety

Their safety, when compared to the safety record of medications, is literally many thousandfold safer. In humans there is usually one or two verifiable herb deaths per year- usually from herb abuse - taking high amounts of one herb for a ridiculous amount of time or most often from mistaking a poisonous plant for a near look alike non poisonous one. I think it's safe to surmise that most plants that we work with on a daily basis have never had a dangerous reaction attached to it. I don't know if we have a single drug including over the counter preparations that can state that safety record. The number of human prescription medication deaths per year (used as prescribed) hovers somewhere between 200,000 and 700,000 per year in this country alone. It depends on whose numbers you go with, the lower numbers always being the American Medical Association numbers. Even aspirin, which is also used in pets and livestock, has about 25,000 human deaths per year attributed to it mainly from GI tract damage. According to James Duke, PhD, about one half of all medications for humans that are released, are recalled within 10 years because of serious safety concerns. That's one out of two medications. I'm sorry I don't have numbers on animal products, but I expect findings would be interesting.

Along with safety I want to mention Hippocrates forever quoted phrase of "…first, do no harm'. Herbs fit this Father of Medicine's ideal in wholistic therapies. Not a single drug can claim this phrase. Remember; do no harm also means that you and your creature will not get harmed in the process of administering herbs while working with them. The last thing you want to do is to have to herb you or your creature for a moderate to severe injury or worse sustained while trying to help them!

Satisfaction

Working with herbs is quite rewarding.   Besides the therapy of picking herbs on a gorgeous day,   you become part of the process for providing resources for the herdsmanship of your creatures.   What a delight to watch the plants and the creatures thrive under your care.

Vitalism versus Allopathy (Atomists)

Just what is vitalism anyways?   And what is allopathy?   Here I'll try to briefly explain.   Understand that vitalism is a narrow field, most herbalists and alternative trained people are allopathic

as is the trained medical profession.

A Vitalist is going to look beyond the symptoms they are seeing, and start asking WHY their creature is in the condition that they are in.   For example,   when I see a skin issue on an animal, besides being allopathic, and working with the skin issue topically to bring comfort to the creature,   I'm going to want to address the immune system, the liver, and probably the kidneys which are all likely contributing to this scenario.   Otherwise I can throw herbs at the visible problem- the skin and expect in the future to have to address it again and maybe again and then maybe larger issues later because I did not address the other organs and systems involved. This is incredibly important in chronic issues and of course is supportive in emergencies.

A Vitalist will try to work WITH the body that they believe IS functioning correctly in the situation and will tend to work with the whole body and being. Herbs are used generally as a tool to nourish and cleanse.

A Vitalist will also concern themselves with things like exercise, fresh air, sunlight, hydrotherapy, body work, and other safe alternative therapies. Hippocrates is perhaps our most well known Vitalist of all time.

An allopathic or atomist approach will be more focused on the symptoms. Often drugs and sometimes even herbs are used that force the body to comply or react in a certain manner. Please note that veterinarians also tend to consider nutritional issues and that is highly commendable- I am not commenting about that here. A personal example of this is my allergies. At the age of four I suddenly one day had high pollen allergies (I suspect my tetanus vaccination which is linked anecdotally to that problem). Of course we did the standard allopathic diagnosing with scratch tests and did drug treatments for years which semi controlled them, but often kept me partially drowsy (slowing down neural activity- now that's not a 'smart' thing to do!) until the later medications came out. Then there were the years of weekly shots that controlled them but didn't heal them. In fact, I kept acquiring more allergies like some foods, chemicals, and some of the smaller furry animals. Then as an adult I switched to homeopathy for them and controlled them marvelously well with a product that was harmless to me. But I still had allergies off of the product until applying to myself what I was learning in my herbal education on cleansing and nourishing. My allergies now are gone, almost 4 decades after acquiring them. I went gung ho, so it took me only 7 months to clean them out of my system instead of the one year average. Now if I repollute myself, they do try to return. But who wants to go back there?!

Controlling a fever is another one of those atomist things. We like to let fevers run their course as long as it is safe for the creature, as a fever really ramps up the immune system exponentially to attack the invader and monitoring the fever gives me a way to know if I have enough herbs into the creature to support the body into going after the invader. Once the fever dissipates itself I know the invader has been conquered. If I purposely eliminated the fever I would only be able to guess if my dosaging was correct in that case. Controlling the fever will kick the immune system in the pants. I write more on that in the Immune System chapter.

Additional Issues Impacting Health

There are many additional things to consider when attempting to encourage an animal to better health. I will list several. This list is probably not exhaustive, but will cover a lot of bases for thought.

First, because herbs do NOT suppress symptoms, as drugs do, they may not appear to help the body heal itself as fast, or they may (see healing crisis) seem to get worse. The cells finally are feeling nourished enough to dump their trash and clean the lymph, which has to recirculate through the body to get out or come out through an injury site. You will see this pattern over and over in symptomology as you support creatures through chronic issues. However, I find in most situations, that I can see some evidence of improvement often within hours on acute (fast onset conditions) situations. I usually get clues of increased wellness in just days after starting to work on a chronic (long term problems) problem.

Second, using the right herbs actually speeds cell division to allow tissue regeneration to be accomplished quicker. In a human, a well nourished person replaces 100% of the cells in their body every 2 years, with many organs, blood, and bones being completely replaced, cell for cell, every 3 to 4 months. An unhealthy cell can't regenerate back to 100% health in one regeneration, so it may take several. It is said that it takes 7 years for a body to heal itself with correct food. With proper feeding, cleansing, and herbal nutrition, that process can be sped up considerably- perhaps as fast as 2 years with many things being noticeable much before then if one is being steadfast. Sometimes in just days. Do be patient though, in chronic situations the problem hasn't been going on for only a day or a week, but rather for months or years, so you can't expect the body to resolve it in only a day or a week.

Third, the constitution of the creature will impact how fast healing occurs. A constitution is part of one's genotype (DNA inherited traits). It is the residual strength of mind and physical body that one is born with. Obviously those born with stronger tissues and mind and less toxins can withstand more stress and abuse than those born with weaker ones. Stronger ones will heal faster than weaker ones once attended to. Of course one with a strong constitution that abused itself or was exposed to serious toxins   will still become damaged.   As cleansing and nourishing come into play these types usually still respond faster.

Fourth, the mental and emotional state of your animal will affect its rate of healing. Anyone that has worked around animals long enough knows that they CAN get depressed and stressed.   Like people they can range through a full spectrum of emotions, which require a healthy endocrine system and healthy and clean liver to run those chemicals called hormones and break them down correctly.   And don't forget that all important ingredient- Love.

Fifth, the body temperature of the animal will affect its ability to heal. We say that cold is death and heat is life.   I would personally, rather have the animal on a bit of a warm side, then hypothermic- under normal temperature.   Remember that body temperatures can range a bit tending to run a bit cooler in the colder months and a degree to a degree and a half warmer in creatures in warm months and up to an average of 2 degrees warmer in young stock.   I'm real quick to blanket an animal that is having health difficulties whether it is fever or cold.   They do not seem to be able to regulate their body temperatures as well when under large amounts of system stress from injury or illness.

Sixth, the diet of your creature will affect its ability to heal.   If a larger percentage of its diet is processed foods which are less in whole food nutrition and life force and usually higher in synthetic 'nutrients', are the wrong ph and mucous forming within the body constipating the cells, its body will not recuperate as fast as one on a traditional raw diet.   Thankfully I don't have to coax my dairy goats to give up hamburgers and sodas,   but I have to watch what types of treats I offer them, as well as their grain. Cats and dogs are largely on processed bagged or canned foods in industrialized countries.   Even your cats and dogs will benefit from raw fruits and vegetables, and some sprouted grains in their diet a well as a switch to naturally raised raw meats.   Be careful of diet no no's though.   Some plants and fruits that one species can have, will be disaster for another, so learn more about those from your veterinarian and university websites.

Seventh- the amount of toxicity in your critter will decrease its ability to respond to herbs.   When a cell contains toxins and is in a state of hypoperformance (lowered performance) ,   it is unable to fully react or take benefit of nutrients.   This is because the toxins take up space and make the cell weaker, negatively impacting it's metabolism (nutrient and waste exchanges). Our animals are exposed to the same toxins we are- air, water, herbicides, pesticides, vehicular exhaust, heavy metals, compromised air cleanliness coming down in the rain, grooming products, iodine, airborne bleach in milk rooms, feed contaminants *ad infinitum*. If you have not done a routine cleanse on your animal consider it. I'll explain more on that in the related body systems chapters. Every Spring we do spring cleaning here- on the outside and on everyone's insides including mine! And I do it again before our breeding season.

Eighth- the amount of cellular damage affects how quickly they are able to heal. I get this question a lot, "How long will it take for my goat's or cow's udder to even up after mastitis?". My answer, "I don't know." I haven't been able to crawl inside of the mammary gland to see the extent of the damage, nor do I know at what rate your creature is shedding damaged cells and replacing them. Nor do I know how many cellular regenerations this animal has to do to get that mammary to full health. What I DO know is that if you keep at it, those mammaries, knees, wounds, bones, ligaments DO heal as we clean and nourish that animal with those plants appropriate for their situation.   So it may take several days, weeks, or a few months, or an entire season. Two critters affected at the same time may heal at different rates. But don't give up. I've even had people come back and tell me later that their creature now milks more on the side that was affected! Go herbs go!

Ninth- the efficacy of the herbs you use will affect the rate of heal. That was discussed earlier in this chapter.

Tenth- selecting the correct herbs for the situation also was discussed earlier in this chapter as well as assessing the situation correctly.

Taking Care of the Herd/Flock Owner/Manager

Now why would this be in a livestock herbal? Simply stated, your stock are only going to get as good of care as you yourself are feeling up to giving.   There are far too many people out there that make sure their creatures have the best of feed and nutrition, and then shortchange themselves and sometimes even their human family. I've even had my husband tell me years ago "I wish I was a goat". That told me I had my priorities wrong. So I'm going to give you some basics. If you follow them, you will have more energy, feel better, and with that will come more physical and mental ability to care better for your herd, kennel, or flock!

Toxins. The same toxin sources that make their way into your creatures make their way into you. Besides anything they consume that we in turn consume when we eat meat or their other products, we usually are exposed to more car exhaust, trips to town, daily chemical shampoos and bathroom products, sodas, packaged food, baked and processed foods, and most restaurant foods. And we do that for decades, not just 5 years, 10 years, or perhaps 30 plus years that the longer lived creatures may be here for. I have yet to counsel one of my goats to quit going to the fast food burger place and to give up fries cooked in hydrogenated oils or to quick drinking on the caffeinated plants. None of my guardian dogs use hair spray, underarm deodorant, or fluoride & chemical sweetener filled toothpaste. Our stock also tends to have better access to live raw foods then you will find most people consuming on their plates.

Considering some of these things, it seems good to choose to clean things up. For a person that usually means about a year of bowel cleanses if they've never done a long term one before. I get tired of seeing all of the products out there for 3 day, 10 day and 2 week cleanses. They can open your bowels, but what about the often decades of glued on animal products, refined flours, junk food, et al in the 25 to 27 feet of small and large intestinal surfaces? It takes time to get those layers back out, and time for the peristaltic action and linings of that digestive tract to heal itself. So we work with people for a year on that. It is simply AMAZING to me how many health conditions begin to fade into distant memory once this area is attended to. It is interesting to note that the inner zone of the iris is the small and large intestine areas. That is surrounded by the other body tissues and organs in the outer zone. We can see in iridology (iris viewing) toxins from one location in the bowel affected organs in the adjacent zone. Interesting indeed.

It is oh so good to maintain those main detoxifying organs that maintain you. Those are largely the kidneys and liver, but also the lungs and skin. Stress in one or more of these organs places additional strain on the other cleansing organs and they too, over time can degenerate from that distress. 1000 to 1500 quarts of blood are filtered by the liver and kidneys in a human every day and toxins build up in our society at rates faster than they can clean themselves. Those unkept toxins are then free to settle in other areas of our body slowing those cells' metabolism (nutrient and waste exchanges), leading to degeneration. So I encourage all to regularly clean these. Never start an organ cleanse before one has 2 regular bowel movements per day. I like to do this myself quarterly, and I do a longer 'spring cleaning' tune up as well. Four months is not too short for a first time and my preference on these is also a year to really get them going well. If you've had a history of problems in those organs, then doubling that would not be a bad consideration. Remember about being visited by a healing crisis! So consider when you start. The afternoon of the end of your work week is usually a good place to start. I like to start my clients at below normal maintenance dose to give their bodies opportunity to adjust slowly and to try to minimize the healing crisis that is sure to come.

So what about the other cells in the body? Once the bowels are operating regularly, and the major detoxification organs are in process, it's time to release the toxins that have been cooped up in the cells and between them. Again, four months would not be too short of a time to work on this with a year being much better. If you experience any degenerative type of disease I'd think about doing it longer. Then consider visiting the liver and kidneys again for a several week tune up, as they have had to process all of this excess released from the cells. The cellular cleansing also addresses the bloodstream. It is impossible to have abundant health with trash living in your body. My wish for you is abundant overflowing wellness so that you can become all that God intended for you for His glory.

Diet changes. This is somewhat simplified but the more raw fruits and vegetables you have in your diet, the more distilled water, real non caffeine herb teas, and fresh juices from your own juicer, the more quickly you will watch your body benefit. Add to that cooked legumes, steamed squashes, and sprouted grains and raw nuts and you'll really be humming after you get into your cleanse program for awhile. Remember, dead foods cannot support a living body to abundant life. If you eat animal products, and I do on a very limited basis with a bit more during the cold months, treat them as a condiment and sprinkle some (1/2 ounce, perhaps an ounce in cold winter weather) over your salad as a dressing. I never treat animal products as the main meal. If I do, then I can expect to have the level of health that most Americans face today. I don't want to go there.

Sleep- that elusive item on the daily schedule especially during kidding, foaling, calving, lambing, whelping and every other birthing type of season! Do the best you can. To bed by 10, no later than 11pm is ideal to allow the natural cycle of light and dark and rest and body renewal to occur in accordance with our body's circadian rhythm. This is in part controlled by your pituitary and pineal glands. You can't push it for too long before taxing your adrenals and immunity. I even took a nap this year in the middle of the day in a kidding pen with one of my LaMancha does while waiting for her to kid. I wasn't going to get enough sleep in otherwise. Barn clothes, a good winter hat, a pile of straw, a warm doe next to me. Thirty minutes of glorious rest!

Though this book's primary focus is not a human herbal, much of what I'll be sharing in here can be applied directly to humans. Just match the human size to the creature size (usually the goat/sheep weights for adults) and work from there dosage wise. I expect in the future I'll be penning a human herbal as well. Ask for it and it will get done sooner…

I trust that you find some of this information helpful in your quest to keep your stock doing well.

Chapter Two- Husbandry

Husbandry is caring for a creature in a husband-like manner. A good husbandman sees to it that his/her charges are well fed, safe, secure, warm, dry and loved. It amazes me how many animals I see as I drive along the countryside that cause me to wonder if that case is true for them. Please do not ever let that be thought of you or of me! Herbs can be thrown at animals all day long but if you are unable to provide the above, they will not be nearly as effective as they should be and you'll have many more issues to deal with than normal. Herbs simply will not make up for bad management.

For specifics on any one animal type, please consult some good books or perhaps a county extension agent, your local feed store customer service counter, successful breeders of your chosen animal, etcetera. As a general rule I like to see at least three reputable references agree on something before I feel I may have some valid information. That is not to rule out the one or two source that you know God has directed you in a time of need. His advice certainly is worth more than man's. Also remember, that for each person you seek advice from there will be another way to do something. Each herd or flock owner is going to manage things a bit differently depending on feed availability, facilities, herd and flock size, herd and flock goals, state or local ordinances, education, time, budget, personality, special needs, past or current health issues, biosecurity issues, climate, regional culture, and so on. Use their information as a starting point on what is working for someone and go from there to build what works best for your situation. So if you want one simple answer from me be assured you are not going to get it. Hopefully this book will provide a basis for you to build on, however, and get you asking the right questions.

Shelter

Shelter is that which protects your animals from the elements and potential predators. In a hot dry climate that may be as simple as shade trees to rest under during the heat of the day. Or in an area like mine with wet winters that definitely means a barn where my goats can be out of any wind, rain, or occasional snow. Then in our hot dry summers their barn and a couple trees also provide for their

The Accessible Pet, Equine and Livestock Herbal

shade.   If your creatures can be set up so that they can go in and out of their shelter at will that would be the best scenario.   Be careful of overcrowding which may increase injuries and nearly always negatively impacts immune systems due to increased stress from bullies picking on lower pecking order creatures. Even beef cattle and meat goats, which have thicker hides and can deal with more inclement weather will still benefit from better feed conversion, better immunity and stronger progeny if you can supply shelter.

Shelter also means that you will need to plan somewhere to keep any hay, supplements, grain, bedding, root crops, and the like where it can be dry and secure from spoilage, vermin, temperature or humidity fluctuations and accidental raids by your livestock.   If you are fortunate and able to build something to suit your needs always plan to build bigger than you think you will need. Always. Trust me, you'll find you need it!

When building or remodeling a shelter seriously consider building in such a way that you can tractor clean your facilities.   They are more likely to be kept clean, and cleaned more often if it doesn't have to be by pitchfork and wheelbarrow. Even if you don't have a tractor now you may find yourself with one or the ability to rent one in the future. Plan ahead. Your back will thank you!

Fresh Air and Sun

Nearly nothing is more heavenly then smelling fresh spring air kissed by the sun. Fresh air does not mean that the wind is blowing on your stock but rather while in their shelter, there is fresh air movement overhead that can draw urine, humidity caused by urine and respiration and other odors out of the barn.   As mentioned above, if they can have access in and out to their fresh air so much the better. We have a metal tarp frame set up outside of our goats' doors like an awning to which a tarp is attached.   In the wet months this allows our goats to stand out in the fresh air without being rained on. And that is where they tend to congregate. Very few actually go into or sleep in the barn during daylight hours unless we get some wind going.

Sunshine is used by creatures and humans alike to form vitamin D in our bodies which must be present to fully utilize calcium. Calcium is responsible for bone strength, is in all connective and muscle tissue, regulates heart beat and is a vital part of our nerves. Animals that spend much of their lives indoors will never reach the fullest health possible. Neither will people. There are a few vitamin D plants. Some of those will be mentioned in the Supplements chapter.

Exercise

Muscles and tendons and bone that are not subjected to resistance training from movement will not remain as strong as intended. Movement also encourages larger intake of oxygen into the body which is needed by every cell. The lymph circulatory system is three times larger than the cardio-pulmonary system and it requires muscle movement to function. The lymph collects waste, dead cells, killed bacteria and viruses and carries them down to be excreted eventually via the intestinal tract. Without movement these accumulate and stagnate and can cause cellular degeneration or dis-ease. Your lymph also carries nutrition and oxygen to the cells that your capillaries do not reach. Movement is also necessary for the emotional well being of your creature. Please allow your animals some type of regular daily exercise. For their mental state some of that should be free choice if at all possible. Their immunity will also benefit. Movement is also important to encourage healthy peristaltic action in the intestinal structure.

Blanketing or Not

This is a question I get asked about from time to time. Animals generally benefit from not being blanketed when in good health, having access to shelter, and proper feed. Blanketing compresses their hair coat and if they are not removed daily and rebrushed, the air layer that is supposed to be trapped in their fluffy fur as an insulation layer is no longer able to insulate your creature. Some blankets actually will leave your animal colder than it would be had you left one off of them if they are not allowing air to insulate between the hairs. Some when wet (like cottons) will draw heat out of your animal putting them at risk for hypothermia. Blankets not removed daily can also create an itchy animal from waste buildup in the skin. That itchy animal rubbing on things can catch the blanket. If the animal panics or the blanket doesn't tear, you may gain an injury to deal with. You will learn in Part II that the skin is an important organ. If not allowed to breathe properly you will actually increase the load on the kidneys to process more toxins that the skin is now not free to remove. Blanketing also prevents the winter protective coat from coming in.

There are times I do blanket, however. If I have an ill animal I will blanket them. Real sick animals have difficulty maintaining their body temperature. I've even blanketed a very sick goat when it was in the 90's outside. He was going hypothermic and 95 degrees Fahrenheit was still far too low for his stressed system when his normal temperature should have been 102.5 to 103 that time of year.

I would blanket if I did not have facilities to protect my animals from a wind or rain or a snow storm. In this case you would need two blankets per animal. One blanket should be drying when the fresh one goes on your creature with a good brushing in between the changes. But you are a GOOD husbandman and are going to have shelter for your animals so you shouldn't have to consider this.

When we lived in the 'frozen north' of the North Cascades I would start blanketing my healthy and strong horses at about 10 degrees below zero. This was in an area that did not have winter wind to create a wind chill. If you have wind, you are going to have to consider wind chill factors in your blanketing decisions. This was for a foundation quarter horse type and a larger Arabian in his early 20's. My well fed, properly housed dairy goats were never blanketed unless ill or kidding.

If you have clipped your horses with a winter harness or riding clip so that you can cool (dry) them easier from winter exercise, then you will need to blanket them daily. However, do get that blanket off of them every day and give them a vigorous brushing. If it's unseasonably warm with the sun out try and get that blanket off of them for at least two hours so they can soak in some Vitamin D.

Some short haired pets that live indoors will want a blanket in the winter when you take them outside but then again get it off and give a good brushing once you are back inside. Keep in mind their sunlight needs too and take advantage of a sun-break if possible.

Grounding

Grounding is something you don't hear a lot about but it is important. In our ever increasing technical societies with more computer this and cell phone that and everything else in between, we need more than ever to be sure our animals are grounding out every day to encourage a healthy nervous system. Without a healthy nervous system every cell of the body will be negatively impacted including those that make hormones and can affect their personality. Our indoor pets may live their whole lives inside walking on carpets, concrete, tile, or flooring but never the earth itself. Their feet need to touch the beach, or yard, or a dirt path to discharge any accumulated electricity picked up from around them. Taking dogs for a walk on concrete and/or asphalt won't accomplish this; it needs to be the real created ground. The same goes for us. And the same goes for poultry and livestock some of which also may spend their entire lives in a barn on a non earth floor. At least have an outdoor paddock for them so that they can have their feet come in contact with the ground.

Grooming & Bathing

Just as humans ought to dry brush their skin for optimum skin health your mammals require that as well. On a human the skin is the largest organ in the body at about 9 pounds for the 'average' 150 pound person. It acts as an additional kidney, excreting toxic waste and uric acid. A completely plugged up skin would see its inhabitant perish within about 24 hours. This IS an important organ! You can either groom them with a moderate hardness brush or you can do what we do for our dairy goats. Many counties have road cleaning equipment that involves a plastic bristled brush of some sort. Often you can obtain their worn out ones for free just by asking as it saves them dump fees to discard them. Preferably a long cylindrical shaped one but other shapes will do with some creativity. My husband supported ours by strapping the top to a post and the bottom to another post so that it is at about a 45 degree angle touching the ground. The girls love it. They walk under it scratching and dry brushing their backs, rumps and heads. Then they step over the low part to do tummies and necks. It sure saves me tons of time on brushing that you know I wouldn't get to. And it saves on fencing wear

The Accessible Pet, Equine and Livestock Herbal

and tear which is worth a lot!   If you can't do this then try to spend some time brushing every day.   Our horses accomplish this by rolling but of course that doesn't reach all of their itchy spots.

Consider trimming back or shaving off the beards on your goats if they are drinking water from buckets or stock tanks (or other non fresh water running source). Trimming or braiding exceptionally long manes on horses is a good idea as well.   Just the other day I scrubbed, cleaned, and refilled a 100 gallon stock tank just to watch Shekkinah drop hay, straw, and I expect also barn dirt into it that had been clinging to her beard.   Your tanks will stay cleaner longer if you keep their faces 'clean shaven'. This is very important for bucks during rut when they urinate on their beards to smell 'pretty' for the ladies. They will not get adequate water consumption if their water becomes tainted from urine soaked beards.

Bathing is also a good practice, but be sure you use something gentle for the soap that won't damage the skin.   My favorite to use is homemade goat milk soap; especially those with lavender, tea tree, eucalyptus, rose geranium, patchouli, carrot oil or rosemary essential oils added. All of these essential oils listed benefit the skin for differing reasons. Beneficial base oils could be almond, jojoba (wax), olive, rose hip, shea butter, or avocado to name a few. Goats' milk has been used for millennia to nurture the skin, rather than strip it as most store bought products accomplish. I avoid all of those with synthetic fragrances in them which will just add to the toxic load in their skin. We're trying to clean them, not repollute them. I'll put a resource for very nice quality soap in our appendix.

Bedding

This again is a topic you'll have to do more research on for the creature you are working with, but don't ignore it. It can something as simple as soft grass hay or straws of differing kinds or as expensive as rubber matting. Your floor base may determine what will work best as well.   At all costs avoid concrete, if possible as those were made for ease of care for the "EntreManure" mover, but any stock that has to spend time standing on these day after day is going to have extra joint trauma and inflammation at the cellular level at some point. There will be pros and cons to any type of floor and bedding you have, and some types are better for some animals than they are for others. Ideally, the bedding should keep animals that lay down warm and dry, and soak up or drain urine. Be sure that your bedding choice is not something that your animal can overeat on if it is not used to it as that can cause problems we'll address later in the book. Do avoid black walnut shavings in equine and camelids as these can founder them. Also avoid green shavings as opposed to kiln dried in any creature. They can carry mites and can also splinter into any mammary tissue causing mastitis whether the creature is male or female, milking or not. Some goats will nibble at shavings to the point where they cause an impaction in their intestines, so I tend to avoid shavings with my goats altogether. At fairs where that is all they supply I will apply a generous amount of straw that I purchase over the shavings in my kid pens. You will also want to learn for your area if you need to purchase a year's supply when the product is in season or if it's available all year without fail. Also see if there are times of the year when the price is better. We try to purchase a bit more than a year's supply of straw once a year to save us both time and money. As with hay be certain that your bedding choice is clean and dry and free of mold when you purchase it and store it where it will remain that way until use. Frequency of stall cleaning for each creature, climate, and set up varies as well. With goats we often topdress and let the underneath compost creating additional warmth for the goats. That works fine AS LONG AS you have adequate ventilation. If you can smell urine or feel wetness when you put a knee to the bedding then the time to clean that stall/barn was yesterday! The other extreme is with horses where often daily cleaning is necessary as their weight on their feet churns it up in the bedding or they will pack manure in their hooves setting them up for hoof health problems. Your level of air humidity will also affect timing on cleaning. We have to clean more often in the wetter months than in the drier ones, both because the animals congregate inside more and because the evaporation rate of the urine is slower.

When a stall is stripped here is a recipe for you that I was inspired with. I take my lovely bottle of lavender essential oil (remember not to use this around barn cats), and put 12 to 15 drops per cup of baking soda. I mix it real well (the best way is to pre-make it and let it age a bit), and then sprinkle that along the stripped flooring. It doesn't just 'cover' bacteria but actually kills it as well as discouraging fungi and some insect pests, is calming for your stock, beneficial for their respiratory tract and is enjoyable for you. It is safe enough to use this way

The Accessible Pet, Equine and Livestock Herbal

around your baby animals too. I shouldn't be surprised with how well this takes away the odor but I still am every time. Then we recover it with new bedding unless we want the stall floor to have some air dry time.

Fencing & Security

Unless you've been blessed with a multitude of acres far away from other farms or ranches you will need to address fencing. And for sure you'll at least need good fencing to keep your creatures out of any vegetable, herb, or flower gardens you may have. Again, the 'best' fencing is going to vary with the livestock, pets or poultry/ratite type that you have, where you live, accessibility, cost, your facilities, etcetera. It is way worth it to build it right the first time and in the long run will be cheaper as well. Sometimes you can find used fencing on craigslist or in a paper. Just remember with used fencing you may be bringing home some diseases with it so be very sure of what creature type the fencing was used with and consider sanitizing it as with an essential oil/water/soap blend like 80 drops of thyme, cinnamon, oregano or tea tree essential oil per quart of distilled water/vinegar and a tablespoon of dish soap in a sprayer. I like the sprayers that people use for spraying fruit trees for this solution. For biosecurity reasons with the goats we've always gone new with goat specific fencing though sometimes I've picked up and disinfected gates that were used for horses from yard sales.

Remember two things about your fencing, well, maybe three. The first is that the fencing should be built to keep your creature or creatures in (profound statement, I know). Secondly, be sure your fencing choice is SAFE for your creature. Vet bills and/or lots of salving and herbing are not something I like to do on something I could have avoided! Third and oft forgotten, is that your fence is there to protect your creatures from predators or areas of endangerment such as neighbor dogs (sometimes even your own dog!), coyotes, wolves, cougars, bear, sometimes humans, poisonous plants, unsafe geography, field 'junk' collections and more.

Because there is no fence that can completely keep out a bear, a cougar, a venomous snake, a bird of prey, or even a determined person you might consider learning about Livestock Guardian Dogs and how they can benefit you. There are several breeds that fit differently for various situations. Do some research and talk to different people about them. There is no one best breed for every situation. To us they are worth their weight in gold! Besides predator protection they also have called us when a goat has been in trouble. Our dogs have also doubled as goat midwives, stripping placenta fluids from nose tip to shoulders and carrying in just born kids out of the snow and keeping their mother with them while keeping the rest of the herd at a distance. A good one is amazing indeed. We have yet to lose even a chicken to a predator in the decade we have owned them.

Hoof & Nail Care

Please consider taking good care of your creature's feet. If they can't get around well due to neglect in this area their longevity can be negatively impacted and their feet or nails can be prone to infection. Some animals are able to get enough exercise on hard enough ground to keep nails or hooves worn down, but unless you own the rare exceptional animal you will still need to correct angles and lengths in areas not worn down. Incorrect hoof angles put additional stress on fetlocks, pasterns, knees, hocks, stifles, shoulders and hips which can cause the beginning of soundness issues.

I occasionally run into situations where people let their horses 'self trim'. I have yet to see a self trimmed domestic horse with correct hoof length and pastern angles from this practice. Usually they are quite grown out with chunks of hoof breaking off. 'Self trimming' works for wild horses because they put miles and miles on their hooves every day keeping them worn down, not self trimmed. They are also from generations of strong hooved horses (weak hooved foals become prey) so don't tend to break their hooves by chucks. Please keep your horse collection to the number that you can either keep up with their feet on your own or can afford to have them professionally trimmed on a regular schedule. They deserve that. Horses should be done every 6 to 8 weeks. My fjords require me to rasp and trim their feet in between farrier visits to keep pastern angles correct. My limit is two feet per day, but I don't let that stop me even though I have four horses. On kelp they grow that quickly. I'd rather have them well mineralized and deal with faster growing feet then to leave our mares undernourished. I still have them done professionally at two month intervals to keep them done correctly and to relieve my back of full duty. If your horses can be barefoot allowing the frog to come into full contact with the ground they will be healthier. I understand that some horses with weak hooves may need boot or shoe protection while that problem is remedied. Also some horses are ridden on ground that can be very damaging to hooves and do need shoes in those cases. Please don't let your horses go in the winter months. It took me into September to regain correct hoof angles on my horses that I acquired in January.

Livestock like sheep and cattle have a different trim schedule and some of these do keep their hooves worn down on their own. Keep an eye on them and find out from breeders that use their stock in the same way you use yours what would be the appropriate timing for additional hoof care if needed for your creature.

I trim my dairy goats' hooves monthly. Sometimes they go as long as 6 weeks but monthly is the goal I try to keep up with. I keep a written record on my barn white board so I can remember who I've done when. It is amazing how tiny of a portion of goat hoof you can shave off and how drastically it can change their hoof angle. My show string sometimes gets their hooves trimmed or rasped weekly. Hooves that are let go and curl and trap mud and manure against the sole sets up that area for rot. It also puts pressure in all of the leg joints just as it does in other livestock.

Animals that have nails that don't keep them worn down may be more likely to inflict injury on their (or your) skin which could set up the area for the possibility of a nasty infection. We once had a dog whose dewclaw nail curled around and started growing into the dewclaw pad area. Remember that those nails are full of bacteria too. You need to be able to clearly see where the 'quick' is so that you do not cause bleeding when you trim them. Seek advice from someone experienced in trimming the nails of your pet if this is new to you. I've never had to trim our cat or chickens, but have had to keep up with our older guardian dogs, my iguana when I had one and trim dewclaw nails on our younger Pyrenees.

Transporting

Please consider how you transport your creatures! If it's cold make considerations. Keep the wind off of them as even a tough hided animal will dehydrate as the wind whips off moisture at a faster rate. If it is below about 72 degrees my goats get a goat coat put on them when traveling. My girls (or boys) are body clipped for show in this case and even though they have a nice stock trailer with good bedding there will still be some wind chill from air circulation. My theory is I would rather have them a little bit too warm (NOT hot), then too cold. Warmth is life, cold is death as mentioned previously. In addition I don't crowd them.

On long drives I stop and offer water and light feed like hay. For the goats we might throw in an extra milking to keep them more comfortable. Many shipping fevers (pneumonias) could be avoided if this were thought through more.

For those shipping an outdoor animal in your vehicle during cold weather do not have your vehicle at 70 or 80 degrees in the cab and then just toss your animal back out in 30 or 40 degree weather (or worse) upon arrival to your destination. Keep your cab somewhat closer to the temperature that they will be moving to, if possible. Temperature swings are hard on them. This is especially true with young, old, or fragile creatures. I once aborted a trip I was making that was 4 ½ hours in 17 degree Fahrenheit weather. I was taking my bucks (male goats) to a semen collector. Though deeply bedded and double coated I still checked on them 30 minutes into the drive. They cried and complained to me loudly when I peeked in on them. That's all I needed to know that they were not going to do this trip. We turned around and took them back home where I gave them hot black strap molasses water to drink and then put them away with coats on and additional servings of hot black strap molasses water. The coats came off a couple days later on a sunny late morning when the temperature came back up some. It was not worth jeopardizing them.

We've had to equally plan on hot weather trips. I've hauled a few times in 107 degree weather through the central Washington desert and even just down I-5 in Oregon and California! In those cases I wet the animals down so that the evaporation from their skin would cool them. Stops I made were no longer than a minute to be able to keep airflow on them from driving. Parking in the shade does help some though at those temperatures, but you still don't want to be still very long. Additional water is always on board in case I need to have quick access to water for an animal. It takes thought, additional work, and PLANNING. Sure, this may sound like a lot of fuss to some people, but I have heard of too many people that have had animals die during or after transport during temperature extremes. Don't forget to have your vehicle maintained to do trips in this kind of weather if you must travel then. Getting stranded in temperature extremes is a recipe for disaster.

Animals can be calmed during shipping a number of ways but my favorite is using lavender. When I load an animal in a kennel for air transport I will either dab a touch of lavender essential oil on the hairs under their nostrils or will drop 2 to 5 drops, depending on animal size on the kennel bedding. I sometimes will have 60 to 80 drops in a quart spray bottle with distilled water in it, shake and spray it around in the air. Or you can do the stall freshener mix of lavender with baking soda and put that under your bedding or on the stall mats. Other herbs that can be drenched or fed include hops strobiles (flowers but not to dogs as a single herb), chamomile, clary sage essential oil cut at the same rate as lavender essential oil, and valerian root. Know how your animal will react to valerian ahead of time as a small percentage of animals it will excite rather than soothe. Remember to not use the essential oil products with your feline family members. Try to use whatever herbs you chose 20 minutes before traveling to allow time for them to take effect.

Size of Herd, Flock, Cattery or Kennel

I am certainly not here to step on anyone's toes as I want this book to be an encouragement. However, for the sake of our own sanity, and the well being of our entrusted creatures, this is one topic that shouldn't be overlooked. Look at your facilities, your pocketbook, your time schedule, and your family's needs and decide how many creatures you can really take care of fairly- for them and for you, and try to stick to that. You will need to figure in time for chores, time and physical ability to purchase, load, and move feed. Time and money for pen, fence and stall maintenance and cleaning is also a consideration. And then consider that the costs of those items will likely rise faster than the pay you bring home. If they are pet like in their nature like our goats and horses, then small group or individual time with them is important too. Take on only as many creatures as you can take care of well. If you find that all of your time and all of your spare change is going to support your creatures you will burn out emotionally, physically, financially, and likely spiritually. Your family will also burn out and your creatures won't receive the care that you really hoped to give them. Expect more health issues in this situation both for you and your creatures! A wise friend mentioned to me when I was first getting goats that if one gets behind on their hoof trimming then they have too many goats. I've had other people mention that they gauge their herd size by if they get behind in their stall cleaning. The hoof trimming gauge works real good for me as we trim all of them every month and record it on our barn whiteboard. Keeping our numbers reasonable means that there are that many less tons of hay and straw per year that we have to handle by hand and that many less bags of grain. You need to have family time and personal time too. For us that includes one day a week (usually Sundays) where nothing but the essentials are done. Every month or two includes a day trip of some type that is not farm related to get us off of the farm. We also try to take a vacation once per year where both of us can go somewhere together. After all, my relationship with my husband is infinitely more important than that with my goats! I'm not saying to choose the schedule that works for me and my husband but that farms have a way of running us. Be sure your family is scheduled in for some times for fun and refreshment. Your herd and pets will thank you for the better care because you are refreshed and not strapped financially or time wise with their upkeep.

Feed and Hay

Different types will be available in different parts of the country. I'll cover some specifics in the next chapter. However, your feed should be clean, of good color and completely free of mold and bugs. It should smell clean and taste clean. I will literally take a few kernels of the grain or a few leaves/stems of the hay and taste it. I don't eat it, I taste it. I taste for any off taste or bitterness that could be indicative of mold; as long as I am sure I am not tasting a clean herb that can be bitter, like dandelion. Grass hays and alfalfa should be sweet. The EXCEPTION to the taste test is this; If you do not know what the plant is in your hay and you do not know for sure if it is toxic or not, do NOT taste it. Most of us have heard stories of animal poisonings due to poisonous plants being mixed in the hayfield. If you think there could be chemical contamination of the grain or the hay do NOT taste it. Blister beetles can inhabit and be baled into alfalfa hay in several parts of the country and are severely toxic, killing the stock that accidentally eats them. I reemphasize that you be sure there are no poisonous plants in your hay. You can consult your county extension agent or local agricultural office to learn what those may be in your area or the location your hay/feed is from. You can also peruse some websites or check out books from your library. As well, be on the lookout for GM (genetically modified) alfalfa, corn, soy, beets etcetera. Europe calls our American GM foods 'frankenfoods'. If you are curious do a web search for Morgellon's disease if you have computer access to learn more. This terrible disease has been linked by matching DNA studies of Genetically Modified foods. Labeling is not required for GM foods or products in the United States at the time of this writing.

How one knows they are feeding enough hay to their goats is a question I get sometimes. We feed hay two, sometimes three times per day at our farm. When I go out to feed if I find that there are no stems left over equating a 'clean' plate, then I didn't feed enough. It's likely that the goats on the bottom of the pecking order did not get enough hay to eat. If I find, however, that there is a lot of stem left over and pushed around then I fed too much. We try to strike a happy medium between the two extremes. This will not work for some types of animals like horses, which will usually eat everything they are fed even to excess. We will also watch their individual weights which I explain more below.

Water

Ideally water should be clean pure H2O. Nothing more and nothing less. All water other than distilled water is hard water, containing inorganic (nonliving) rock minerals. Those rock minerals are taken in, a little is assimilated, some is eliminated, and some to a lot is retained. The retained minerals may never show up as a causation of symptoms in your farm creature or pet being that they generally live a few decades less than we do, but they do collect and they certainly can cause problems. You may find them in body organs (like kidney stones), on veins and arteries, in the urethra (urinary calculi), in joints (some forms of arthritis), and even in brains that begin to harden (some forms of dementia). Depending on where you live, differing minerals will be building up. At my farm calcium is prevalent. I can sometimes get a teaspoon out of one gallon of water that I distill! I won't even mention what appeared (and we smelled) in my distiller when I took it on vacation with me to a large west coast city. Yuck! Let's just say that municipal waste water purification systems sometimes offer a false sense of security. Plant minerals are fully assimilable and fully eliminable, and don't build up due to the living carbon atom that is attached to a mineral when a plant uptakes it and assimilates it into its cells. Remember that areas that have soils that are very high in a particular mineral, like selenium or arsenic to name a couple, probably have water that is also high in that mineral. That water can be the key to an inorganic mineral overdose. Not usually right away but over time as those rock minerals accumulate in the tissues of your creature and slowly poisons them.

There are many water systems out there but unless filters are changed or cleaned very regularly (often weekly) then virus, bacteria, and fungi will breed and grow in them. City water comes complete with synthetic add ins and pharmaceuticals that do not filter out of the water. So what does one do?

Personally for my drinking water I use a water distiller and run our well water through it, not city water. It is the closest we can get to pure H20. It is said to be 99.9% pure. I'll have a link for contacts in the appendix. Some people's argument against distillers is the ph, as it comes out acidic. BUT if that water is chewed as all liquids should be to mix your saliva with it then the ph will come in around 7.4 which is right at blood ph. Perfect. Without impurities. This is also the water I will use when I make teas and decoctions for my goats, me and my other creatures. This water, called a 'thirsty water' will draw 30 to 35% more of your herb phytochemicals (plant chemicals/nutrients) into your water, making a stronger product. It also upon consumption will slowly dissolve those nasty inorganic accumulations in the body and carry them out. It will not dissolve organic, plant based minerals that have been assimilated into your body tissues.

The Accessible Pet, Equine and Livestock Herbal

I would love to have nothing but distilled water for my goats but that is not possible for us at this time. But what I do, and we are in a cleaner area to do it (Siskiyou mountains), is I rain barrel our water during the wet months. It does keep the rock minerals out of their water. And then again as no air is 100% pure we do herbal cleansing in the goats which they would need anyways since no air is pure and no feed is pure.

During the summer months I have to use our well water. In those months I compensate by giving my creatures raw apple cider vinegar either in their water or in their grain. A 100 to 200 lb animal can have between 1 and 3 tablespoons of this in their water intake or food per day. Calibrate up or down for your creatures sizes. This will help dissolve out any rock mineral accumulation and reduce some toxic accumulation.

In the winter months it does not hurt to offer warmed water if you have the ability to do that. Your creatures will drink more water, increasing their wellness and decreasing the possibility of an impaction in the gut which is more common in the cold months of the year.

Weight

Learn from your veterinarian or a trusted experienced breeder of your creature type how to check and look for correct weight on your animal. In general in dairy stock and most racing stock, you should be able to just barely see some of the framework, but have a healthy fat covering over that framework including the ribs. I am not talking about protruding bones or a sharp feel over them, but they should be easy to feel with an easy to slide over the ribs fat layer between your hand and their body. Draft, meat and other stock will tend to have a bit more covering. Also learn where to check for weight on your creature. I cannot even count the multitudes of times I have had people point at my goat's stomach or rumen area and exclaim what a fat goat that is. Then I go into my spiel that what they are looking at is the milk factory production unit where large amounts of feed must be processed to be able to milk their genetic potential. Then I show them that I gently but firmly pinch skin behind the elbow, on the barrel of the animal for weight. On my dairy goats that should be ¼ to ½ inch in the summer, and ½ inch in the winter. In very cold weather climates where it is often below freezing, then up to ¾ inch wouldn't be too much for the winter. On my horses I like to see an average of ½ to 1 inch of cover (easy moving tissue) over their ribs, depending on the time of year. Learn what the numbers should be for your breed and type of creature. An animal of proper weight will have less health and structural problems, will have better longevity, and less reproductive problems statistically when compared with underweight or overweight animals.

Remember that our animals are entrusted to us and depend on us for their care. They will reward you with companionship, memories, entertainment, productivity, a good working relationship, and perhaps a wink (yes, the goats wink) or sloppy barn kiss as well. It's a rare day that my 4 year old mare doesn't get horse slobber on my arm or coat.

Chapter 3 Supplementation and Feed

I used to buy the rock minerals available at the feed store for my creatures just as I had been taught to do as a youth.   I do still keep one block in with my bucks (of Redmond real salt mineral block), in case we don't get kelp out to them from time to time,   but I'll list several supplements and why I like them along with a couple to be cautious about.   Then you decide what may work for you.

I want to take a minute to talk to you about 'Offensive Herbalism™" my own phrase.   Most of our society is into defensive this, defensive that. By that I mean to try to help an issue after it has become observable.   I'm into Offensive Herbalism™ rather than defensive herbalism.   If you decide to follow some of these recommendations, you will be building a stronger, healthier animal that will be able withstand stresses to its system and stay healthier than its counterparts with similar constitutions.   Season this information with love and good husbandry and you have a powerful, synergistic combination!   It's much easier, cheaper and time effective to nourish healthy animals then to deal with issues caused from nutritional neglect.   I wish our humans in our world would figure that out with themselves.   I had one person suggest to me that they thought the purpose of herbalism was to build a strong immune system so that invaders could be readily fought.   Though an admirable premise, and in part, true, I expect you have gathered enough information from this book to see that my suggestion is building a healthy entire animal from the cellular level. This gives us an internal environment that is unfavorable to invaders, thus making the immune system's job a much easier one.

Alfalfa

Why would I list alfalfa under supplements?   Alfalfa is currently the most mineral rich land herb that we are aware of. Having tap roots that can draw minerals 12 feet and further below the earth's surface, it reaches minerals that other grasses, legumes, and even many trees can't.   It's also one of the rare plants containing vitamin D.   We take this herb for granted because we can buy it so cheap (price it per pound or ounce at the bale or ton rate, believe me, it's cheap compared to other herbs that I purchase) and it comes to most of us in a bale. It is also a slow gentle cleanser for the system. Please don't miss this herb. Alfalfa is an important prenatal herb and is very important for unborn creature development as well as for young stock growth. Lucerne as it's also called, helps build that all important mineral and calcium store in the bones of milking stock starting in their youth which helps to prevent milk fever (hypocalcemia) and loss of bone in the fetlocks during third trimester. It is also very valuable as a portion of the dry feed for working animals such as horses that are worked at moderate to high levels daily. In those I suggest a minimum of 1 big handful as a starting point. Horses with known HYPP problems probably will need to forgo alfalfa, however.

I feed alfalfa hay to pigs when we have them to use our excess goat milk and then we sell them to people that want drug free raised pigs. Our pigs receive no grain. They reach finishing weight at 5 months of age on the raw goat milk and alfalfa verses the "normal" 6 months and finish with tender, yet firm meat. I feed alfalfa hay to our chickens and our baby goats. Sometimes mix in powdered alfalfa or other herbs for my dogs' food and I drink powdered alfalfa in my greens mix and smoothies. Literally everything benefits from the nutrition in this herb.

If you have an animal that is an easy keeper or one that is not working hard you will want to feed alfalfa as a supplement and not as the whole meal. That would be at normal dosage rates as discussed in other portions of this book. My fjord horses would get too fat and would try to founder on an alfalfa diet. So they get two small handfuls of alfalfa stems that the goats don't eat or one handful of the hay with the leaf still in it twice per day. Then they also get a small flake of grass hay and a large flake of oat straw also twice per day along with whatever herbs I'd like them on.

Non working dairy goats (not bred or milking or growing) should also be limited in their uptake of alfalfa. For them (100 to 200 pounds goat sizes) just one or two large handfuls out of a flake of hay, or 1/4 cup of alfalfa pellets twice a day would be a sufficient amount of alfalfa for nourishment. Use this principal with any of your stock. If they are growing or working hard then their bodies will utilize more nutrition. If they aren't working then just feed at normal supplement rates.

Watch when you buy alfalfa hay that it is dry. Not so dry that the leaf shatters off of the stem, but it should be dry enough so that when you break open a bale and take out a few stems it should pass the 'twist test'. While holding the stems in both hands twist them. They should break within 3 twists. If it is still holding together it is too wet and quite likely be starting to mold (become toxic) and even could combust and start a barn fire. I've had to send hay back that I didn't want to stack in my barn due to fire & health concerns. Also be sure there is no 'dust' in the hay. Sometimes that dust really is dust but often it's a fine mold that goes airborne when you pull flakes (sections) of hay apart. Taste that hay. It's likely to be bitter and off color having some grayish and or whitish tint to it. Again watch for unidentifiable plants, beetles, etc. A reputable farmer will let you break open a bale to look at it. If I have one hesitant then I would purchase the bale and break it open. I've yet to have a farmer not let me break open a bale though to inspect it. They usually are pretty proud of hay that they worked hard to put up well and don't mind showing it off. I was at one farm this year looking at hay and when I rolled over a bale in the field I found a wet bottom and slugs underneath it. Needless to say, we didn't get any.

If you are using alfalfa pellets please be sure of their quality. Smell them, taste them, check the color- they should look fresh and should not be 100% uniform in color. Make sure they are not overly dusty. Sometimes companies will take damaged hay that should never be consumed by anything, put it in pellets, spray paint them, and resell them so they don't lose their hay crop that should have been compost instead. Pellets would not be my first choice as they are high heat steamed in many cases to press them- giving up nutrition in the process and sometimes binders are added and not always on the label. If you feed alfalfa pellets, then feed them at a lesser amount then you would alfalfa hay (25 to 33% less by weight), as there will be less or no waste. Also be sure an animal doesn't gorge on them, and then hit the water. They will expand in volume immediately and can cause an impaction or bloat emergency. Introduce any new feed to your animal gradually over a couple of weeks. When we used to feed pellets, I'd feed some hay first to prefill the greedy gobblers, then put out the pellets after at least a half an hour of hay eating so they couldn't overdo it. Your livestock will still need the hay as their GI tract REQUIRES fiber that has length of stem to it to keep a healthy peristaltic action. Remember, you are feeding alfalfa for its rich mineral base, along with quality protein. If you have pregnant, growing, or lactating stock it is imperative in my mind.   Try to find organic, non GM, or unsprayed if possible.

Have an unused corner of land, even just 10 feet by 10 feet?   Prep the ground and plant alfalfa in it. You can harvest it with a Scythe or machete as it grows and feed it fresh.   Start at one end and by the time you work through to the other end ideally the front will have grown up enough to start harvesting again.   NEVER feed frosted alfalfa (or clover).   It will cause frothy bloat which is an EMERGENCY requiring quick action and is very difficult to work with. Wait until it thaws out. Make your mini alfalfa crop even better and plant some oats with it. Livestock candy!   I can imagine them pushing on the fence for it even now.

Here's a quick and likely unpopular note on 'cattle quality' hay. It is a common practice for hay that is starting to mold or suffer water or other damage to be sold as 'cow hay'.   Just because cattle are larger and can stand inferior food longer, that does not mean that they are not sustaining liver damage from this practice making them more susceptible to dis-eases, parasites and lower production or rate of gain. If it wouldn't be clean enough for you to eat consider before you feed it to something else.   Spoiled hay on our farm goes into our garden aisles where it composts down and provides nutrition for our soil and plants.   This is a WONDERFUL use for spoiled hay. I also line the edges of herb beds with it which makes those areas easy to mow and maintain. As it rots down my beds become larger or I can add it to a bed I want more soil on. Reputable hay farmers will replace bad bales. Find out if you need to return the bale to them before you toss it on your garden though. They may require it to exchange for a good bale. I always ask what their policy is before I buy from them.

Baking Soda

I am listing baking soda here because it is often used with dairy goats as a support in conditions of bloat or acidity.   Though it can be put to good use in an acute situation, I want to caution people about the practice on some farms of using it as a daily supplement.   Some people add it to their daily grain ration.   Baking soda does dissolve organic minerals that your animal needs to support its tissues and body functions and causes your creature to flush those much needed minerals out with its urine. So using it daily can put your animal into a state of mineral deficiency in bones and other tissues (including the heart) and also can be hard on the tender kidney, urethra, and bladder tissues. If one does use it for an occasional situation they will want to address soothing the renal system and feed some additional kelp for a few days to replace any minerals stripped out by the soda. If your animals have a chronic acidosis problem then you will want to address their entire diet, pasture exposure, and GI tract health, not just cover it up with baking soda supplementation. I'm sure glad I don't have to counsel my goats on giving up their soda pops. I couldn't imagine keeping their hard working bodies mineralized if they were consuming those!

Barley

Juliette de Bairacli Levy, in her book, <u>Herbal Handbook for Farm and Stable,</u> mentions barley as the goat cereal. Barley has been used for millennia and is even mentioned in the Bible as a common livestock feed. King Solomon who was blessed with phenomenal wisdom by God about creatures, plants and judicial matters had his horses fed barley. Besides being mainly carbohydrates for energy production, it contains some protein and has been used to help support those recovering from chronic conditions as well as being soothing to the digestive tract. Barley has been used to help the body slowly but surely remove congestion in the lungs and urinary tract. See also Oats below. I prefer a blend of both.

Black Oiled Sunflower Seeds

I like to feed these to my goats, a small handful each milking. They are used sometimes to feed to poultry or ruminants due to their higher protein and fat contents. Unfortunately spoilage in these seeds can be hard to detect and I almost killed my two best does with them several years ago. If you get a batch that has molded you will see the mold often start on the inside of the seed first before you can smell or see a light mold dusting on the outside of the shell. The seeds are harvested late summer and early fall and then the year's harvest is stored.

If those seeds are harvested in a humid climate it's difficult to dry them properly. If they are stored or transported at any time in a way where they are exposed to condensation, excess humidity, or fast temperature changes they can mold. When you do get a problem, the mold will accumulate and begin to damage the liver. So if you use them upon opening a bag I'd suggest smelling well to see if you could catch anything at first. One should also look carefully for any fine whitish or grayish 'dusting' and you ought to look for any holes in any seeds indicating possible insect damage. You can also crack several open and look inside. Don't be afraid to take the bag back if you are not sure of its safety. However, if you have lung conditions do not breathe the contents of the bag. Most of the bags I purchase are fine but occasionally I need to return one.

Black Strap Unsulphured Molasses

All molasses is NOT created equal. The first and second refinings of molasses result in a product that is high is sugar and low in minerals. The first refining being the cheapest product and that which often finds its way into our livestock feeds. This type of molasses has the same problems as other highly refined sugars like white; being an excitotoxin. Excitotoxins cause rapid firing of the nervous system while at the same time depleting the precious minerals from the body, including the nerves, heart, adrenal glands, kidneys, musculature, bones, and brain. It also increases body acidity and is traumatic for the pancreas to keep up with. These refined sugars ask the system to perform above a healthy normal while burning out and depleting the tissues. Also sugars as in these first and second refinings shut down the immune system. In humans that averages eight hours. Sulphur is sometimes added to the process to get more volume to the finished product. Sulphur on its own can be caustic. Sulphur is what makes garlic and onions hot. Watch out for its use in prepared pelleted feed and sweet feeds. We try stick to whole feed types without molasses and then add black strap if we want to. The easiest way I've found to dispense it is to fill used food grade containers like ketchup squeeze bottles and keeping it in my milk/feed room areas. Then I can just squeeze out the amount I want in their whole grains or herbal supplements right before I feed. As much as I don't like to store feed in plastic it is much safer for me to keep plastic containers in my concrete floored rooms than glass. My goats have been known to flip things off of the counter in my milkroom. Goofy 'children'!

Black Strap molasses, unsulphured, is the third refining and is considered high in minerals and low in sugar. It's a very nourishing and powerful blood building supplement. I take it myself due to it being a rich source of B vitamins, calcium, copper, iron, magnesium, selenium, manganese and potassium. So when I mention molasses in the text, know that I am talking about unsulphured, black strap. You can find this in most health food stores. Small animals like cats, iguanas, and young baby goats and lambs and similar sized animals may get ¼ teaspoon mixed in their feed and medium sized dogs can get ½ teaspoon to 1 teaspoon. Miniature sized goats up to 100 pounds and similar sized stock can have ½ tablespoon. From 100 to 200 pound creatures (large dogs, goats, sheep, alpacas, etc) I like 1 tablespoon twice per day. For creatures up to 800 pounds (ponies, llamas, larger pigs, mini cattle, etc) I prefer to supplement them with 1/8 cup and for standard sized horses and medium sized cattle ¼ cup works well for them, again twice per day if possible. Draft cattle, draft horses, large mules and warmblood sizes can be increased about that. I prefer a heaping ¼ cup in those cases.

Browse and Pasture

This would be pasture and/or meadow or wooded access where possible. Our animals do not benefit from the monocropped (single plant variety) pastures of today. They perform better receiving the varied nutrients and fibers from a selection of pasture and browse. The longer stem fibers benefit and encourage peristaltic action, the smooth muscle movement within the intestinal tract which moves digested food remains down towards their outward goal. The exercise obtained as they wander about grazing and browsing is an additional bonus; as will their exposure to fresh air, breezes, sunshine and country harmonies like birdie choirs. Even traditional grazers, like cattle and horses, will eat some shrubs and brush if given the chance. Just ask anyone that has had a horse, cow, sheep, or pig get out to find out what happened when they got into the orchard, flower or vegetable garden! We won't even mention how fast goats can clear a garden here if given the chance. Ugh.

Cayenne- Capsicum annum or C. frutens

Yeehaw! You should see the eyebrows rise when I mention this hot little daily supplement! Cayenne is THE FIRST AID HERB. If there were only one plant available to us on earth for alternative help in emergencies, this would have to be my first choice. When you don't know what to do in a situation, this is what you do first. Even when you know what to do this will still many times be what you do first. What creature would not benefit from having an herb that helps the body build a healthier circulatory system and stronger heart? This is another supplement I take. Chock full of B Vitamins and also quality Vitamin C you can hardly go wrong with this herb, as long as you are working with at least 40,000 HU (heat unit) cayenne. You can use a hotter pepper, but there is not a medicinal benefit to do so; maybe just some bragging rights which I certainly can't claim. It is also an amazing endurance herb and can help a person or creature gain more energy even after the first dose.

Always dilute this herb with some type of suitable liquid before using because it is hot. If you don't, your creature can feel like they have a hole burning through their stomach. How do I know? Because I've done it to myself! Remember it won't harm, but you'll be hard pressed to get another dosage into them if you forget to dilute it. I have a goat that will suck it right out of the syringe when diluted in water. Carrot juice, fruit juice, and runny black strap molasses are great things to mix with this. On occasion I'll also use a milker's own milk to dilute it with. I have a girlfriend that takes a piece of bread and wraps garlic and cayenne into these mini sandwiches for her goats. They gobble it right up for her. It can also be mixed into wet feed which works especially well for pets and poultry and pigs. If you are using the powder as a daily supplement start with a very small amount to get them used to it. Over 2 to 4 weeks work them up to a small pinch for the small animals up to 20 pounds. For the 20 to 35 pound group I like ¼ teaspoon. For the 35 to 100 pound group I like ½ teaspoon. For the 100 to 200 pound group I like 1 teaspoon, then ½ tablespoon up to 800 pounds and 1 tablespoon for the standard sized and larger group.   For emergencies sometimes we'll double that but for daily supplementation at twice a day those amounts are nice goals.

Carrots- Daucus carota

I remember a bad joke my high school agriculture teacher told us one day. "What is invisible and smells like carrots?" Bunny farts… Ha ha ha ha ha…   I guess it co (liuldn't be that bad of a joke as it has caused me to remember this intelligent and hard working teacher all these years later.

Carrots are one of those superfoods that we consider for a prenatal program. Several minerals, very high in assimilable calcium especially, liver supporting, alkalinizing.   If I could not get a hold of alfalfa hay or if I had an animal that I could not give larger amounts of alfalfa to (like HYPP horses or very easy keeper animals), this would be an herb I would be feeding LOTS of!   I have heard it said that one pint of carrot juice has more usable calcium to the body than 40 jars of calcium pills. That may be an exaggeration, but it may not be. The point being that the juice will be completely bioavailable and the pills, especially those made from inorganic sources, won't. I often juice carrots for my own personal benefit and add some cayenne to it for a kicker and some Practical Synergy…   Ok, it's an herbalist thing. But try it, I dare you. Maybe you'll even like it. Sometimes an un-well goat or other creature will get carrot juice as part of my herb plan for them. If you have a choice, selecting the more brightly colored carrots like the deep oranges, reds and purples will have greater amounts of nutrition including higher antioxidant activity. Consider that when you purchase seeds for your garden. My juicing pulp gets shared with my goats at milking time. Sometimes my chickens get some and our dogs also. My horses get carrots thrown in with any other herbal supplements I give them. I wish I could 'hay' carrots and get them by the bale. They'd be put to excellent use here.

Cod Liver Oil

I sometimes hear about people giving cod liver oil to their pets, and sometimes even to their livestock. So what exactly is cod liver oil? Modern cod liver oil is made from the fat found in cod fish including the oil from the liver. The liver, being one of the two primary internal organs for detoxification, is where buildup of toxic fat soluble chemicals remain unless purposefully cleansed out with herbal cleansing. Body fat also, as a protection to the body's organs, is another primary storage center for toxins that the liver and kidneys were unable to process and get out. So when one is supplementing with cod liver oil they are also supplementing with the highest concentration of any toxins the fish has been exposed to and not cleaned out during its life. I'm not just talking about the mercury that people associate with fish but any and every of the thousands of synthetic toxins that are out there as well. I do not know of any cod fish on a four to six month herbal cleansing program before they are turned into these types of products. There is also the danger of toxification from an over accumulation of vitamin A from these animal source products. Since they are not a whole herb product, the body will have difficulty eliminating this source of extra vitamin A. Now remember this the next time you want to feed your dog beef or pig or other types of liver or kidneys. In today's world even organic is going to have some level of toxic exposure and accumulation. If that weren't true I wouldn't have to reclean my kidneys and liver quarterly- even though I live in the country and am pretty careful about what goes in my mouth and on my skin!

Comfrey- Symphytum officinalis

Every farm and even every apartment balcony ought to have some comfrey growing on it. It does for tissue regeneration what probably no other single herb can do which could be why it's not a popular herb with the FDA. It can survive very low temperatures- up to 40 below Fahrenheit and can do hot summers as long as it has some shade. It does benefit from regular water, so plant it where you water a lot- near a stock tank, around orchard trees, at your garden's edge and similar locations. Do beware that in moderate temperature or damp climates it will take off and be invasive, so be sure you put it where that won't drive you crazy. Along a fence line would be ideal. Just keep it far enough from the fence that the stock doesn't reach through and eat your young plants. I like my plants 1 to 2 feet further out then the longest goat neck in our herd. Otherwise they'll kill it out before it has a chance to get going! Make sure that fence line is strong or they will work that fence for it. If you can get roots, cut them into 1 inch or larger sections and then plant. Or put some in a spot where you can rototil it. The following year til it up, then when the leaves start popping up you can usually just gently pull on those and dislodge them, and plant them in their new home.

This is another deep rooted, very rich in calcium and mineral plant that I would feed lots of if I didn't have alfalfa access. Like alfalfa, comfrey sends down incredibly deep roots and it can be hayed and stored. Even with free choice alfalfa available, I like to feed my goats and horses comfrey a couple times a week. If I had an animal with a weak or damaged liver I would do some liver support work for a few months before feeding this in any large amounts due to one or two human anecdotal cases of liver tubule blockage in severely compromised livers from the phytochemical allantoin in the comfrey. It has been calculated that the human overdose rate for comfrey would be 40 cups of tea per day for 40 years, so we consider it a very safe herb. Just use wisdom. This is another plant I'd love to be able to get by the bale!

Diatomaceous Earth or DE

Even though this isn't herb I'm going to discuss it here as I get asked a lot about DE. First let's think about what DE is. It is the sharp skeletal remains of tiny sea creatures. People that dust their animals with it never seem to remember to put a respirator on their animals within breathing distance nor to wear one themselves. So they in turn, as they dust, they breathe in these tiny sharp particles which could be compared to breathing in fiberglass. Then these sharp little diatoms can go slicing and dicing on any tender lung tissue they come in contact with. I do use DE but I use it as a bug control under and around the outside edges of the house in areas where animals won't be exposed to it. It works mechanically. As the low crawling bug bodies come in contact with it their body is pierced and they lose their life fluids and die. Is that what it does in the lungs one cell at a time? The bag

I have here mentions that if the product gets wet then it needs to be reapplied to be effective. So take that thought and think about it's sometimes use as an oral dewormer. The animal you are giving it to has a wet digestive tract starting at the mouth and ending many feet later at the anus. Thinking about these two points causes me to have a hard time with wanting to add a crushed sharp glass like product to my creature's menu. Remember just because a product is 'natural' does not mean it is beneficial in the long run. Mercury is natural, but you won't find me using that either even though mercury is still used today in medicine as an ingredient in vaccines.

Flax Seed

Flax is our omega oils super plant. Others to consider are purslane and chia seed, which also contain high levels. I always suggest flax seed over the use of cod liver oil. First, flax is less expensive and that really does matter in today's economy and if you are facing supplementing several animals versus only one or two pets. Second, there is not the risk of mercury toxicity that cod can have. Third, cod liver oil is from the liver which is the cleansing organ of the fish which will be full of what? Toxins! Toxins are what I'm trying to get out of my stock, not put back in. Fourth, it is an animal protein product not being a living noncholesterol nutrient source. And if you consider taste there is NO comparison! Simple stomached animals should have it ground FRESH so they can utilize it as it begins to oxidize immediately from air touching it causing free radicals. A simple coffee grinder in the feed or tack area will suffice for grinding with a small pastry brush to clean the grinder out good. In the house I use my Magic Bullet. Ruminants can have it fed whole in the seed unless it is one with GI tract damage then it should also be freshly ground. A 100 to 200 pound animal can take up to a tablespoon per day, but a teaspoon once or twice per day is sufficient for most.

Garlic

Garlic is a wonderful herb. If there were only two medicinal herbs on the planet garlic would be my other choice. But I don't have to choose so just know I am very thankful for this gift!   Allium sativa is one of those plants I use anytime a creature is ill.   There are 23 to 35 known antibacterial phytochemicals in garlic. I think it is safe to suggest that as we learn more about nutrients we may find even more. It is also antifungal, antiparasitic, antimicrobial, antiviral and an immunostimulant.   Garlic is also a wealthy source of probiotics/enzymes.   In humans we like this herb to assist the body in cleaning veins and arteries, which also is something to consider in pets that eat animal products.   It's a great general health supporting herb but for absolute best results it MUST be used fresh.   One of the most important ingredients is gone about 15 minutes after it is cut into or crushed.   I feed it blendered with water, carrot juice, or olive oil, whole, pressed into feed, mixed with black strap or any way I think is the easiest way to get it down them.   Remember my friend that makes garlic and cayenne sandwiches for her goats. I've even heard of people pressing it into peanut butter (use organic please).   A 100 to 200 pound animal would use 2 "woman sized thumb joint" sized cloves, sometimes double that.   Two cloves is roughly the equivalent to one human dosage of penicillian for activity.   That means your 9 pound housecat is going to have just $1/8^{th}$ of a clove for its regular dose.   Occasionally there are reports of Hemolytic Anemia in cats and dogs consuming large quantities of garlic. It only seems to be a problem in some domesticated pets and I wonder if there isn't a relationship between the amount of vaccines they and their ancestors have had along with their personal toxic load, plus the garlic that causes this.   Studies would be great to have here.   I have no problem with giving reasonable quantities of garlic to my pets. I have found that most of my goats will take this readily if they are not feeling well, but usually pass on it when feeling well. Or they will take it for one or two days then pass it up. So if you use it as a supplement you might follow this pattern at the correct dose for your creature- 1 or 2 days on, then 1 or 2 days off, unless you need it longer for an acute situation.

Grass hay

This takes in a whole number of grasses- brome, orchard, timothy, couch or quack, blue grass and more. I am not talking about the high protein hays here. I prefer not to use them. I believe our high protein fixated society has created something that may be damaging to kidneys and joints in the long run from creatures being fed these things having to process and clear out too many proteins. This if often the case in large dogs that are fed the high protein puppy foods as puppies. Their body grows too fast; the joints fail to keep up with the growth rate and don't develop to be as strong as they should. I believe many hip dysplasias et al. in dogs could be avoided. I use grass hay to add variety to the diet of my dairy goats during the times of year when the pasture is dead or the weather is too wet for them to go out and graze. When I lived in snow country there were several months a year where the pasture was also under snow. Some of you are nodding your heads right now! Anyhow, this is how I would continue to give my goats variety. If they are lactating, then I would only let it be 25% of their hay (pasture access counts for that), the remainder being alfalfa (of course!). When they are not lactating and before they are third trimester in their gestations I may increase the grass hay amount fed by weight to 33% of their hay.

Your livestock animals that depend on hay for their diet should have either quality pasture access or some grass hay as part of their total hay ration. Some animals, like camelids or non working (not pregnant, lactating, or working) stock should have quality grass hay rather than alfalfa as one half to ninety-five percent of their hay diet. Horses, unless they are working extremely hard should have at least half of their hay diet in grass hay. Drafts, some ponies and horses that are easier to founder should have grass hay for the bulk of their hay diet with alfalfa at supplement levels as mentioned in the alfalfa section.

When the weather turns extremely cold additional grass hay will help them generate additional body heat internally, as well deep bedding, blanketing and housing them out of the wind and elements. Always plan to buy more grass hay then you think you will need in case you have a colder than normal winter season. I like to try to buy enough to get me into second cutting of the following year in case first cutting is lost to rain.

What is my favorite grass hay? Good old fashioned meadow grass which has a combination of grasses and herbs in it, not monocropped (singular type of plant) hay fields. As I have mentioned before do be on the watch for poisonous or annoying plants. Also watch for any of those annoying plants to take seed and get established on your farm. Get rid of them immediately. I ripped some puncture vine out of my yard last summer and am I so glad that I took the time to root it out every two weeks last year. I haven't seen it back.

The best grass hay I've ever seen in my life was in the Austrian alps- grasses, ladies mantle, yarrow, herb robert (cranesbill geranium), dandelions and more swaying in the breeze, soaking in glorious rays of alpine sunshine, all to become that year's hay to well nourish its partakers through the winter months. Oh how I wish I could duplicate that here!

Kelp

Remember the name of our most nutrient dense land plant? Very good (alfalfa)! Here is our ocean counterpart. The interesting thing about kelp is that there are no nutrient deficiencies in the ocean. Just be sure you are using cold water kelp to avoid more toxic areas of harvest. Also watch for adulteration of your kelp with salt. That is done sometimes to be able to make more money on the kelp. It should have a hint of salt flavor but not be overpowering. My favorite brand of kelp is harvested in Iceland and we are able to get it with an organic label. The kelps from cold water are cleaner from toxins than are temperate water kelps.

I add it to my milkers' grain every feeding and sometimes to my dogs' goat milk. I mix ¼ cup of it with my horses' herbal supplements too. My poultry benefit from it being mixed in their mash. I also add powdered kelp to my kids' lambar (baby bucket with nipples for their milk). Sometimes I add additional herbs to their kelp. A 100 to 200 lb animal can use up to a tablespoon per feeding, but 1 teaspoon is sufficient for most. Lactating and third trimester animals should have double- one dose for them, one for milk production or the babies. My very heavy milker gets 3 tablespoons every 12 hours at milking time. She is currently nine years old (that is considered old) and is still incredibly strong on her pasterns. This is an awesome supplement for those of you with reptiles. It's another great calcium/supporting mineral source for those fast growers like iguanas. You can sprinkle a pinch to ¼ teaspoon of the powder on their salad depending on their size.

I believe that kelp allows animals to adjust to times of stress and weather conditions better just as kelp supplementation helps garden plants resist temperature extremes better. Plants have proven to be hardier, withstanding heat waves and unexpected frosts better when given high mineral supplements such as kelp. It makes sense. The more nutrition allows the body to build healthier and stronger cells.

Moringa oleifera

Moringa is a fascinating tree of the tropical and subtropical regions. Being very high in several nutrients including vitamins A, some B, C, the hard to find D and several more nutrients including protein (all of the essential amino acids plus many more), selenium, and calcium, this tree is a Godsend to tropical regions. All parts of the tree are used including the pulp that is left over from pressing the seed oil. The leftover pulp is used to purify water. I look forward to moringa becoming more affordable in the future as supply increases, so I wanted you to at least be aware of this plant. It seems to work in a gentle manner in its nourishing abilities, so moringa has been used quite a lot in failure to thrive types of situations in humans. Seeds can be obtained in the US and it can be grown in pots for the leaves and brought inside before freezing weather hits. In very southern locations that don't freeze it can be grown outdoors.

Nutritional Yeast

Nutritional yeast is a B vitamin powerhouse including B12 which is harder to find in plant foods. You can serve it with feed or add to kelp. For myself I put it in smoothies or on popcorn. Any animal under any kind of stress or workload will benefit from this. Do NOT mistake it for brewer's yeast, which is used to make fermented drink products and can also feed Candida albicans. Brewer's yeast often is the yeast found at feed stores. Why? Because it is cheaper that nutritional yeast and you will usually find that the least inexpensive choices are selected for animal feeds rather than the wisest choices. One teaspoon per day split up between two feedings, is plenty for a healthy 100 to 200# creature. Consider supplementing more if it's ill or working, pregnant, or lactating. I like N yeast so well that I have it in our Better Daze herb mix product.

The Accessible Pet, Equine and Livestock Herbal

Oats

Warming, energy giving and soothing are all important things to remember about oats. From skin irritations to nerve and stomach irritations this is an herb to consider being a part of your feeding program. Oats, especially the straw, are also another quality calcium food which is beneficial to every muscle (including the heart muscle), to the nervous system sheath, the nerves, bones, tendons, and any connective tissue. Without enough plant based calcium in the diet your creature can not thrive. Our goats love it when we throw out fresh oat straw for bedding. Besides rolling in it we have to make sure and put enough out as they will consume some of it as well. As mentioned previously oats with alfalfa make a good team. The best oats for nutrition will be those that still include the hull instead of the rolled and sometimes steamed dead product. My horses also benefit from clean oat straw as a part of their hay diet. Since I can't feed them as much grass hay as I would like to because the fjords get fat very easy, I remain guilt free knowing their tummies are full with a quality tummy protecting high plant calcium feed. In animals that can't eat the oats or oat straw, a tea can be made with distilled water and given with their other foods.

Olive Oil

Olives might be the most calorie dense food around. No wonder I love them! Olive oil is also nutrient dense and antibacterial. Used along with water intake, olives and their oil can completely support life and do it abundantly so. Young stock to old stock that can't eat or won't due to nausea, get olive oil skin/mammary rubs as well as measured olive oil drenches (carefully give orally). Even the oil on the skin or a back end enema (anal) will get pulled in by the body and utilized. I use it often as a base when giving herbs orally or I mix herbs with some then mix it in the grain/feed so that the herbs stick to the grain. When you purchase your olive oil remember a couple of things. Extra Virgin and virgin are going to be your highest quality, being from the first pressings of the olives and the most nutrient dense. That fact also makes them expensive for livestock use. It is what I use in my kitchen. For my stock I find regular olive oil that is cold pressed or expeller pressed, NOT solvent (petrochemical) extracted. I also purchase from places that have a very fast turnover of products. You do not want to use any oil of any type that has gone rancid- that is very dangerous to the liver because the fats in it will now be free radical loaded. Though olive oil keeps 2 to 3 years, sometimes an unpopular brand can sit in a warehouse or store shelf for years before being sold. Please do not substitute another type of oil for olive. Other oils 'twist' in their molecular structure during the heating to process them, creating a dangerous level of oxidants. Some, like canola (rapeseed), even if cold pressed, are toxic. And none match the nutrient profile of olive. Coconut oil is another oil that may not twist under heat, but I have not been able to find definitive information on that at this time. However; your olive oil still has the greater phytochemical profile and is less cost.

Peanut Hay

As I do not live anywhere near areas that grow peanut hay there isn't a lot I can say here. But, if you use it do try to get organic. Peanuts, grown conventionally, tend to be a very heavily sprayed crop and very prone to liver damaging dangerous forms of mold. This is why I suggest you use only organic peanut butter if using it to make herbs more palatable for your creatures.

Raw Apple Cider Vinegar

Raw ACV, as it is often referred to, is another mineral powerhouse with the added bonus of lots of enzyme/probiotic activity. A 100 to 200 pound animal can have a tablespoon up to 3 times per day added to their feed, or put in their water. This is another daily supplement that I like to take for myself. It will also help the body rid itself of inorganic rock based minerals and can be used in emergencies in larger doses. When buying my ACV I look for the types that are unpasteurized (raw) that are also made from whole apples verses just the core and peels. I also like them to contain the mother which contains many of the probiotics we are after. Whenever I open a new bottle of ACV I always put the dregs from the previous bottle in it and shake it well. My understanding is that there are some Amish batches around this country that are 100 years old or older from doing that.

I have used ACV to get a high doeling (baby girl goat) birthrate several years back. I put about 1 cup of it in their 5 gallon water bucket changed fresh every day. I started doing this TWO months before breeding season and continued it into breeding season. Part way through the Fall I stopped giving it. The following Spring I had several births in a row of twin, triplet, and single doelings. It wasn't until later in the year that we started getting bucklings again which corresponded with when I quit serving it. Amazing.

Raw Honey

Another wonderful probiotic source which is also antibacterial is REAL raw honey. And yes, I will use it with newborns without any fear, as long as it is REAL honey from correctly cared for bees. Real honey never goes bad. Two thousand year old raw honey has been found in Egyptian pyramids and was still viable. If it crystallizes just gently heat it in a double boiler type of situation or place your container in hot water (not on the stove). In fact at some point real honey should crystallize. If it doesn't, that should raise a red flag for you. This is a "know your beekeeper" type of product. You want honey that is centrifuge extracted (not heat extracted) from bees that are allowed to eat their own honey year round for nourishment rather than the industry standard of sugar water laced with antibiotics. It should also be from bees that have access to wild land or pesticide free land as opposed to those shipped around and placed in sprayed orchards to collect pollen from. A tablespoon up to 3 times per day is a wonderful supplement for 100 to 200 pound creatures. If they have a blood sugar problem, then use just a fraction of that amount, if any until you've made progress on that condition. All of you beekeepers out there that are doing honey correctly- THANK-YOU!

Raw Meat

For those that are feeding canine and feline friends consider their diet. In the United States we like to feed them processed bagged and processed canned foods usually made from the junk that is leftover in meat processing plants. I suggest that this diet also can give them issues with constipation. How many of us have seen a dog straining to eliminate? That should NOT be. Sure, with their straighter alimentary canal (the route from mouth to anus) than ours they still tend to have regular bowel movements. Eating that processed dead food is going to cause weaker stomach acids and allow for some sludge and mucous to glue itself to the intestinal tract. Look at the health problems they have nowadays. Increases in cancer, diabetes, and more, similar to the human health situation. I realize that there are better quality dog foods out now but remember they are all processed DEAD food.

Consider taking some time to slowly adjust their diet over to some raw organic or natural raised meats, some sprouted grains, and some raw or very lightly steamed vegetables, and some fruits. I suggest switching no faster than then ¼ of the diet per week taking one month to change their diet over. First I would consider adding some raw vegetables and fruit, up to 10% of your cat's diet and up to 25% of your canine's diet. This change can be made the first week. The second week I'd start adding some organic or naturally raised raw meat to their diet and removing some of the processed food. As mentioned earlier in the book I do not endorse feeding liver or kidneys to pets due to their toxicity levels. Now if you are fortunate to have a resource that has been raising the animals naturally for generations on clean ground in a cleaner air area then you might consider it in the diet once or twice per week. Just remember there is not going to be a pure set of liver or kidneys so you may need to compensate with your pet's herb program, or just avoid these organs. The third week you might add two teaspoons to a ¼ cup of cooked whole grains for over 100 pound dogs to their supper dish. Better yet, soak the grains overnight and serve them soft but raw. This could be barley, oats, hard red organic wheat, emmer, spelt, quinoa, chia seed (does not need to be presoaked), amaranth, millet, cooked wild rice or cooked brown rice. I also like herbal supplements like Vitalerbs by Dr. Christopher or Fir Meadow's Better Daze or God's Greens. These and kelp can be sprinkled and mixed into their feed. Watch their wellness improve as they become well nourished. Raw goat's milk (NOT pasteurized) can be given in a small amount daily and REAL farm raised chicken eggs can be given about 2 times a week. Herbs can also be mixed into part of an egg or the goat milk and then mixed into your pet food.

The Accessible Pet, Equine and Livestock Herbal

My dogs relish carrot pulp left over from my juicer and they love apples and pears. Grapes, raisins, and similar should not be fed to dogs. Though wild dogs and foxes can have them, I suspect our toxicity levels in our dogs, mixed with grapes is what can cause renal (kidney) failures. Also avoid any sugar types of products. I had a client once whose show hounds got into a bag of a health food store sugar product and it took their livers to 10% function. If they get any sweetener at all it should be real green (not bleached white and containing anti-caking fillers) stevia, evaporated cane juice, agave, maple syrup, real raw honey, date sugar, figs, and etcetera. Avocados should also be avoided in dogs. Heavy onion or garlic feeding should be avoided in cats and dogs. I have heard of very healthy vegetarian dogs out there so I know that can be done with proper herbal supplementation. Afterall; before the flood during Noah's time all creatures ate vegetation. If you have a hard working dog or are in a cold climate be sure they do have some raw animal products.

Salt

Salt is one supplement that we need to provide for our creatures. I prefer sea salt but if blocks are needed one can look into Redmond Real Salt blocks for livestock. Their salt is earth mined out of old salt beds that accumulated after the great flood. Celery is a good plant source of sodium, but feeding it in quanities large enough to meet the needs of livestock would prove to be quite a challenge. A teeny pinch of sea or celery salt can be added to the raw food diets of small pets, increasing that to a teaspoon for the 100 to 200 pound animals and a tablespoon per day for the large creatures like equine and bovine if you serve it with their feed. They will need increased amounts on hot days and decreased amounts on cool or cold ones. I prefer to let them free choice their salt so that they take the amount they need; not the amount I think they need. There is no need to be afraid of real salt. That is a far cry from the processed and refined white stuff with toxic additives like aluminum to make it flow freely and be well preserved. That is the problematic 'salt' that will cause circulatory system problems. Lactating animals should have access to free choice loose salt as many of them will not be able to consume enough salt off of a block to keep up with their body's demands.

Soy

Soy is another controversial product that doesn't have to be.   Very high in protein and containing all the essential amino acids that humans don't produce on their own, it is used sometimes in cheap feeds to get the protein levels up higher. The key to soy is to be sure you are using WHOLE SOY, not a protein or soy product; and be sure that it is non GMO. Most soy in the US is genetically modified. If you use whole food organic soy which will also be non GMO, you should not run into the estrogenic problems that can occur with soy products or isolated soy protein products. Certainly don't let it be a major portion of the diet-human or creature. Other complete protein profile foods to consider are chia seed, nutritional yeast, watercress, and moringa.

Sprouted Grains

Whole, unsprouted grains are quite acidic once processed by the body and many of their nutrients are not bioavailable in this form.   Sprouted grains; however, contain 300 to 1000 percent MORE nutrition that is available to the creature and they become alkaline to support a healthy bloodstream.   I sprout grains and pulses (pulses contain legumes and seeds) in jars and food grade buckets.   Use lukewarm distilled water if possible at room temperature and often within 12 hours they are already sprouting.   You will know by tasting them.   They should be soft and sweeter than the unsprouted form. At that point the grape sugars have converted which increase the digestibility and utilization of the seeds.   You can see from this how the same grain can be fed at one third to one half in quantity of the unsprouted rate,   to achieve even better results. Just account for the increase in weight and volume from the water they have soaked in. I also soak wheat and barley in the winter time for my mid to late morning breakfast cereal. I put hot distilled water in a canning jar with the whole grains of wheat, emmer, barley, spelt, or whatever I feel like the night before. I use about ¼ to ½ cup of the grain per person.   Then I drain and rinse in the morning and add some raw honey, cinnamon or pumpkin pie spice, Mexican vanilla, raisins or currants or blueberries, maybe coconut and some gently warmed almond or coconut milk. Now we're talkin'. Who says eating healthy has to taste funky? You can share this with your cat and dog without the raisins also.

Stinging Nettle

This herb probably would make it into my top 5 or 6 herbs. This is such a favorite herb that I started some from seed and have a nice little bed of it going now! My friends from Washington state where we are originally from think I'm nuts for planting this one. Nettle can be fed wilted, dried cut and sifted (crushed), powdered or made into an infusion (tea). It is one of the few herbs containing vitamin D, the sunshine vitamin. It contains sufficient amounts of all the macronutrients (protein, carbohydrates and fats- the seeds being especially rich in fats). Urtica dioica is useful for nutritional support for animals that are very ill, lactating, pregnant, need blood panel improvement, working, in need of gentle cleansing, internal organ support, etc. It's a nice all around herb and another I think every farm should have. Nettle is also one I would gladly hay and bale and fill a barn with if I could.

Feeding Fast Growing Vegetarian Lizards/Reptiles

Anyone that has worked very much with iguanas or other vegetarian lizards can appreciate the challenge in feeding them to help them reach their potential size and health. They grow so incredibly fast when they are young that they can get into calcium deficiency problems quite quickly. Remember how important calcium is to the heart, bones, and nerves. You are going to focus on a wide variety of foods not just one or two types and you will want to feed it fresh two times per day to encourage adequate food uptake. By focusing on whole foods and herbs, their body will be able to eliminate any minerals that they don't need from their food avoiding dangerous buildups in organs or the skeletal structure.

Foods for them (may your lunch or dinner plate look similar) are berries such as raspberries, blueberries, grapes, apple, blackberries and strawberries. Try to keep raspberries and/or raspberry leaf as a daily food. Pick at least two or three from this list every day.

Dark leafy and green vegetables should be a part of their daily diet as well. Collard greens, alfalfa, romaine lettuce, broccoli, asparagus, and some mustard greens are all vegetables to look at. Consider others as well, but try and get two or three of this list in every day and rotate the vegetables used every shopping trip or walk to the garden. Do not feed spinach, lambs quarter or other greens that are high in oxalates very often if at all. These foods can tie up the calcium from being usable and is not a wise thing to do to such a fast growing reptile.

Include some orange into their diet. Grated carrots should be daily (give them some of your carrot juice pulp), some yam sliced thin and steamed (not overcooked), orange melon, organic pumpkins (sliced thin and sautéed or lightly steamed). Do not feed pumpkins to them that have had candles in them. The fragrances and lead in the candles will make the pumpkin toxic. Try to pick one more orange food besides the carrot.

Herbs beside alfalfa and red raspberry leaf fed daily can be white oak bark, comfrey (perfect for growing lizards as long as you have maintained their liver), nettle, dandelion, kelp, slippery elm bark, marshmallow root, or moringa leaf. Try to have two or three of these. Moisten their feed and sprinkle the powder on, or mix it with their fruit or orange foods. Blend a few of the herbs and give just a pinch per feeding. Fir Meadow has a Hi-Cal herb blend for these situations.

You can also serve a very mild herb tea (made with distilled water of course) for their water. Raspberry and/or nettle here would be an excellent choice. They can have it every day. Once your animals are mature, because they will not buildup rock minerals in their body, you can keep them on this same diet.

If you have an Ig, give it a hug from me!

Feeding Insect or Rodent eating Reptiles

That could be snakes, lizards, or you name it. If their food is mealworms, crickets, and the like, you can spritz their food with moisture and then sprinkle herb powder on them. Start out with barely any to be sure they still eat their food. You can also sprinkle the herbs in their bug's food for the bugs to eat. If their food is rodents then you can feed the food an excellent diet supplemented with

The Accessible Pet, Equine and Livestock Herbal

herbs which will enable them to better nourish your reptile. Giving herb tea to both the food and your reptile is another sneaky way to increase their nutrition. You might start with a mild one like stinging nettle or raspberry.

Grain Mix Recipes

I'll share a recipe with you that Kristie Miller of Michigan (www.landofhavilahfarm.com) and I came up with. She asked me to help her develop a recipe in 2009 with what she had available to her. This recipe comes in at about 12.9% protein, and is chock full of nutrients. Use nonsprayed and GMO free where possible and sprout it if you can. 12.9% protein is completely acceptable for a lactating dairy goat IF they have free choice access to high quality alfalfa. I have fed goats for years at as low as 11% protein grain and still have had competitive show goats that can milk top ten milk records and keep body condition and sound production for years in a row. If you are not feeding alfalfa then you will have to increase the protein on working, third trimester, or lactating stock. Approximate protein amounts are listed. Remember they will vary a bit due to plant species used and where grown. You can buy the parts yourself and mix it or if you live near a feed mill sometimes you can have them make up your mix for a minimum order of one half to one ton. Do NOT use mills that also process chemical fertilizers with the same equipment! Besides goats, this could be used for horses, cattle, camelids, mules, donkeys, poultry, pigs, and even a bit for the farm dogs- especially if sprouted.

5 pounds of barley (11%)

1 pound Austrian winter peas (22%)

1 pound of wheat (10.8%)

½ pound of millet (12% protein)

2 pounds of oats (12%)

This makes a total of 9 ½ pounds of mix. Then she sprouts it, and adds flax, comfrey, raspberry, and carrots to topdress it. In warm months she adds raw ACV to discourage mold.

If you don't have access to one of the above grains, then substitute another similar percent grain or readjust the amounts of the others to keep the percent where you need it. You'll notice I don't have corn in the mix. Corn has a high propensity to mold as well as a high probability of being genetically modified. Correlations have been found between corn feeding and parasite loads in some studies so I avoid it when I can.

Kat's EZ Goat Mix or a Nice Ruminant Mix

Here is a grain recipe that I use for my high performing dairy goats. Without the sunflower seeds it can be used for other stock as well. Sprouting it makes it even better, but in warm months you will need to add raw apple cider vinegar to it to keep it from spoiling. Here is the recipe and the math to get the protein percent.

3 Parts/pounds whole oats   (12% protein) $3 \times 12\% = 36$

3 Parts/pounds whole barley (11% protein) $3 \times 11\% = 33$

1 Part/pounds black oiled sunflower seeds (15% protein) $1 \times 15\% = 15$

$36 + 33 + 15 = 84$ 84 divided by 7 pounds total mix = 12% average protein of this blend.

This is a very simple recipe that gives us 7 pounds of grain mix at 12.0% protein. Then I add kelp and herb mixes like Fir Meadow's Kop-Sel, Fresh Start, Better Daze, Dworm BWW or whatever I think they need at the time. Goats that need additional support in weight because of their age or strength of lactation may get one or two more ¼ cup portions of black oiled sunflower seeds or 2 to 3 carrots added to their grain pan to increase fat and carbohydrate levels for them. You can also use olive oil or organic cold pressed sunflower oil (never heat it). Remember to start slow with your oils. See the Olive oil section for more advice. If you sprout this without the sunflower seeds you can give a bit to your dogs and some to your poultry and other stock.

Kat's Horse Mash or Other Simple Stomached Animal Mash

My horses have a different program. Our fjord horses are very efficient so we have to nourish them without allowing them to get fat which would put them at risk for founder.

Besides their handful of alfalfa hay, flake of grass hay, and flake or 2 of quality oat straw twice per day they get this mash once per day. The mash can be split up and served twice per day or heavier workers can have the same amount or more as needed two times per day. Whole grains can be presoaked at room temperature for a few hours to allow your horses or other simple stomached animals to gain more out of them.

If you make extra you can scoop a bit of this and add it to your dog's raw food blend.

1 – 2 cups of wheat bran (please note this is the bran, not the problematic endosperm).

¼ cup of oats or oats/barley mix   you can increase this for horses that are working harder or require more feed as some thoroughbred types do.

¼ cup of kelp

¼ cup of any herb blend I want. If I am feeding more than one herb blend I use ¼ cup per herb blend for these small draft horses.

¼ cup of black strap molasses

¼ cup raw apple cider vinegar

Hot water (preferably distilled). Use enough of the water to make an oatmeal or mush consistency with the mix.

My horses LOVE this nutrition packed blend. Just watch out that yours don't slobber this messy mix on you!

Kat's Hummingbird Nectar

Instead of feeding these precious cuties icky white sugar (with aluminum in it), hard minerals and red dye give this recipe a try.

1 Cup of distilled water

¼ Cup of evaporated cane juice (whole sugar with only the water extracted)

1 tsp of cut & sifted raspberry leaves

1 tsp of red berry juice for color

Bring water to boil, mix in sugar and raspberry. Lid. Add berry or cherry juice once cooled. Now doesn't that sound nice?

Kat's Bee Better Honey

1 pint of honey in double boiler on warm heat

1 tablespoon of cut and sifted herb(s) or 1 tsp of powdered

Mix and keep on warm for 3 hours, cool, serve to your bees.

Great herb choices are thyme, sage, lavender, rosemary, garlic. I would rotate the herbs and not use the garlic more than one or two times per week.

Chapter 4- Your Livestock Garden

I'll suggest to you what my DREAM livestock garden would be. You may already have been formulating some ideas while reading the previous chapter. After you read this one you'll probably wonder if I'm trying to recreate some sort of Garden of Eden or something. Well, one can at least try, can't they? Every plant in the ground is one plant closer to ideal. Choose what you want from here knowing that anything you do is more than what you were doing before, for which you are to be commended! My gardens are a continuing work in progress as I slowly improve soils with compost from my goat straw and tincture making leftovers (the millennia old fertilizing method that STILL works), and add new variety to my plantings. I really believe it takes a 3 year minimum to get the soil health where you want it if you are aggressive. I have watched that process up close and personal three times now. You should see the tomatoes at two different friends' houses coming out of areas that have had over a decade of goat compost added. I saw one cherry tomato about 8 to 10 feet high and just loaded with fruit about double expected size. Her husband even had to weld a rebar tomato cage for it! My kind of garden! At last count we have over 70 herbs established on site and of course we are adding more frequently. You will get there too if you want to, one herb at a time. A note of wisdom for you here. It's better to start off with a small bed that you know you can keep up with and get it going well before you add additional beds. That is why ours is still in progress. When the older beds fill we make new ones, knowing that the older beds have grown in more and will require less weeding, less maintenance time and less water than the young beds.

Consider where you put this garden. On my place I've been able to situate most of my plantings near fence lines so that as I clip items I can place them in outdoor feeders or along pasture edges. My vegetable garden is surrounded on three sides by cattle panels making it safe from the goats, but so easy for me to toss nonpoisonous "weeds" and herb and vegetable clippings at them which they greedily gobble. Whenever I go out to weed I have an audience waiting and watching! Part of your herb garden may need a shady area and some full sun depending on your climate. We also had to put in a row of Leland cypress trees to keep hot summer breezes off of the garden which only serve to wick moisture out of the plants at a very fast rate. Remember to consider the needs of your plants.

Unless otherwise stated, all of the herbs listed can be used topically and given orally (drenched or fed which I'll discuss much more of in the following chapter). Also I am listing herbs that are considered by herbalists and even Commission E (like the FDA in Germany) to be quite safe to work with. Do take note of the **emmenagogue/parturient/cathartic** herbs. Those should only be used only under the advice of a trained herbalist with pregnant animals as they have to be used correctly, if at all, in those situations or you risk losing your precious cargo (the unborn babies). Instead, look for another herb that does things you want to do without that concern. The tricky plants to work with really have no place in an herbal primer like this, so won't be discussed. If I don't talk about your favorite herb, don't be surprised. With about 350,000 herbs used worldwide we won't all have the same lists! I am trying to stick with herbs that are easily obtainable, and for the most part extremely affordable for you.

First take a look at the herbal supplements chapter and start your list there. Then consider some of the following. Don't be surprised if you see some 'weeds' in this list that you have spent your whole life trying to annihilate! In fact, when I was transplanting some mullein today, I also transplanted some Plantago lanceolota (grin). That is latin for Plantain. When looking for plants please refer to the latin name to get medicinal quality plants.

Alfalfa. Medicago sativa. As mentioned in the Supplements Chapter plant a strip or corner. If you let any go to flower enjoy the heavenly fragrant purple hues. The flowers and leaves can be added to your salads too. Prime harvest time is just before your alfalfa flowers. Beware of Genetically Modified varieties. Alfalfa is also a nice bee herb to have around.

Aloe. Aloe barbadenis. Aloe is my kitchen windowsill plant that I have used numerous times to cover fresh burns and even my sunburns. You can also use it for burns and tissue damage on your stock; it is wonderful! It's a nice mammary (udder) skin herb as well. Aloe is nourishing, protecting, and an antibacterial cell proliferant (cell division assistant). You can replant any leftover part of the branch that you don't use. It will grow. Do not use it fresh from the plant internally as you may get a purgative effect causing the bowels to clean themselves too quickly and perhaps with cramping. Only store bought aloe drinks that have had the purgative removed should be used internally. Aloe skin products often contain ingredients that are not healthy for the skin such as alcohols. Shop around. Of course I like fresh best but will take good quality gels with me when traveling.

Basil. Ocimum basilicum. Yum, yum, yum. I love adding bits of this fresh herb to salads, tomatoes, and even fresh smoothies and juices. It's heavenly on an olive oil drizzled baked potato too. It is so fresh and uplifting. There is a reason for that you know. Basil, which I like to refer to as 'Brainsil", is a brain stimulant by helping the circulation and enhancing brain function. I am wearing a drop of basil essential oil on the inside of my shirt (not my skin) as I type this so that I can do my best job for you. This herb is an annual which will frost kill. Start some extra plants in a planter and bring it into a sunny winter kitchen window sill so that you and your creatures can uptake its benefits all winter long. If it's winter when you are reading this you may be able to find fresh basil with its stems at a health food store or organic grocery store section. Take it home and try and get it to grow roots while sitting in a jar of water with a bit of organic soil added to the water. Transplant and keep it moist once you see roots forming. Reduce your watering to normal after you see it starting to grow, indicating that the roots are settling in and functioning. You can also start it in moist soil.

Blackberry. Rubus fructicocus. I can hear every Oregonian that reads this saying, "You've got to be kidding!" Blackberry was used by our Native Americans for dysentery and I have used it when I've been away from home unprepared, needing something for a creature diarrhea. Be absolutely sure it's not a plant near a road or one that has been sprayed before you use it and watch out for the mean stickers. I sometimes 'think' they try reach out and grab you on purpose. Oh yes, let me tell you from experience to not forget to watch out for bees and hornets, who sometimes seek refuge for their nests/hives behind the larger plants in this species. You can use the leaves and the root. Sometimes neighbors ripping it out will share them with you just for the asking. It does well in a variety of soils and light though full sun is preferred with moderate moisture.

Black Walnut. Juglans nigra. Remember this cannot be planted where equine or camelids (alpaca, llama, et al.) can get a hold of any part of this tree. Give it room to grow as it can mature to 60 feet or so, although you can keep it pruned down to about 15 feet if wanted.   This plant is a great infection and fungal attacker and can be used internally and externally on the skin for warts or fungal issues such as ringworm. Do remember that the natural organic living iodine in it will stain whatever you put it on.   It is also popular for its anthelmintic (internal worm discouraging) properties. We use the leaves, the hulls (at any age), and the bark.

Blessed or Holy Thistle. Cnicus benedictus. This is a wonderful woman's herb. Does anyone out there have any female breeding stock?   It is a wonderful galactagogue (milk promoting) herb, as well as encouraging hormonal balance, appetite, circulation, and is somewhat antibacterial.   This stickery friend is also an **emmenagogue**- cycle stimulating so it should be used only at lower doses with pregnant stock or as directed under the advice of a trained herbalist. Cnicus b. is an **emetic** (vomit inducing) so do not use above traditional dosage without care. That is however something to keep in mind if you have a nonpregnant creature eat something they shouldn't and your vet tells you to get them to regurgitate it back out. Or a child for that matter.   Get advice from poison control first. You can use the herb, root, and seeds. It is of course a very stickery plant so protect your hands with leather gloves if you are harvesting it. It grows well in sun and does well with light to moderate watering here.

Blueberries. Vaccinium species. Blueberries (nearly any dark purple/blue berry that is edible) are an antioxidant paradise, ready for your beloved animal's nourishment.   Any chronic condition will benefit from the leaves or the berries. The leaves should be picked green and can be used dried or fresh. The berries, well, it's rare they even make it into the house!   When a dairy goat doeling of ours a couple of years ago was recovering from a severe bout with pneumonia this was one of her favorite plants to self herb on. This is also a great heart herb. Any creature at any time can always benefit from heart nourishment.   It does prefer acidic soil so you may have to put some fir bark or sawdust in the planting hole with it if you live in an alkaline soil area (often arid areas).   I was recently able to find a variety that can handle soil that is a bit alkaline and that also tolerates more heat.   They are planted in partial shade and away from inquiring goat faces and are doing extremely well.

The Accessible Pet, Equine and Livestock Herbal

Blue Cohosh. Caulophyllum thalictroides. I don't have any of this growing yet and it's going to be some undertaking for me to get it to grow here, but I'll be trying! It likes wet and in the summer here we are hot and arid. This is a wonderful herb to use during creature birthing to help with contractions and placental expulsion. It is also useful for any creature wanting some balance to their hormones, and is relaxing to your precious mom to be. The neat thing about this herb is if you have miscalculated your animal due dates it will do nothing to get them birthing. It will just nourish and balance in that case. That is not true for the chemical used for this purposed that is available from veterinarians by injection. That one used at the wrong time will abort them.

Boneset. Eupatorium perfoliatum. Is a very nice herb for colds and flu types of problems. It is very drying (try a cup) as well as nourishing, so helps dry up and expel excess mucous as well as encouraging a sweat to help the body blow out toxins faster. Boneset is also beneficial to the stomach and gently encourages movement within the intestinal tract. One caveat though, you drink this herb infusion slowly, or feed it at half dose. It is also an **emetic** (vomit inducer) if you drink it fast. The leaves are used.

Borage. Borage officinalis. If nothing plant borage for its BEAUTY! Its flowers are a great bee attractant and change from blue to pink in color once the bee has pollinated it. Therefore you will see both colorations of star shaped flowers hovering over the bluey green leaves. Float the blossoms in your herbal sun tea and pick the very young leaves for your salads for a mild cucumber type of flavor. It builds endurance by supporting the heart and lungs, is anti-inflammatory, and also is a galactagogue (milk encouraging) herb. It starts readily from seed and once you get it going it will likely reseed for you. Do not feed to severely liver compromised animals; cleanse and nourish their livers for a minimum of 8 weeks first. The leaves are used. My goats like to reach for it through the fence. Remember 'borage for courage' and you'll remember some of its properties.

Burdock. Arctium lappa. Burdock is a wonderful blood cleaning herb with quite prickly burrs. Every cell of the body benefits when the bloodstream is healthier allowing the body to start correcting itself to normal. That is why it is known as an 'alterative'. Burdock being anti-inflammatory is beneficial for joint issues. The root of this plant, like dandelion, is another Inulin containing root and is beneficial for pancreatic support. The roots, seeds, and leaves are traditionally used. It needs to be harvested early spring or late fall, to catch the strength in the roots. If you plant burdock plan to keep it in an area your pets or creatures do not frequent. The burrs can make quite a matted mess to remove in hair coats.

Calendula. Calendula officinalis. Sometimes referred to as marigold or pot marigold in British herbals but please don't mix these up with the marigolds (Tagetes) at the garden center which are not edible! Calendula is a brightly colored yellow to orange daisy like flower with single and double bloom varieties. It is a bit sticky when you pick the flower heads. It is wonderful in skin preparations by supporting the body in its healing. It also is being antibacterial and antiviral. It can be made into an infusion (tea) and used as a wash for skin issues and infected wounds to great benefit. Taken orally it nourishes the heart as well as stimulating and cleaning lymph and being soothing to the GI tract. Eyes too, infected or inflamed will benefit from a wash with the petals. The seeds are high in fat and can be added to the ration of an animal needing more weight. I like this herb a lot and always keep some patches of the flowers going which are easy to start from seed. As true of many flowering plants if you keep the flowers picked they will keep sending up new ones. Late in the season I let them go to seed so that I have seed to get them going in more places. You can also feed the herb whole to your farmstock including the seeds. Calendula is fed to chickens in Mexico which is responsible for giving their skin that bright yellow coloration when you see them in the market. The flowers can be used as a yellow dye and is a nice highlight to red colored coats.

Catnip or Catmint. Nepeta cataria. This is a nice, if somewhat interesting tasting herb to promote relaxation for anything under stress probably due to the wealth of B vitamins that this herb contains. It also is considered a good respiratory support herb and digestive tamer. In flower its waves of lilac blue attracts a lot of bees and is pretty enough to bring a few of the silvery shimmery stalks in the house for the vase (as long as you don't have an indoor cat to wipe out the arrangement). It is easy to start from seed and the older plants can be divided in spring or fall during moderate weather and replanted to create more. I just cut a nice 4 to 6 inch section out by cutting down about 8 to 12 inches deep and then around the chosen section with a spade shovel. It also may reseed giving you more plants to move around. I have one out here that is a mound about 4 feet by 3 feet. Protect it from cats. Because it smells similar to their pheromones it can attract them and they may shred it! Because of this you also may want to keep it in an area that you don't mind cats visiting.

Carrot. Daucus carrota. The Supplements Chapter discusses this herb but please do add them to your herb garden. The volatile oils/essential oils/ fat soluble nutrients are very soothing to every cell of the body. Pair with that the incredible amount of nutrition, liver support, eye support and gentle cleansing action. Have fun and plant some of the redder or purple varieties which are higher in carotenes and antioxidants. It's very nourishing oil for the skin. If it weren't so costly I'd be using it on udders here.

Cayenne. Capsicum frutescens, C. minimum, or C. annuum. Cayenne has already been mentioned in the supplements chapter but I want to mention it again as I feel is a great herb to be growing in your garden. Just make sure it is cayenne or a hotter pepper. You need a 40,000 Heat Unit minimum pepper- most store bought is only 20,000 to 35,000 HU. Ask as it is important to have a therapeutic grade as you'll depend on this plant in emergencies. There is no medicinal benefit to go hotter so if you are a wimp like me you will stay near the 40,000 minimum. You can use the fruit fresh (use 4 to 5 times the dried amount) or dry and crush or grind them to powder. Grinding can be done with the dried fruit in a Vitamix, Magic Bullet, or coffee grinder types of blenders/grinders. I leave the seeds with the fruit. Just beware of any airborne particulate. It will sting (and be good for) your eyes and probably get the mucous moving in your sinus area quite well. Remember, that though it is hot, it will never damage any tissue, not even eyes. I speak from personal experience when a syringe of it meant for oral use in a doe back flushed into my eyes. Yeehaw!

This herb is heart and circulatory EVERYTHING. It is also the FIRST AID plant. If you don't know what to do in a situation grab this herb. It will give the body additional support with its Vitamin B complex and high quality C vitamins and circulation stimulation while you are thinking or praying about what else to do. Cayenne powder is also something I will grab to sprinkle on the ground around plants that I do not want cats or squirrels digging in. Cats will usually sniff the ground before digging their commode. If they get a good whiff of this they will head out somewhere else. It needs to be reapplied after a rain. You will see cayenne mentioned often in this book. I always keep powder and tinctures on hand in several locations, including my purse!

Chamomile or Camomile. Roman- Chamaemelum nobile, Anthemis nobilis. German- Matricaria chamomile, Matricaria recutita. Is it night time yet? Get a good quality tea of this millennia used herb going and it will be sleep time for me. A great stress reducer, mild muscle relaxer, and minor pain reducer to be kept in mind with injured or worried stock. It is also a wonderful tummy tamer for gaseous or other pain causing conditions. Wounds also benefit from washing with this herb. Blonde or palomino coated animals gain highlighting when washed with water in which chamomile flowers have steeped like a tea. You can give it orally in tea form, or use the powdered flowers. This is another easy to start from seed herb. Pineapple weed which has the same appearance sans the petals can be used as a substitute for German chamomile (Matricaria). The German has the more pleasant smelling volatile oils and though more expensive it is my preferred choice.

Cleavers, goosegrass, hitchhiker, bedstraw. Galium aparine. Just ask my patch out here how well it will want to grow for you. This may be one of the easiest to start from seed; watch out, it's invasive! But keeping it in bounds is well worth the trouble for its gentle blood and lymph cleansing work. Any extra I get I either dry or toss to the stock for an herbal snack. It is quite clingy and that does feel weird to bare skin. Wear gloves while picking it if that bothers you. I use the whole upper part of the plant.

Coltsfoot. Tussilago farfara. Its bright golden flowers come out before the main plant in early spring, followed by 6 to 10 inch elephant ear shaped leaves. The leaves are considered stronger than the flower but early in the year the flower is what you get first access to. Flowers and leaves are often mixed together. You can harvest it as soon as it shows and of course do dry some for next winter's stash. This is an amazing lung herb and can be used to support the lungs in any type of issue. It is a favorite of mine to put in lung blends and could be added to an onion poultice (see the Respiratory chapter). Tussilago f. can also can be poulticed over bruises and swellings. It likes damp ground. Mine is growing and spreading well

The Accessible Pet, Equine and Livestock Herbal

in partial shade and looks like it will be very easy to divide if I want to get it going in more locations.   Likely I will. I love this herb!

Comfrey.   Symphytum officinale.   I know I mentioned it in the chapter on supplementation, but I have to mention this favorite herb again.   It probably makes my top 3 list of have to haves.   It knits tissue together par none other that I'm aware of as well as being a great lung support herb.   The livestock LOVE IT! I've heard many stories of that being the first place someone's stock will go to if it gets out.   Thankfully due to the enormous root system it survives occasional assaults and provides more growth almost before you can blink. Well, not quite, but you get the point.   My goats fight over it here when I'm feeding it. Due to the FDA we are not allowed to put comfrey into oral formulations, but you as a herd, pet or flock owner can buy it separate or grow it and feed it orally or add it to blends that you purchase.   I can and do put it into topical use products. Just be aware to cleanse and nourish a liver for four or more months if it is quite damaged before you would use comfrey orally.   Over 99+% of the time it will cause no problem, but there have been a couple of known human cases over the thousands of years of use.   We won't reiterate how many cases of human adverse effects there are from just plain ol' aspirin per year yet that is allowed to be sold for oral use over the counter. Hmmmmm.

Dandelion. Taraxacum officinale. "Oh my, what is that doing here?" Is that what you are thinking right now as you roll your eyes? Another weed that has caused you distress, perhaps?   Well now it has a purpose. Yes you most definitely will find it growing among my flowers and herbs and even in my vegetable garden as I consider this weed probably in my top ten groups of must haves.   Taraxacum is another one of the elusive vitamin D containing plants, along with A, B, and C. So just remember that with Dandelion you get you're A, B, C and D's. It is one of the highest iron containing herbs we are aware of making it a huge help in blood building for those with blood issues or events causing blood loss. Since the iron is organic (living) it is completely safe, unlike supplements for iron that are not whole herb based.   It is another calcium and potassium containing herb making it a good support for pregnant, lactating or egg laying stock or pets.   Dandelion is a friend to the liver, spleen, and kidneys, allowing them to tone and clean themselves.   The mild flavored root contains Inulin which makes it an important herb for use with pancreatic issues. Its gentle blood cleaning and mild relief for constipation should not be overlooked either. I have counseled several to use this with good results when more preferred plants were not available to them for plant poisoning in pets and farmstock. It is a blessed herb indeed! I would also use this herb as part of an injury/tissue healing program for the nourishment if comfrey were not available. This is an important herb to dry and keep a winter supply of as you can see from the partial list of its benefits. Dandelion would be a plant that I would gladly welcome in my hay in volume. If you must weed it from somewhere at least allow your creatures to obtain the benefits of it. We use the whole plant and root. The flowers add lovely color to salads. I enjoy it personally as a tea. It can be fed daily as a supplement. We won't even discuss how easy this one is to propagate.

Echinacea. Echinacea purpurea, E. angustifolia. Oh yes you can grow this from seed- easily! Its beautiful purple petals and nearly black cones sure add delightfulness to any garden scene. I start more every year as I'm not sure anyone could have too much of this plant! Well known as an immune system stimulant and a protector of cell integrity in cases of venoms and animal poisons, this is a must have in your creature garden. The key to this plant is QUALITY (see my efficacy section in the foundations chapter). This plant is so often sold as poor quality due to the good money that people make collecting and selling this herb to wholesalers. So if you've ever taken it, then decided it didn't work it was the quality problem, NOT the herb! Good echinacea should give your tongue and mouth a tingling numbness when you chew on it. You can use this herb as often as needed (hourly is great) for up to 10 days at which time in the case of an illness it will no longer fool the immune system into going into an enhanced mode. You don't want to overwork your immune system that way anyways. But for several days in a row you can go for it and then take at least a three day break. The only limit being with stock to not give so much as to cause an enterotoxemia or founder problem by overdoing a plant their systems are not used to. We'll discuss more on that in those sections in the Digestive Tract chapter. So, any form of illness or toxicity has me reaching for this herb. It contains vitamins A, the B's, C and E and is also rich in iron and has many minerals. Because wild stocks have been largely annihilated by plant poachers, please grow your own or obtain your supply from reputable sources and resist the temptation to wildcraft. In fact, I have a challenge for you. If you get a good crop going why not plant a few in areas they are likely to succeed in the wild? The entire plant can be used, with the roots needing to be 2 or 3 years old before harvesting.   I prefer to use the above ground parts on plants when I can so that I don't have to sacrifice the whole plant.   That just requires me to use more.

Elderberry. Sambucus nigra, S. Canadensis. Make sure you are using the blue berried type and not the red berried which is toxic.   This is a great respiratory support herb, helping the body to clear mucous out of the lungs and upper respiratory. It's used widely for cold and flu support.   It has a candy/syrupy type of flavor in tinctures, so can be an easier one to get stock or pets used to.   We use the flowers and berries and yes, it really tastes that good.   When you work with herb tastes for awhile, you appreciate the real pleasant ones! You can get these to grow well and they like full sun. They can do moisture to arid as long as there is some water for them and good watering while getting established.   This is a moderate to large sized shrub so give it room to grow. I've seen some 20 foot tall specimens in the wild. Make sure you harvest the berries before the birds do! You might try gently tying paper bags over the berries just before they ripen as the birds seem to hit them the day before you want to collect them.

Eucalyptus. Eucalyptus globulus.   There are other varieties of eucalyptus but this one is considered the best and is probably the most readily available and the most affordable. It does grow in several areas of moderate climate and as long as we have it in a somewhat protected area it will even grow in parts of southern Oregon.   The leaves can be used in tea and are a favorite of mine when supporting respiratory tissues. It even dilates the bronchials after a deep breath in of the essential oil which can be important information for those creatures that have spasming or closing bronchial tubes.   They also make a great wash for infections or external parasites.   You will want to keep this tree away from your stock as some animals could overdo the leaves to a point of toxicity.   Unfortunately we started my tree the year we got an incredible cold snap. Needless to say I plan to obtain one again (God willing).   I remember driving along the wet side of the big island, Hawaii, a couple of years ago through some groves of eucalyptus trees. Even with the windows up their intensity wafted into the vehicle.   Oh, I delighted in this respiratory treat! But I was the only herbalist on the trip so the windows stayed up.

Eyebright.   Euphrasia officinalis. Now what do you think this herb might be used for?   Yes,   nourishing the eyes during any type of distress. From allergy caused, mechanical caused like dust or injury, or illness related problems.   Make a tea, strain well, and use as a wash. You can drink it as well.

Fennel. Foeniculum vulgare.   A fragrant plant and a favorite of mine in the garden.   It is useful as a purifier of the lymph, to assist with retained fluid release, and as a digestive stimulant and reliever of bloat and discomfort in the GI tract.   It is a traditional obesity support herb, taken morning and evening to encourage the body to release accumulated lipids.   It also has a very nice nutrient profile, even containing the elusive Vitamin E.   The urinary tract benefits from the cleansing and antiseptic qualities of this old time vegetable. Generally the seeds are used for traditional medicine, but the stalk itself is considered a table vegetable and can be fed to stock. The next time you have an upset stomach, chew a few seeds and see if you notice anything. Safe enough for the youngest of creatures. One note though for your garden. Plant fennel by itself. Most other plants do not do as well as they could if fennel is in their vicinity. Do not use the essential oil with children under about 6 years old or with young stock of that 'human age' equivalent. It's too potent.

Garlic. Allium sativum. Do not mistake this for the larger but much weaker elephant garlic.   Previously mentioned in the Supplements section this is another particularly easy plant to have in your garden. Plant it in an area where you can limit water to it when it's near harvest and knock the tops over on all of them once about 25% of the tops have fallen over. You also want to let them dry out a bit in between watering after established. Then I pull them up and dry on a wood slatted table, basket, or a corner of my deck.   Anytime you buy a bulb of garlic make it a practice to plant a clove or two out of it. Plant the biggest prettiest cloves to improve the strain in your garden. You'll have a good supply growing in no time. Yes, there are better times of the year to plant it (spring and fall depending on the type and climate),   but much of the time I can get this one to grow no matter when I plant it as long as the ground isn't frozen.   Stretch yourself, bend the traditional 'growing rules' on these herbs, and see how many more you can grow because you tried and God blessed. Garlic is a must have for me.   I always have a big bag of it and replace it every week with a fresh bag! I use it OFTEN for a myriad of issues.

The Accessible Pet, Equine and Livestock Herbal

Never rely on pre-jarred garlic, powder, or pills. Some of the large firms allow too much air, too long and often too much heat to come into contact with this herb when processing, losing much of its value. Odorless products are pretty close to worthless, so don't waste your money on those either. Your average dosages with garlic would be two to four cloves for a 100 to 200 pound animal. So for a cat that may mean just 1/8 or 1/9 of a clove! Cats that are overdosed routinely can get problems with Hemolytic anemia. So keep at the low dose for them, and don't use as a daily supplement. Animals that are on blood thinners need to be careful with this herb if used long term. If your creatures are on prescription drugs it does not hurt to check with your vet to see if garlic will be a problem.

Ginger. Zingiber officinalis. Warming, stimulating, energizing, and a circulatory enhancement especially for the legs, feet, head, and reproductive areas is what comes immediately to mind on this herb. This is THE antinausea herb. I also use it to relieve tense muscles anywhere in the body. Besides oral use I like using it topically nearest the area of concern. If a creature is trying to birth prematurely, we can try to relax the early labor contractions with a strong ginger fomentation applied warm to the abdomen. We also use it to encourage other herbs to stay in the system longer. It's another great assistant in cases of cold or other illness. Though there are not many places this subtropical plant can grow in the United States it can grow in a planter in the house. Consider it. Let it roommate next to your aloe. Roots can be acquired from many grocery stores.

Goldenseal. Hydrastis canadensis. This is one of the tougher plants to get going, but if you have the right conditions you can. This is one I'd like to get started here. Due to the effort involved I'm going to do some more study before I try to plant it. Please respect its place in the wild and think before you wildcraft this herb. It is another that has been subject to a lot of poaching and loss from the wilderness which is another reason to grow it yourself if you are up to the challenge, or live in the Midwestern or eastern US or Canada where it grows naturally. Then the roots need to be a few years old before you use them to reach a high berberine content causing their orangey yellow coloration. It is an herb that is definitely worth the wait. I use this plant rhizomes in nearly any infectious condition. It is expensive, but I think worth every penny in the results we've seen. Goldenseal is NOT an herb you want to use for a long time by itself; especially in pregnant stock. It will eventually tie up the Vitamin B available to your creature. So when you use it always be sure and supply a Vitamin B herb along with it such as cayenne or catnip or even Nutritional Yeast or Black Strap Molasses and don't use it at large doses by itself for a long period of time.

Hawthorn. Crataegus lavigata, C. oxycantha. I call it, "Heartthorn". Traditionally the fruit of this European native has been used, but studies show the leaves to be even more powerful. I like to use both. The powder has a nice 'Vitamin C' type of flavor to them, which they are high in, as well as A, B complex, iron, selenium and silicon to name a few. This is an important heart herb enabling the body to rebuild heart tissue after even substantial damage as well as to support its strength to avoid damage. It is a vasodilator allowing blood vessels to relax improving circulation. It also helps the body lower blood pressure due to this effect and by helping the heart to increase it's strength allowing it to pump more efficiently. Memory also benefits from this herb. It grows to be a fairly large tree and makes a good hedgerow planting. Due to its thorns you want it where you won't brush up against it all the time. I like nibbling the chewy leaves whenever I walk by this tree. By now you've probably figured out that I graze and browse as I am out in my gardens. It's not a bad plan, after all, our animals do that and most of them have better health then most humans.

Hops. Humulus lupulus. Quite the climber, hops will need to be planted where it has something strong to trellis upon. Hops is a beautiful, vining, unique strobiles (flowers), and very relaxing for nervous creatures both in cases of anxiety or sleeplessness as well as aiding digestion. It is considered another anthelmintic though I have never used it that way so I can't comment on its effectiveness. It is very nutritive with Vitamins A, B complex, and many minerals including calcium, magnesium, phosphorus, zinc, selenium, silicon, iron, copper, and iodine. The flowers are used, either whole or powdered, and can be fed or made into an infusion (tea). They can be stuffed into pillows so that the herdkeeper can get a good night's rest as well! This herb used by itself in moderate quantities can pose a problem for your canine family. This has been discovered by home brewers who have lost dogs that have eaten the used hops after brewing. I have never seen a problem with small amounts of the whole herb powder as part of a blend, however. It is picked in late summer or early fall as the strobiles begin to lose a bit of color and sound papery when you rustle them. The powdered glands under the scales should be orange and smell beer like. I pick mine in the late afternoon as they definitely will relax you.

Horseradish. Amoracia rusticana. Pungent, and wonderful when a bit is added to a salad dressing! This "make your eyes weep" root is just what is called for with sinus congestion by helping the mucoid matter to break up and flow out often quite rapidly. Very useful in lower respiratory (lung) conditions by helping to break up mucous making it easier for the body to expel. In small amounts it can be used as a poultice in the chest area as long as you put olive oil on the skin first and then remove it after three hours as longer may still allow the skin to burn. It is stimulant to the circulatory system and a tasty digestive aid. It needs moderate moisture to get established and somewhat regular watering. I have mine near my peppermint which also has higher water requirements. You can carefully dig around the root and harvest any portion of it any time of year that the ground is not frozen. You can divide it into segments containing a rootlet and replant to have several more plants including one in a pot to bring into the kitchen for the winter if you live in a snow or a frozen ground winter climate. I obtained my roots from a health food store in the produce section. Just a piece with a root eye will get you started. As mentioned earlier the essential oil from this root is extremely toxic. Do NOT use it. If you add horseradish in your juicing it needs to be a piece no larger than a ½ by ½ inch chunk or it will be too overwhelming for your system. The most common way to use it is to grate some and mix with raw apple cider vinegar. Keep it in your refrigerator.

Horehound. Marrubium vulgare. I really like using this silvery green, mint family herb when addressing lung issues. It is also a digestive aid and anthelmintic. I have several growing and once established it is a low maintenance plant and can tolerate quite dry conditions. We use the leaves and flowers.

Hyssop. Hyssopus officinalis. An herb of Biblical fame, hyssop is a powerful antiviral and is supHerb for expectoration and nourishing in the lungs. From allergies and bronchitis to pleurisy, this plant has been usefully employed. I love the fuchsia-purple hued blooms on this rather tall plant so give it some room to grow. Any of the upper (above ground) parts of the plant may be used. Be sure and cut it back in the fall right down to near the crown to prepare it for its winter's nap. Pruning it down a bit in the spring when it first starts to send up stalks will give you a bushier plant with more herbs to harvest during the year. Hyssop was the herb used in the Bible for purification after handling those that had departed. It was also the herb that a stalk was taken from to dip the blood of the Passover lamb and then put on the door mantle to protect those within the house from death. Powerful word picture.

Lavender. Lavandula officinale. Lavandula angustifolia. This is one of my very favorite plants. So much so that a bottle of lavender essential oil resides in my purse and it certainly makes my top ten list of herbs to keep on hand. Lavender is relaxing, antibacterial, antifungal, tonic (giving nutritive and a balancing effect to each body cell), a wonderful skin aid and cell proliferant (enhancing cell division). Aching muscles delight in this herb. Several types of bugs, especially moths, despise it. It is a wonderful first aid herb, helping to calm your creature, battle inflammation, and disinfect and encourage healing. I've used it for sunburns, lameness caused from joint sprains, very infected dog bite wounds, and blood poisoning streaks with wonderful results. This is a wonderful herb on lactating mammary glands to promote skin wellness and is safe for the offspring if they ingest some. I also use it in my stock trailer and air shipping kennels to encourage a more restful move. The fragrance is the icing on the cake! This plant is easy to grow and can tolerate some dryness. For those of you in areas plagued by deer this is one plant they will leave alone. Be sure you get a Lavandula officinalis/officinale/angustifolia to have a medicinal grade plant. Most lavender plants, you will find, have been developed for the cosmetics and perfume industries due to their greater volumes of less quality oil per acre and are not therapeutic grade (lavandin and spike types). I use the leaves, stems, and flowers. Since it is evergreen you may be able to harvest some stem throughout the winter if you are in a mild climate, though the growing season months, picked just after the dew is off of them. This will provide you with the highest amount of volatile oils. It can be used orally or topically. The prime harvest time for the blooms is when they are picked at full maturity before they fade.

Lemon Balm. Melissa officinalis. Watch out. Once you have this herb growing, after it seeds you will DEFINITELY have plenty of this herb the next season! It can be invasive to consider that when you decide where to plant it. It makes beautiful light to dark lime green mounds that grow to around 2 ½ feet tall in shade and sun.   A wonderful lightly lemon after dinner tea or evening chore time tea, your livestock and pets will also benefit from its nervine (relaxing and nerve nourishing/soothing) and highly antiviral properties.   This is a very popular herb in Europe that is sadly most overlooked here in America.   It dries well, but loses its medicinal properties more rapidly than other stored plants so keeping it in a tincture is best.   When using dried herbs, using a larger than usual amount as your herb stash ages is imperative.   I like cutting and feeding the extra to my goats in their hay feeders during the summer and fall months.   It helps to soothe them which I believe indirectly contributes to better milk production.

Lobelia.   Lobelia inflata.   Do not confuse this with garden lobelia bought at farm and plant stores that people like to plant in containers.   We are not talking about the same plant, so in my writings I am usually always going to refer to this plant by its full Latin genus and species name.   Brought to herbal fame by Samuel Thompson back in the 1700's this plant is still of much value today.   Besides being a bronchial dilator and lung nourisher it also helps the body to better utilize any herbs taken with it so is a wonderful herb to work with when you are not sure what is going on or for sure how to support your creature.   Being nervine it can help relax muscles and the nervous system when tight or under distress due to illness or injury or emotional state.   I've used it to relax cramped loin and abdominal muscles in dairy goats after a black widow bite with great results. This same effect is valuable in giving the body the nourishment it needs to relieve a seizure. It is also an emetic in moderate doses, meaning it will cause its partaker to vomit, which can be useful in some types of poisoning.   This plant is NOT poisonous when used in whole herb form.   Now to those that have extracted and used lobeliene, the alkaloid, by itself and have used it that way shame on you. That is a dangerous drug separated from its parent plant and is responsible for the bad rap on this extremely valuable herb. In low doses it can alleviate nausea. L. inflata is definitely a great herb to work with and disburses readily in the system going exactly where it's nourishment is needed and will lead your companion herbs to that area which is something we refer to as a 'lead (leed) horse' effect. It's very safe orally or used topically.   When using orally, use less than the average herb dosage and give slower so you do not get to the emetic property unless of course that is what you are looking for.   It grows readily from seed and the upper (above ground) parts are used. The seeds are the strongest part of the plant use at lower than usual dosages.

Mallow. Malva parviflora. Another weed works its way into my list and it's probably one you won't even have to plant although I've been known to move them around in my garden. It is often known as 'little cheeses' for its seeds that are in the shape of cheese wheels. It also has a unique round duck foot shaped leaf, and can either be low- sprawling along the ground or have a tall growth habit. My two foot tall one has purple streaked lavender-pink blooms and the wild low one has soft pink smaller blooms. The leaves and root are used in poultices to help draw infections including gangrene. For something as serious as gangrene you need to be more determined then the problem. It will require 24/7 poulticing with fresh herbs and soaks applied every hour along with oral use. That's A LOT of herb and not a lot of sleep until the problem is resolved. Internally the herb is a demulcent- being soothing to damaged tissue. The cheese heads are high in protein and considered a good survival food but I don't know why it shouldn't be enjoyed in salads on a regular basis. So you guessed it, some of this weed does get to stay in my flower and herb beds next to my lavender.

Marshmallow. Althea officinalis. A pretty, moderately tall herb bed plant with a beautiful pinkish whitish bloom that is easy to start from seed. It is a powerful anti inflammatory so is a wonderful injury herb to work with. Like mallow it is also very soothing to damaged tissues. It is another good herb to use in gangrene or areas where tissue has really hardened. Over time the body will take its nutrients and use them to rebuild the hard tissues back into soft, living, beautiful tissue. Because of these properties it is a good herb to use with damaged udders or mammary systems. Throat inflammations are another good use of this herb. It is a good overall body nourisher and supports the lungs by adding additional oxygen to the bloodstream. It, like common mallow, has a high amount of quality, very bioavailable protein. Your flower garden hollyhock plant can be used interchangeably with marshmallow, if needed.

Milk Thistle. Silybum marianum. Milk thistle is an amazing liver herb and a very safe one at that. The whole plant can be used, but often just the seeds are used due to its extremely stickery nature. I remember reading in one book how they hated this herb as their experience was that people would get worse on this herb. What he didn't know is that can be a part of the healing process. The alternative would be to just leave the toxins in. To me that's not a wise choice. As this herb enables the liver to let go of toxins at a much faster rate than it accumulated them, do expect a healing crisis and Hering's Law to demonstrate themselves as mentioned in the Foundations chapter. Then you can expect amazing improvement. From cirrhosis to hepatitis and toxic plant issues like tansy damage, watch this amazing herb enable the body to work wonders over several months to two years of use. I do not recommend this plant for pregnant animals in large doses, as we do not really want to run toxins at this rate through the unborn babies. It is better to wait until after they have birthed, and then give it to the dam at one half normal dosage so that they clean slower at a rate that the nursing babies can work with. They will get the herb and its benefits too- though the milk.

Mullein. Verbascum Thapsus. What would we do without mullein? This is not a plant for the compost pile! A respiratory blessing and a powerful pain controlling herb without any drugging effect at all to the brain puts this nice find on my top ten herb list also. All glands from tonsils to mammaries specifically benefit largely from this herb. Even damaged testicles may heal themselves and retained testicles may drop with judicious use of this herb when combined with the synergy from Lobelia inflata. It's a great choice for chewing some leaf up and then mashing it onto poison oaked skin or a bug bite for fast relief. Mullein tea can also be used to wash wounds, the flowers mixed with olive oil is great for earaches, and is an anthelcide (internal parasite killer). Verbascum t. is a great lung herb, helping to dry the lungs out and being demulcent or soothing to the damaged tissue. One of my favorite herb stories with this plant is when I accidentally removed the top part of my finger with my Champion juicer. The screen wasn't on and I didn't know that. Needless to say after hitting the top of my raw meat finger tip with cayenne to stop the bleeding (which would also offer some pain relief), I gulped about ¼ cup of mullein tincture that was in a raw apple cider vinegar base. That was before chore time in the morning. I wrapped my finger, fed hay, milked goats (by machine and hand), and did office work that day. About 9 hours later while heading to an evening church service my finger began to throb and ache. That mullein had covered all of that for that long! I was impressed to say the least. You might be too.

Commission E from Germany has found no toxicity level in the leaves and flowers. The seeds, however, are toxic due to their high saponin content. It is very easy to start from seed and can be very carefully transplanted if you take care to dig around its taproot when small and keep some of its native dirt with it.

Mustard. Sinapis species. Mustard is a longtime folk remedy to plaster onto chests of those with respiratory congestion. Again, like horseradish, use care or you can burn the skin. The main reason I mention it here though is that it also has a wonderful ability to help cleanse ground from bacteria and worm ovum (eggs). Simply grow it and then rototil it under just before flowering to help purify the ground. Repeat with a second crop if wanted. This is a completely safe non chemical way to clean your premises. Remember if any of your milk stock has access to the plant around milking time that their milk will pick up the pungent flavor. Easily grown from seed I let mine mature in the garden so I can have seeds to plant a new crop. Rotating it through your garden and tilling it in will help cut down on garden pests too. As always if you are planning on saving seed be sure you have open pollinated non GMO varieties. Hybrids don't breed true and are not an option to collect seeds from. I don't know that we have GMO mustard at this time, but as always watch for it as it is the unfortunate trend.

Onion. Allium cepa. Oh, the smell of sautéed onions. Every time I make an onion poultice, which I'll explain later in the book, it smells like mealtime around here! On a serious note, this is one serious plant for support in lung issues from mild to scary. Besides giving the body tools to go after a fever in an illness due to its antibacterial nature, it also helps liquefy mucous in the lungs facilitating easier expectoration by the body. My preference is to use white onions as they tend to be the sharpest, containing the most active phytochemicals (plant chemicals) that I am after. This is one of the few times I prefer a white plant to the colored ones. Other onions can be used in a pinch, but always keep some strong white ones on hand if possible. The wimpy ones that you can eat right out of your hand are not helpful when the going is tough. This is an easy plant to grow and likes the same conditions as garlic so allow the soil to dry out between watering. Living in a mild climate I am able to plant sets in the fall or seeds in the late summer which allows me to have early spring green onions most years. Overdoing oral use of onion on dogs and cats day after day can cause Hemolytic anemia in some. In these animals, especially the smaller breeds I would use other herbs after the first day or two of working an acute situation. External use as in poultices would be fine.

Parsley. Petroselinum crispum. This is not just a 'look at it on the side of your plate' plant. Parsley is a wonderful source of iron and also a good kidney supporter. What body part does not benefit from its Vitamin B complex and antioxidants? This is a helpful plant when blood building. I mix it in my salads and use the plant, seeds, and root for kidney support with stock as long as they are NOT lactating. It will encourage lactating stock to dry up (**galactaphygous**) so is something to keep in mind if you are having a 'fight' trying to dry up your animal that is trying to produce after you would like her dry. I often laugh at this thought. Here we are breeding goats for long, steady and strong lactations and then we fuss when we have to encourage them to dry up against their will after a full ten month lactation. Figure that one out.

Peppermint. Mentha piperita. Peppermint is used more than any other herb worldwide. And you just thought it was a tasty taste bud treat! Headaches, pain, lung issues, bloat, digestive issues, nausea, circulation, nerves and more, favor this scentful herb! Swollen or congested mammaries benefit too, but use only when necessary as mint can reduce milk production with prolonged use. In pioneer times it was often planted in barn, home, and milkroom areas to detour spider, ant, and mouse traffic. Some veterinary stomach preparations even contain oil of peppermint in them. It also helps to stimulate circulation which also benefits clearer thinking. Just remember every time you tea this herb that the wafting minty air is your herbal remedy floating away so be sure and keep a lid on that tea! It likes moist areas so mine hangs out by my stock tank where I dump extra water on it when I fill it. In Eastern Washington I have seen huge irrigated fields of it in direct hot desert sun. Peppermint is easy to divide and move around spreading through underground roots. Cuttings are easy to start too, just keep them moist like your basil. Try to stick with the real peppermint as most of the different 'flavored' varieties don't have the medicinal punch we are looking for. Some of the chocolate mints with the dark stem are good too.

Pine. Pinus species. Try this fun recipe I learned from Sandra Ellis, one of my teachers. Fill a jar with soft new growth pine needles (for me that is late June most years). Don't pack them tight but do fill the jar. I use canning jars but you could use any jar with a tight lid to keep out bugs and dust. Then fill with raw organic or natural raised honey. Lid it well and place in the sun for two months to let it draw out the antioxidants and high quality Vitamin C in those needles. I use mine in my tea as well as adding it to infusions after they have cooled a bit for drenches that I make for our animals when I'm working with conditions in them. Make up several half pints if you like, tie a ribbon on them and give them for festive Christmas gifts for people to add to their holiday tea. You might consider avoiding Ponderosa pine, although the dosage in your honey will be quite smaller, as there are veterinary reports of cattle aborting when eating the dried mature needles. Until we have more detailed data I think it's wise to err on the side of caution and skip using that particular pine tree. I have a batch of Coastal Redwood honey steeping right now for its lung assistance properties. You'll be surprised where you can grow redwoods. If your climate doesn't stay frozen in the winter; go ahead and plant one or two. Our temperature ranges from the rare 8 degrees Fahrenheit to the 111 to 114 degree range in the summer and ours grow just fine with watering. We do like to spray the branches with water as this tree will uptake moisture through its needles which it gets from the fog in its native coastal California and Oregon environments. Do give them room to grow as they are the majestic redwoods!

Plantain. Plantago major, P. lanceolata. Plantain is another friend, not foe that pops up in my yard and garden. Did you know that a toad might seek out this plant and eat it when stung by a bee? Toadally fascinating if you ask me! So remember our friend the toad when you, your children, or your creature gets stung or bit by something poisonous. Grab a few plantain leaves, chew them up and place the pioneer made poultice right on the offending spot. Replace with fresh chewed new leaves every half an hour as needed. It will help draw out the poison. Please teach your children this easy to identify plant and how to use it both on themselves, their playmates, and their creatures. It is also useful as an anthelmintic (dewormer) and on bruises, sores and wounds. Plantain is also helpful once applied to your skin after your faithful dog shares poison oak or ivy with you. Young leaves can be fed or added to salads.

Poke. Phytolacca Americana.   A tall plant, with strong smooth pinkish red stalks with beautiful dark blue/purple berries late summer and fall that the bluebirds cherish!   I like it for its amazing glandular support, even nourishing the body in mammary gland malignancies.   It can also be used to wash wounds, soften a hardened liver, on skin irritations, lymph gland swellings and more.   The root is considered the strongest but should be used fresh or tinctured as it does not store well.   The leaves and berries also can be used.   Do not use this plant, especially the root, orally as it is a POWERFUL **emetic** that is slow in action.   Translated this means that what you nibble on now or feed to something won't start it vomiting for perhaps hours so there is no good way to monitor or establish an oral dosage.   Use it topically over the area of concern in poultices, salves or fomentations.

Red Clover. Trifolium pratense.   Red clover is a blood cleaner par excellence and a delightfully fragrant one at that.   Any condition, especially chronic ones can benefit from cleaner blood.   Just remember as with any herb, start with smaller amounts to enable the digestive flora a chance to get used to it. Translating that into practical use that means that you don't throw out armloads of the plant to your stock in one day if they are not used to it.   I know someone that killed their goats doing that. Always feed by the handful if using a fresh herb and adjust animals to larger amounts over 10 to 14 days. Clover should not be fed in large quantities day after day, month after month due to possibility of changing the thickness of vaginal mucous to more runny. That damages fertility by it less likely for sperm to make it to the uterus when bred as is documented with white clover in sheep. Reasonable normal therapeutic dosages are just fine and even better when included in a blend. The pink blossom heads are preferred but the leaf can also be used. When I pick them I keep the top leaves with the blooms as they come off together. Mine dry quite well in a basket tray which I can shake around each day until dry. It also makes quite an enjoyable tea.

Red Raspberry. Rubus idaeus.   This herb will reward you many times over for giving some space to it in your herb garden.   Considered a valuable prenatal due to the wide range of minerals within and for those same reasons it is also a valuable lactation support herb. Calcium, selenium, niacin (a B vitamin) and iron are just some that come to the top of my head. It is interesting to note that niacin deficiency contributes to ketosis/pregnancy toxemia.   You can tea or feed the leaves. Its gentle cleansing action is also good for upset GI tracts, for chronic or acute conditions of all kinds, as a wound wash, during colds and flu given in copious amounts as tea (just replace their water with the tea) and for general nourishment even in fragile situations. Once you plant it as long as it gets some water you should have it for a long time as it sends up new shoots via its runners. This is another plant the stock heads to in order to gobble it up if they should get out. Wisdom.

Rose. Rosa canina, Rosa species. Now here's a delightful herb! You can use the hips of any type of rose, but the old time varieties bred for the large hips like Frau Dagmar, are the easiest to work with. Wild roses also often produce moderate to large sized hips. They are very high in vitamin C and considered another good survival food, but why limit it to that? It's beneficial for abundant wellness too. Taste one sometime. They taste like a mild apple. Just chew them carefully as they do contain many seeds. Harvest them after first fall frost and dry. You can use it in teas and put in herb blends and tinctures.

Rosemary. Rosmarinus officinalis. Memories... It stimulates each cell of the body including your mind and is invigorating as well. An excellent "start your day with" herb friend. This herb is considered one of the better encephalitic support herbs which is the brain stem. It increases circulation, is antibacterial, antiviral, and antimicrobial and a favorite of mine. Rosemary helps to restore hair by nourishing, cleansing and stimulating the skin and hair follicle. I like it as an addition in goat milk soaps because of those properties. It can be used to wash internal or external wounds and increases the ability to digest and break down fats. It's a good wash if made strong to gargle with for gum infection support. I also like rosemary in blends for lung support. True to many of the pine like scented plants and trees it is antioxidant packed. It grows well in hot to moderate climates but will freeze out at around ten degrees Fahrenheit. We can occasionally get colder than that, so mine are planted where they have some protection from other plants and buildings and get a straw bed after the first good freeze. Otherwise grow it as a container herb that you can bring inside for the winter. It's great crushing a few needles into baths too! I like working with the essential oil from this plant too. Rosemary ranks pretty high on my must haves herb list.

Sage. Salvia officinalis. Sage is another antioxidant herb with several key minerals of value when dealing with infections and colds. Sage can help the body lower blood sugar problems and aid in digestive distress. Sage also helps to make one sage (wise) by nourishing the nerve cells in the brain and is a good antibacterial aid in dealing with colds and some viral conditions. I like using it in respiratory conditions that involve wetness due to its astringing nature. Salvia o. is also good to use as a wash hourly for infected wounds. It is drying to lactating creatures so I don't use it as a simple (by itself) in those cases. I DO use it when trying to encourage something to dry up its milk (**galactaphygous**), but in regular doses only or externally as this herb in large doses can harm a pregnancy. It is MUCH more potent than wormwood, which I consider safe, in that area. Many of our livestock animals are rebred before they are done producing milk for the season so this is something to keep in mind. In those cases I would make a salve with it and apply it directly to the mammary and forgo much oral use. I also like it powdered or tinctured to put on fresh navels. This is another easy to grow herb that comes in sage green, purple, and variegated varieties.

Scullcap (skullcap). Scutellaria lateriflora. Scullcap is a nervous system's friend; especially the nerves along the spinal cord make this an herb of great value in any back or neck injury or distress. If the nerves along the spinal cord are not working at their best efficiency then communication from the brain to the other parts of the body and return will be less than desirable. This herb nourishes the nerves rather than controlling them. Scullcap is also valuable to start using if a creature had to be on a course of medications that could be addicting for any part of the body as it will ease and soothe the nerves during the withdrawal process. We sometimes get these cases in transition when a creature or person is switching from drug therapies to natural herbal approaches. Always do this under medical supervision! This is another herb that is pretty easy to grow from seed. I've found that my chickens think of it as a delicacy so protect it if you need to! Maybe they have achy backs from their daily 'pregnancies'?

Sow Thistle. Sonchus oleraceus. "Ok, Kat, so what's up with all of these stickers?" You have already guessed that I let some of these come up in my gardens as well! If I ever get a gardener they are going to be besides them self, wondering "Is this a weed, is it not? Can I pull it, should I leave it there?" I can picture it now... Maybe I have you doing the same thing at this point. Hang in there, you will get it and keep your sense of humor in the process! Sow thistle can be used in the same way as wild lettuce (do not confuse wild lettuce with milkweed) and makes a good after dinner tea for human or creature. It is soothing and helps reduce pain levels. I wonder if it also mildly helps the body dissipate inflammation. It can be used in higher amounts than wild lettuce too so I favor it for that reason. I use the leaves and also feed my 'weedings' to the stock. I have never had to plant any yet! I do always leave a few to go to seed both to share with the birdies and so that I can keep them propagating.

Stinging Nettle. Urtica dioica. Nettle, probably another one of my top ten must have plants, was covered in the supplements section. I do have a patch, it does like shade and it also is easy to start from seed. The seeds are very, very tiny so just press them into soft soil and keep them moist. If they dry out while sprouting they die. Remember to wear gloves if you don't want to endure the stings from picking it, which are used by many to decrease inflammation. Personally I'm not into stinging myself on purpose, but if you are careful you can pick it without gloves on. Practice, practice. This is a wonderful companion plant for other herbs, allowing them to grow better. Nettle also makes a nice tea, any time of the day. I drink it often.

Strawberry. Fragaria vesca. We're actually considering the leaves here, though the berries are certainly a treat and sometimes were poulticed (smashed up) onto wounds by pioneers. You can use tame or wild varieties; the wild ones usually have a greater amount of phytochemicals. I use it as another herb to support a GI tract that is experiencing diarrhea when I'm in a location where I don't have my herbs on hand. Remember that you must then ascertain the cause of the diarrhea. If it is parasites, a fast feed change, toxins, or some other cause you need to know and address that as well. Strawberry does make a nice ground cover and I love the beautiful white blossoms.

Thyme. Thymus vulgaris. What a beautiful, dark green, ground spreading mat to smaller sized shrub this plant becomes, while sharing its awesome antibacterial, antifungal, antiviral, and antimicrobial powers with us. A blessing in lung conditions due to its afore mentioned anti-everything properties, it also encourages the bronchial tubes to dilate. This allows more surface area for oxygen to penetrate within the lungs. Colds or infections are good reasons to make use of this herb. It makes a great herbal wound wash and also a skin wash in fungal activity such as ringworm. This makes a choice for equine or camelid skin challenges where black walnut can be problematic. Being a stimulant herb, this one is quite hot so you will want to be careful when using topically. Tasting a leaf every day or two will help you pick it at its peak nutrient value. Pick it at its hottest, usually just before full bloom and just after the dew is off of it. It is easy to grow and will reward you by spreading and increasing bee activity to your garden. This is a GREAT herb to carefully infuse with real honey and then feed back to your bees! Once it has spread you can carefully divide out sections with dirt in the spring or fall to create more. Have a good thyme!

Uva Ursi. Arctostaphylos uva-ursi. Pronounce that one! Bearberry or Kinnikinnik are other names for this renal system support plant. The kidneys in humans contain 70 to 75 miles of tubules in each one! In addition they filter about 1000 quarts of blood each for water soluble toxins every single day. Whatever the creature, having kidneys working to their fullest ability are extremely important. Bearberry is a good antiseptic for situations causing infection in the kidneys, urethra, or bladder. I prefer it in blends as its higher tannin content can make it drying to the mucous membranes and milk production. Its astringent properties (to which the tannins contribute) do make it of value in using as a wash for pus and discharges as well as used internally for those same issues. This is especially true with urinary or reproductive tract problems. The leaves of this plant are the parts that are used. It makes a nice little evergreen bush and its berries can be enjoyed as well.

Valerian. Valeriana officinalis. Now tell me, how can such sweet smelling plant blossoms produce a root that smells so much like very dirty socks? The older this root gets the more odiferous it becomes! Valerian root is used to calm the nerves of those under distress, and can have a mild effect in pain reduction. Occasionally (perhaps 20% of the time) this herb may excite rather than calm an animal so I prefer to use this in blends then by itself. Even though it grows to about 6 feet tall it does not take up a lot of room in the garden. It does like moderate water. Valerian will die back in the fall but don't worry; it will send new shoots back up again come springtime. Keep a plant marker near it so you don't accidentally try to plant something else there while it's hiding in dormancy.

Wheat Grass. Triticum species.   This herb is not a problem for gluten sensitive pets or people as the gluten is found in the endosperm of the seed and not in the grass.   We consider wheat grass to be green 'blood'.   Any blood issue, irregular blood panel, blood needing additional cleansing, blood needing to be rebuilt or replenished, or blood loss condition benefits from the nourishment of this completely nontoxic herb.   You can also use it to wash wounds, apply to skin conditions, and help with internal cleansing.   It's not very hard to grow if you get viable seed.   Some health food stores carry it in bulk.   I soak a cup in a quart canning jar in warm water for half of a day and drain, then let it sit another 12 hours in the jar at room temperature.   Then I take black plastic plant trays, fill them with one inch of compost and spread the seeds on them quite thickly. I gently water (not flood) them and place plastic wrap on them, leaving it in the house.   In a couple days I remove the plastic wrap.   In about 5 more days, once it is 7 inches tall, I start using it in a wheat grass juicer.   Use just 2 ounces of fresh juice at a time for a 100 to 200 lb animal or two big handfuls of the grass that I harvest with scissors. It is potent so don't overdo it or you could get an acidosis or enterotoxemia condition.   You can harvest it before then if you need it before it will just be shorter.   I cut close to the seed.   You can get three total cuttings from one planting.   After I remove the plastic wrap from one tray I start soaking another set.   Wheat grass juice has to be used when you make it as it starts losing nutrients within minutes.   We also make good use of the wheat seeds in a mix called Rejuvelac as a probiotic. I will discuss more on that in the Digestive tract chapters.

Wild Lettuce. Lactuca serriola, L. scariola.   When I first learned about this herb I thought they were kidding.   They are not, and I have the tea on my counter for an evening tea to prove it!   It is sedative (relaxing) and nervine (nervous system quieting) and is also beneficial for mild aches and pains.   Just tea the leaves and drench or add to your creature's water. A quart jar filled with the fresh herb (or sow thistle herb) and filled with hot water and lidded to steep for 15 minutes makes a great addition to a five gallon water bucket. Even your horse might thank you for this treat after a workout. It is stickery so you may want to wear gloves as you pick it.   Latuca likes company so it tends to grow in colonies and will grow in quite well in dry conditions. An interesting name for the plant is "compass plant", as the leaves turn during the day to follow the sun. This is another gift I have not had to plant but rather just control where I want it.

Yarrow. Achillea millefolium. Clouds of white, yellow, red, or dusty pink flat blooms in an umbel pattern and delicate lacy leaves make this a plant that I enjoy in flower arrangements. Yarrow does much more than that though, being a diaphoretic (pore opening and sweat inducing herb) of choice in times where toxins need to be released from the body in quick manner such as in feverish conditions. It is a very nourishing cold and flu assistant and to many a pioneer was the first herb gathered to support the body in any condition. Yarrow is a digestive tonic as it strengthens the tissue in the GI tract and may reduce bacterial issues. It is not an emmenagogue (cycle promoting herb) so is a great choice to use for toning reproductive organs during pregnancy with its vitamins A, B complex, C, E and multiple minerals and bioflavanoids (Vitamin P). Achillea gently cleanses and supports the liver being a good wintertime herb and is a gentle blood cleanser too. It is also anti-inflammatory and antiseptic, lending to good use as a wound poultice or wash. Yarrow is also a wonderful restorer of hair color as long as copper deficiency isn't the culprit. It grows wild in a wide range of climates and can tolerate quite dry conditions. Once it is going it will spread rapidly for you with some care. You can use any color interchangeably and we use any of the upper parts of the plant. This is another herb that makes a great companion plant to others so I have a few scattered here and there throughout the herb beds besides having a patch. I also have a couple of goats named after this esteemed plant. One is named Yarrow and her daughter is called Achillea mille, affectionately referred to as 'Millie'.

Yellow Dock. Rumex crispus. Curly dock is another name for this alterative herb. What is an alterative? An alterative increases the body's ability to adjust an organ or tissue back to normal over time making this a nice herb to add to blends. It is another liver support herb which my goats like to nibble on in the spring to break up winter cellular stagnation and an aperient at the same time. Aperients help to gently reduce constipation so is an herb easy to use with pregnant or young stock. It helps move lymph fast allowing toxins to be more readily removed from the body. This is a power packed anemia herb being rich in iron. Due to its oxalic acid, this is not an herb that you use in high doses over a long period of time.

Oxalates tie up some minerals including calcium from being able to be utilized. Spinach is another commonly known oxalate plant. Even though my goats use the leaves, herbalists usually harvest and use the roots. EARLY spring or late in the fall is the time to look for these. As you dig up the roots and then clean them and slice them, look for a brighter orange to orange creamsicle looking hue. If they are barely yellow or cream colored then they will not do you any good. Replant that before you cut it up any more in loose soil to see if you can salvage it. The loose soil is so that it is easier to dig up the next time, as I find it likes to hang out in harder to dig areas such as tree roots and unirrigated areas. You might do as I do and cut the first root you dig up before you dig a patch; to be sure your timing is right. Seeds can also be harvested after they are rust colored and dry and rescattered in areas where you would like to see them come up.

I realize that I just gave you a very large list of plants. There are many others that could make it on here as well. But now you get to have now the fun of seeing what God has already provided for you and of choosing what you want to plant and tend. Over time you will also add plants not on this list as I do, to have personal or regional favorites to use or look at. For the most part this list contains plants that will grow in quite a wide range of areas being of use to a larger amount of people relying on this book.

A Few Garden Tips

Here are a few tips just for fun. That in itself could make another whole book so just a few will suffice.

I like starting my seeds in paper egg cartons. Just carefully tear the lid of the carton off and place it as the base then fill with your favorite planting medium. I use year old rotted goat straw compost or swipe soil from a corner of my garden. Keep them where it doesn't matter that what they sit on gets wet. I keep them in my little homemade greenhouse. Once your baby plants are ready for their permanent homes, dampen the cartons and they will readily pull apart. Plant just as it is so you don't disturb the tender roots which may be adhered to or even have grown through their egg carton base. Be sure that your soil completely covers the carton paper or any exposed paper may wick out moisture from your plant baby. I

The Accessible Pet, Equine and Livestock Herbal

tear off any edges that could stick out above the ground level. Baby plants should be planted at the right time for your climate and really try to avoid the hot months unless you can be watering them twice per day. If it's hot provide some shade for several days until their roots get settled in better.

I use one year old rotted compost from our goats and side dress established plants. Before we plant, we completely top dress new beds four to six inches deep when we have enough compost soil. If there are still big lumps in it then it is not ready to use and could burn your young plants. Just one quarter inch of compost like this will renew damaged or depleted soil but I like my plants happy and we have rock hard clay soil in the summer months, so we put on much more.

I also use the bottom damaged comfrey and mullein leaves as mulch. In compost they will speed up the composting process if that is wanted. Comfrey leaves or organic alfalfa put in your water tank to decay for garden watering will release nutrients to feed your plants. You can also do this with kelp too, but as mentioned earlier be sure that kelp has not been cut with salt by the manufacturer before you use it on your plants! Comfrey is cheaper for this use as I don't have to buy it. The kelp I have to buy. If you live where you can harvest kelp, be sure it is still a cold water very rural area to reduce pollution problems. Then wash it well to get all of the salt water off that you don't want in your garden.

Your plants will do much better if given their drinks from warm water than from cold well water. Because of this I keep a stock tank filled with water so that it will be air temperature rather than ground temperature (think 40 degrees Fahrenheit like your refrigerator). Your baby plants will really appreciate this. A couple of goldfish in the barrel or used stock tank will help keep up with the mosquitoes. Tadpoles do a nice job of that too.

Nettles, yarrow, and comfrey all increase the health of the plants growing near them. Even though my beds have patches of certain plants I also have sporadic yarrow and comfrey throughout many of my beds. Comfrey, once established, will increase the water and minerals available to your plants. This Fall I want to place some comfrey root at the base of each of our baby fruit trees for that purpose. If the comfrey plants get too big for their space I can just cut them back and make instant mulch for my fruit tree feet with them.

Tree or shrub injuries can be supported with comfrey poultices or salves and then splints and breathable wraps if needed. Really! Richo Cech showed me a beautiful Lebanese cedar tree at Horizon Seeds a couple of years ago that had been damaged by goats as a sapling. They applied a lot of comfrey poultice to the plant and wrapped it with fabric that could deteriorate over time. I looked hard and could not even find any indication of scar on that tree now over 1 foot in diameter.

Fungal or mildew issues on herbs or plants can be worked with a much diluted amount of lavender essential oil (60 to 80 drops per quart of distilled water). I've used it very successfully with roses. You can also make an infusion (tea) cooled to air temperature of the lavender herb and spray on that on early morning. You want it to dry before nightfall and you don't want the water's magnifying abilities to strengthen the midday or afternoon sunlight hitting the leaf which could cause a burn. I have not tried this with aphids as we hardly ever see any here but one sure could. A very, very mild dish soap diluted with water will dissolve those pests.

I always use open pollinated seeds when planting. Hybrids will not breed true to the plant you are looking at but will revert to whatever the parents are. Many times those parents are inferior to the hybrid. I do like to use organic seed as that lessens the chance of genetically modified seed making its way here. I let my lettuces, mustards, arugula, a few onions, herbs etcetera go to seed once I'm done harvesting any particular patch. I didn't even plant any curly lettuce, kale or chard this year; I just moved baby plants as they came up on their own. I do harvest some of that seed as well as share some with the wild birds who double as bug hunters when they are raising their young around our farm.

Seed stores well in glass jars like canning jars with a well sealed lid. I put the packets in the jars and then keep them in the refrigerator. A seed that would be viable for only three years now might be viable for ten with hibernation.

Ducks? When we used to live where we had slug problems we had ducks. They love slugs and unlike chickens won't scratch up your beds. They will on occasion crush a young plant, but we found they did far less damage than the slugs would if we had not had them. They were comical to watch and listen to as well. We have friends that are using cedar chips around plant beds to dispel slugs and it is working very well for them. Some people use beer traps but then you have to keep up with them all the time. Thankfully we don't battle slugs here! We'll talk about slugs a bit more when we get to the parasite section.

Everyone that has read a bit on gardening knows about microclimates. For instance, our little creek valley next to a larger river valley tends to be drier and also cools down more at night then the neighboring one which is the one we are considered a part of. However, don't forget that you have mini microclimates all over your farm. Think about your shady areas, sunny areas, windier spots, wetter, and the like. I use this to my advantage when planting. Our garden area is prone to warm to hot breezes in the afternoon that like to suck the moisture right out of my plants. So, we have put in a Leland Cypress row on one side that will eventually block that wind and provide some later afternoon shade to plants placed close to them. I also leave sections of weeds in my garden. I weed out a one to one and a half foot wide path around the rows or squares, and then let weeds grow for a two foot wide strip on the windy side. That has gone a long ways for keeping more moisture in my plants and soil on those hot afternoon breeze days. It sounds strange but it works well for us and didn't cost me anything. Be creative, you'll come up with some great ideas too.

Square foot gardening is a fun concept to look into if you are new to gardening. I use this at times. Basically in this method you plant your plants closer together in square foot sections which really does cut down on weeding and allows you to grow more in less area as they claim. I use it with some of my herbs as well as some of my vegetables. You probably can find books and maybe videos that you can check out from many library systems for free.

Use a mulch composting system of gardening to get maximum benefits with minimal work, weeding, watering, pests and no fertilizer. The way it's meant to be! I have a link to a wonderful video of this method on my website.

Chapter 5- Dosage and Methods of Administration

There are numerous ways to administer herbs; probably about as many ways are there are minds that work with them. I will guide you through several different methods, definitions, and dosages that are practical and workable with pets, poultry, and livestock. Select the ones that work best for you and your creatures as well as for the situation at hand. As we all know; working with animals can take some creativity at times. But then, if you have children that can be true for them as well! Cats tend to be, as a whole; the most difficult to work with due to their personalities and sensitivities as well as their teeth and claws, but usually a way can be found for them as well. My vet has told me she doesn't work on cats because she knows they are going to get her! She'd rather subject herself to the perils of working with larger stock.

Remember when working with pets and livestock that their and your safety comes first. You are not trying to help them in order to gain an injury or loss to them or yourself or others helping you. Please exercise wisdom. This book or any person or entity attached to it shall accept no liability for any injury or loss that might be sustained.

Dosages

When you control the efficacy (strength) of your herbs you will find that they are much stronger than many store bought herbs and products that are out there. Yet you will find my dosaging often to be higher than what you would normally expect to find on the bottle of a tincture or capsules. When working with safe plants or blends we can work at dosages that are large enough to work with the body at a faster pace. That's opposed to the puny worn out herbs and doses that prove to so many people's minds that herbs are worthless. In those cases I have to agree. Always feel free to run any dosage by your practitioner of choice as the ultimate responsibility falls on you, the herd, pet, or flock owner for making choices that will work for your creatures in their situation. If you are not comfortable with administering herbs in one of the following forms, such as drenching, then please get training from someone well versed in doing them safely or choose another method you are comfortable with.

Herbs do not have a 'half life' like drugs, where a percentage of the drug lingers in the system for X number of days, months and yes, some even for years. I know that one of the mental drugs for humans (I shall leave it unnamed) stays in the system for 30 days with just the FIRST dose! No wonder conditions under that protocol continue to degenerate. How long does it take to get a week's worth of that prescription out of the system? (Just a note here- if you or your pet are on a mind support prescription you do NOT just stop taking it. You MUST work with your physician in any type of prescription reduction program. Your safety can be at risk if you don't heed this warning). In a healthy individual herbs will be digested, utilized, broken down, and ready to expel in four to six hours. In an unhealthy individual where metabolism (nutrient and waste exchange) has been reduced in ability, it may take twelve to fourteen hours or even longer to break down and expel. In the case of goats, they may work through the herbs and break them down at an even faster rate than other livestock. Drug companies recognize this physiological difference and often label higher dosages for goats or formulate specifically for them due to this reason. So in some cases in goats, you will be dosing higher and/or more often, especially when faced with acute situations.

The herbs are expelled from the body in four ways. The water soluble excess nutrients are expelled through the moisture exhaled from the lungs, through the sweat glands in the skin, and through the bladder via the kidneys and urethra. The fat soluble nutrients go through the liver and then they and the insoluble nutrients (like cellulose or fiber/roughage) and bile are excreted in the feces or manure. Remember these four paths of elimination and detoxification as we can use them to our advantage with working with certain conditions that affect those areas. In those cases we may topload herbs at a higher rate to get those excess nutrients and phytochemicals running through those elimination organs in higher amounts.

Acute Dosaging

Acute situations are those that appear rapidly, or have now come to a dangerous level of risk to the well being of the creature. They can be an injury or something like pneumonia or previously undiagnosed organ disorders or chronic disorders that are now degenerating at an extremely fast rate.   In acute situations IDEALLY we like to work herbs into the creature every hour they are awake. Knowing that is unrealistic in many cases, and knowing that most herbs will stay in the system for at least 3 to 4 hours,   I like to suggest that people get herbs down their animals AT LEAST every 3 hours while they are in the acute stage, but we will increase the amount of herbs used in those situations, especially the first herbs given.   For goats I often suggest people give herbs at least every 2 hours due to their faster metabolism rates.

The pain levels that your creature is experiencing will give you valuable information.   Besides signaling to us that something is wrong, pain also informs us of a nutrition request by the body so that it can attempt to fix the problem. Therefore, I also monitor the amount of herbs I am using by the amount of pain shown.   If they begin to show more pain I carefully increase the amount of herbs used.   If they look comfortable I gradually reduce the amount of herbs used to the point where I keep the pain covered but I am not using more herbs then their body is working with to repair the problem.   I also like to work with chronic cases as if they were acute for the first day to get a good jump on them.   In general I will continue them on their herb program for at least three days past the final symptoms.   It is a lot of work but the stories I get back as well as my own personal experiences show how it is so worth it.   If you want to just give herbs one or two times a day like one would give drugs in an acute situation, then herbs are probably not for you.   Call your medical practitioner. You can still add herbal support but you won't have the herbs in their system long enough to benefit you in most emergencies.

When working with unconscious or barely conscious animals or any with their swallowing ability impaired; do not give oral herbs that you need them to swallow. I do, however, place tinctures onto the gum line knowing that they will absorb them through their capillaries in the mouth.   I do not put it on in a way that it would run back towards their throat towards the lungs.   For example; if they are lying on their side, I may put some on the gum line where some may trickle across their tongue to the other side of their mouth, teeth, and gums. That is fine.   But to lift their head in a way where the tincture could run back into their lungs and aspirate them would not be okay. You can also give them enemas, elevating the back end higher than the front end to get herbal nutrition into them. Use common sense. You'll learn more methods in this chapter so keep reading.

Chronic Dosaging

Chronic situations can be annoying, little issues or they can be conditions that are slowly degenerating into something that will become more serious unless it is intervened. Some situations that start out as acute get well enough to become chronic or non life threatening at that level, but don't finish the healing to be completely well. Chronic situations might be coughs, blood sugar disorders, skin disorders that won't heal, circulation challenges or any number of other issues. In chronic situations the general rule of thumb is that we use the herbs three times a day if possible, but at least two times per day. One time per day is better than nothing and we have some neat stories with just once a day herbing or salving, but it really is doing your animal (or yourself) an injustice if you want to see the body heal the issue. Remember to take one day off a week from your herbing and salving when working with chronic issues at two to three times per day. The body somehow makes better use of the herbs the other six days. That being a pattern set at creation is the only plausible explanation for that; which I find fascinating. This does not include your supplement foods listed in that chapter. They should be available daily to nourish whatever new cells will be formed that day.

I like to use a double barrel approach when working a situation, whether it is chronic or acute. I like to nourish from the inside, allowing capillaries and the lymph system to carry the nutrients to the area needed. I also like to nourish from the skin area located closest to the problem, knowing that the body will draw in the wanted herbs to the area requiring the nourishment. Skin contact is helpful. I use a number 10 size blade on my clippers during warm weather to remove some hair if needed. If it's cool or cold out I use a number 5F blade which will leave a longer coat and is skip tooth, so leaves a bit more hair as well. Do so very carefully in an injured area, such as torn interior soft tissue or fractured bone. The vibrations will cause pain to the area, but take note where they seem to be the most tender as that is the area you will concentrate on. If it takes two or three people to safely handle the animal to clip and then apply your herbs; keep that in mind as well. Remember that you getting hurt is not the point of caring for your creature. You want to herb your animal, not add yourself to the list of those that need additional care! If you don't feel safe doing a procedure listed below then enlist competent help or a medical practitioner. A good veterinarian, for the price of an office call or farm visit and some time, often will be glad that you want to learn some techniques to safely work with your animals and some observation skills. Hire their services gladly knowing that you will reduce the likely hood of injury to you or your creatures in the name of trying to help them. I have paid for and have greatly benefited from such services in the past. If that is hard on your budget see if you can arrange with a few breeders or people and the veterinarian to do a clinic and allow you all to pay a reduced fee.

Powdered Herb Dosages

For dry powdered herbs I like to give a small pinch to animals under about 15 to 20 pounds. If they are really small, like chicks, I may spread a pinch out between three to five of them. If they are smaller than that, like tiny lizards, then a pinch might be spread out over 10 of them. For animals over 20 pounds I suggest ¼ teaspoon. At about 35 pounds ½ teaspoon is good. At around 60 to 70 lbs I move it to a whole teaspoon. At 100 pounds to 200 pounds I move into a ½ tablespoon. A whole tablespoon is for the 200 to 400 pound range. Over 400 pounds I move into 1/8 cup and at about 800 pounds to 1200 pounds one quarter cup is good. If your animals are still larger like draft horses, draft mules and draft cattle, then increase accordingly. If you are doing something like we do, putting powdered herbs into lam-bars, then we add the weight of the number of kids that will feed on that nipple outfitted bucket and put that weight amount into their bucket. Do the same with poultry, puppies or other groups of animals you are feeding. It is imperative that if you are feeding herbs for parasite types of reasons to a group that you feed in a way that you KNOW every animal has received enough herb. Powdered herbs can also be directly poured onto and into wounds; even deep wounds as long as you are using ones that are also antibacterial. If it's a deep wound just fill it up with a good quality powdered herb that will assist the body to do what it is you are wanting it to accomplish. The body will absorb and utilize it. See the later chapter on skin for further information.

Cut and Sifted and Fresh Herb Dosages

For cut and sifted (c/s) herbs which are the small pieces of plant parts, you will feed two to four times as much. That is to make up for the volume or airspace that dried c/s herbs take.

For Fresh herbs you'll feed double the cut and sifted rate. For 100 to 200 pound animals that would be feeding large handfuls.

Tincture Dosages

For tinctures always follow label directions unless consulting with a trained herbalist. Do not be surprised if the herbalist has to ask you for the label directions and ingredient list to try and give guidance for your situation, however. Different herbalists formulate them at different strengths and of course, we still often don't know the quality of herbs that were used.

Tinctures are easy to administer and can be used orally or topically. I have also used them intrauterine when diluted appropriately with sterile water or even olive oil. They can be added to bottles or drinking water or juices such as carrot for oral use. I have even added raw milk to them from the goat that I'm going to drench it down orally. They absorb into the bloodstream much faster than herb powders and in real right now emergencies are what I prefer to use. They even begin to enter the bloodstream through the gums and body tissues as they are swallowed. For homemade tinctures in general, this is what I suggest. Note these doses can be higher than suggested for humans, but I've had good results with them and remember we are using plants that are not toxic, poisonous, or habit forming which is not always the case for some products that are out there available for purchase. For freshly hatched chicks I've carefully given one and two drops. For creatures up to twenty pounds up to 5 drops or ¼ teaspoon. From 20 to 35 pounds I suggest two cc's or milliliters (ml). From 35 to 75 pounds three or four cc's.

From 75 to 150 pounds five cc's. From 150 pounds to 225 pounds seven cc's. At 1000 pounds we are up to 30 to 35 cc's. There are times, in acute situations, which I will explain later under different conditions where I give much more than that with safe blends. Tinctures can be made with alcohol (vodka or Everclear only should be used as there are no additives in those), with raw apple cider vinegar, with vegetable glycerine (a glycerite) or a combination. Sometimes brandy (made from grapes) is also used. The alcohol extracted tinctures can store for literally decades and the raw cider vinegar ones for a few years only if they have been made from a high quality whole apple raw process organic type of vinegar. If you use junky vinegar expect a junk product with a crummy shelf life. To remove any alcohol for creature use, place your dosage in a canning jar or mug, pour a bit of at least 200 degree Fahrenheit water over it, and the alcohol will vaporize. Then let it cool a few minutes before you administer and be sure to use just enough water to do the job so that you don't have to figure out how you are getting more quantity of liquid down an animal if it's uncooperative. One final note on tinctures comes to mind. If you are dosing right from the eye dropper in ones that come with a dropper bottle do be careful of the glass. You may need to drop it in a plastic syringe right before you give the product. Some animals have grabbed onto and broken the glass droppers. Do not use tinctures with a plastic dropper suspended in them unless you want a tincture of plastic entering the bloodstream. Not a good thing! So transfer the dosage into the plastic syringe or drenching tool at the time you plan to give it.

Infusions or Teas Dosaging

Infusions are nice. This is an herbalist term for teas. Real tea. Not the wimpy stir the tea bag around the mug three times and take it out, which should be considered a crime. This is taking very hot to boiling water, pouring it over your herb in a canning jar or other heat proof container like a stainless bowl, pot, canning jar, or ceramic mug and then covering with a lid and letting it steep at least 15 minutes or longer if needed to cool to a comfortable drinking temperature. Remember that most of your animals will not be able to tolerate liquids as hot as you can, so normal body temperature would be ideal. If you can use distilled water you will obtain 30 to 35% more of the phytonutrients from your herbs. You can either feed

The Accessible Pet, Equine and Livestock Herbal

it with the herb in it or you can strain it and use it that way. I prefer to leave the herbs in unless I'm working with eyes or have a creature that has a hard time drinking. It will keep lidded in your refrigerator for up to three days. I prefer to make it fresh every day. If you store it do label it with the date made. Sometimes I get more than one tea going so it is quite helpful to know you are grabbing for the correct one! A few very fragile herbs like desert sage need to sun tea (gentle heat) over at least one half of a day to keep their benefits. Remember the peppermint story or any other herb for that matter- if you smell it in the air your herbal remedy is wafting away! Keep it lidded to keep it in the water.

I use one teaspoon of powdered herb to a pint of water or one tablespoon of cut and sifted herb, or two handfuls of fresh herb. This is for soft leaves, blossoms and slender stems. My favorite way to do this is to make it in a canning jar. I measure the herb and the very hot water, place my ingredients in the jar and put a lid on it. It is now portable to take down to the barn or pasture while you wait for it to steep and cool. It needs to stay hot at least 15 minutes so if it is cold outside do wrap it in some toweling. Also cold air hitting a hot canning jar can cause it to break.

For an infusion tea, I would give the whole pint or 250 ml to a horse or cow, two pints or one quart or 1/2 liter for the larger draft breeds. One half of a pint, one cup, or 125 ml to a large pig, pony, or mini version of a large livestock animal. One quarter pint, ½ cup or 65 ml can go to alpacas, standard sized dairy goats, sheep, very large dogs, etc. One quarter cup or 35 ml can go to miniature goats, miniature sheep, medium to large dogs, weaner pigs, young calves, young foals, and etcetera. One eighth cup or 15 to 20 ml can go to small dogs, rabbits, cats, young kids, lambs and the like. Calibrate it down again by one half for animals 3 pounds or lighter. Even down to a few drops for a small pet lizard or chick. A bit of raw quality honey or black strap unsulphured molasses can be used to sweeten and provide more nutrients. Please do not use molasses unless it is labeled black strap and unsulphured. If your animal has blood sugar issues as in diabetes, then forgo sweeteners. In that case a teeny bit of agave syrup can be used. Try to find low heat processed agave if possible so that you are still working with a live food. Please don't even consider using a manmade or synthetic sugar, as those have a possibility of creating brain lesions, brain tumors and neurosystem damage in ones that consume them. I've also had calls on dog liver toxicity problems from pet owners whose dogs have consumed large quantities of these.

If you have fish in an aquarium you will want to estimate the total weight of your creatures and work them up to that size of tea to their aquarium. It is always wise to start at half the normal amount to let the fish adjust to it. In pond situations you would add whole quarts of tea to the area that you feed them. Wild fish are exposed to 'cold water infusions' every day of their life and soak up life giving nutrients through their skin. Try to duplicate that by starting at a lower rate. Wonderful supplements would be raspberry, comfrey, kelp (make sure it is NOT cut with salt!), nettle and dandelion. For immunity supplements you can consider rosemary, lavender, echinacea, ginger and/or sage. Fir Meadow's Better Daze is also a wonderful supplement.

Decoctions

A decoction is a tea made from roots, tough stems, hard or leathery leaves and the like. Licorice root is an example, as are also tougher olive or salal leaves and pine or fir needles. Take your stainless steel or glass pan, put in your herbs and bring the water (preferably distilled) to boiling. Turn it to simmer and with the lid on the whole time, let it go for at least 45 minutes. Then turn it off and let it cool still lidded. Strain and use or store just like the infusion above or the fomentation below. If you need to store your fomentation or decoction for a longer amount of time, like when you are leaving for business or vacation but your help will continue the herb plan for you, then here is what you can do. Add equal the volume in good quality raw apple cider vinegar. You will now have to double the amount of liquid given and give it carefully, preferably mixed with more palatable carriers like carrot juice if drenching your creature orally. But you can store it this way for a couple of weeks at room temperature. Or you can add ¼ of the volume in everclear and shake well. You will have to increase the amount of tea given by another one half (1 teaspoon would go to 1 ½ teaspoons). This will keep for at least one month at room temperature. I still prefer that the alcohol be flashed off with a bit of very hot water before use.

Fomentations

Fomentations are made just like Infusions and decoctions but then are placed on the skin. Take your fomentation liquid, as hot as is still comfortable and soak an all natural cloth (wool, cotton, linen), and apply to the skin. Then cover, if possible, with some plastic and then wrap with an ace, gauze or vet wrapping carefully to not compromise circulation of the area. You must be able to slide your little finger (or a number two pencil) under the dressing or it is too tight. Ideally you renew the dressing with a new fomentation every time it cools down or if overnight, then in the morning. If wounds are open, either use a poultice or a salve, listed below. Do not use gauze or fabric wrappings on an open wound as their removal will pull off some of the new healing cells that are present which will add to the pain of your creature and increase the potential for scarring. Do beware of plastic around some animals- goats, sheep, curious puppies and others may choke or impact their intestinal tract if they chew on or try to swallow any portions of plastic. If that could be a concern then use a salve! I personally find that fomentations work best for use on people that know to rest the area and can keep it covered and of course they won't be chewing on or eating the plastic (be cautious with babies and toddlers and some mentally challenged people, however). Fomentations can work for lap pets if you have a favorite chair and they like to lounge with you. I find salves much more practical and safe for creatures in general and will discuss those below.

Poultices

Poultices are taking the soft parts of plant leaves or flowers and either mashing them (even chewing them!), or heating in just a little water or olive oil until just heated through which softens them and makes the phytochemicals more readily absorbed. If the water has taken on medium to strong coloration you just lost your poultice! Then you wad it onto the area of need and wrap as described in fomentations. You replace them as soon as they dry out. They do work well for open flesh wounds as the moist plants will not stick to nor tear flesh. If a bit of herb should happen to stick just leave it there. The body will break it down and use it, otherwise you may traumatize those brand new cells rebuilding the area! And do not mistake them for pus. Pus will ooze while new little cells will be whitish but will not ooze or be runny. Onion poultices are a favorite of mine and will be explained in the Respiratory chapter.

Salves

Salves are one of my favorite ways to work with creatures when external herbal application is desired. Salves are basically an herb infused in some type of fat or vegetable oil base and then hardened often with beeswax. They are easy to put on and they can be applied as little as twice a day but ideally more often, especially in more serious issues. Salves can be placed on body areas where no bandage can be attached or in cases where your animal wouldn't leave them on anyways. They can be licked by other animals or nursed off of udders by the offspring without ill effect when using the correct herbs as per our rules of safe herbs. Though not necessarily what you want coming in contact with an eye, they will not damage it if they find their way there. When a buck (male dairy goat) of ours had broken a front leg, I used salves to great benefit. For the first week I was only able to salve that limb once a day as it pained him too much for me to remove his splint twice per day. I coated that leg one quarter inch thick and sometimes thicker; then would gauze it and wrap it with his splint to support it. Every time we pulled off the wrap the gauze would be bone dry. The body would pull all of the salve in at the rate that it needed it. I'll probably share more of this story under broken bones in the skeletal structure chapter. It's a fun story and teaches you how to gauge your progress. I apply salves as thickly as I think the job needs. If the area is dry the next time I salve; I either need to apply more each time or apply the salve more often. I keep salves one half to one inch away from eyes. The body will draw it in closer if needed for an eyelid or eye.

Injections- Enema

Injections are a strange thing to find in an herbal, your mind is telling you. When an herbalist uses an injection, we mean to put a liquid product into an existing body opening WITHOUT a needle. Be that the ears, mouth, nostrils, vagina, anus, or teat orifice. Enemas are taking a liquid, putting it into some receptacle, lubricating the end and then gently inserting the equipment anally and carefully forcing the liquid into the animal.   For the goats I use a human fleet enema bottle and put what I want in it. Then I always lubricate the tip with olive oil.   For baby goats sometimes we use twelve cc syringes without needles but do NOT insert them.   Instead we carefully and tightly hold the syringe against the anal opening. For horses or other bigger stock a ladies douche kit works, the permanent kind that comes with a hot water bottle, tube, and then a tip that you screw on. You can do them at body temperature if you want the animal to expel matter (like the first 1 or 2 enemas to remove fecal matter in the way), or cold if you want the muscles to contact to hold the enema in for awhile.   Choose a place that you don't mind getting dirty with fecal matter and wear clothes and shoes that can get soiled. Apply a bit of the enema then withdraw and get out of the way!   Reapply as often as you feel necessary to clear the fecal matter, always using plenty of lubricant to avoid any possible damage to delicate rectal tissue.   Then if you are using an enema you want retained, you can now put that in after you get two or three in that expel the manure in the way.   Please remember human and animal safety.   You are not doing this procedure to see either of you get hurt!   Again, enlist training from a breeder you trust or veterinarian if you want education in how to administer these or any other procedure safely.

Injections- Mammary Infusion

In the case of a mammary infusion into the teat orifice we do need to use a canula, which is a plastic tip made for intramammary infusions. Many feed stores carry them for dairy goat and larger sized animals.   After carefully sanitizing the teat end after milking (I use an essential oil blend like Fir Meadow's DisNFect),   I open the individually wrapped canula without touching the stem or tip.   Then I place it on the 30 to 35 ml syringe that already contains 30 ml of the herbal infusion I want to use.   I then insert the canula JUST BARELY into the teat canal. I'm not even 1/8th of an inch in most of the time. You do not want to damage or cause inflammation to the teat canal. I use my left hand to hold the teat straight and support the syringe and my right (I'm right handed) to push the plunger at a steady but gentle rate. Then I wipe the teat end and resanitize it with a diluted essential oil blend.   Taking my fingers I start at the teat bottom squeezing the infusion back into the udder like you would squeeze up from the bottom of a tube of toothpaste, then I pinch off the teat at the top as it attaches to the mammary gland to hold the infusion above the teat and massage, massage, massage that infusion up into the very cavernous parts of the udder. Try to get it everywhere inside. This is why I use 30 milliliters. The store bought preparations of 10 ml just can't possibly be enough to get all around an udder half or quarter. Any leftover infusion can be put on the udder skin in the area you think would benefit most. For udders I make olive oil based infusions. Never, however, infuse anything into an udder that you are not sure about. Just to randomly pick herbs and then infuse them could have you curding your milk in the udder. That would really compound your problem as you wouldn't be able to milk your animal and you would probably gain a seriously congested and perhaps damaged udder. One nice herb that I like using for many things, stinging nettle, can be used to make cheese so would be a poor choice here!

Herb Balls

Some people call them medicine balls or dosage balls but I prefer to avoid medical connotations as these are not drugs but whole herbs we are working with. Herb balls are fun to make. Take your powdered herb (cut and sifted is okay but powdered is better here), measure out the number of doses you want to make into balls into a stainless or glass bowl. I like doing 8 or 16 doses at a time as then I can keep halving the mixture down to a single dose (keep cutting it in half after I add the binder to get 1/2, 1/4, 1/8, 1/16), making it easier to keep the doses even in size. Then add your binder: raw honey, black strap molasses, low heat processed agave syrup, organic peanut butter or real maple syrup. Just use enough to mix and stick the herb together. Now divide your mix into the number of herb dosages you put in by halving and roll into balls and then the balls in powder to make them easy to handle. Fresh milled flour could be used for the powder, but I prefer cinnamon, slippery elm, comfrey, nettle, rosehips, wheat grass, kelp, alfalfa and other powders. Pick just one for simplicity. You can keep these wrapped in your refrigerator for a week. You can freeze them for longer storage but you will lose some value doing that. Then just feed this 'candy' to your creature or pop it down their mouth if they won't readily eat it. For canine and feline friends and meat

The Accessible Pet, Equine and Livestock Herbal

eating reptiles you can roll it in some type of wet food or enclose in organic hamburger or the like. Or you can leave it all herbal.

Mixing Herb Powders for Better Palatability

Kelp mixes are a favorite of mine! Since my goats (and most stock) readily consume kelp I like to mix powdered herbs or mixes that I would like them to have, then I topdress their grain or other food with it. You can do this with dog and cat types as well. Easy, easy! Or let's sound more astute and call it 'efficient'. I typically mix the herbs half and half with the kelp then just give double the dose knowing that way they will have the full herb dose plus a dose of kelp for additional nutrition. Sometimes I have to apply some black strap molasses over the top of their kelp herb mix but usually not often. For larger stock I just mix it with their grain recipe and molasses, such as in my horse mash recipe in chapter 3.

Olive oil can be used favorably to get herbs into animals.   Take your animal's food mix or grain and add the herb powder to the mix that you would like them to consume. Then add a bit of olive oil to the mix and stir it together to stick the herbs onto their feed.   If they are good quality, alfalfa pellets work well for this as their stronger smell helps cover the herbs and it too is an herb.   I like using barley or oats.   Black strap molasses or other natural sweetener could be added as well. Gently warming your sweetener before adding it will help it blend better.   For me that means putting a jar of the molasses into a small bucket or container with hot water to make it more runny. I can even tote it to the barn that way while I'm waiting for it to heat up.

Other things you can try mixing herbs with is carrot juice, carrot pulp, organic peanut butter, grape juice (except canines), fresh raw applesauce with cinnamon, raw goat milk, fruit smoothies, a portion of raw egg for meat eaters, bread, etcetera.

Injections- Oral Drenching

Drenching is not my favorite way to dispense herbs, but it is a common way and sometimes is very necessary. Drenching is to give an infusion or liquid orally via the mouth. Herb powders can be mixed with some liquid, shaken well, and given this way if needed. Some liquid choices are water, raw healthy milk of the species (or raw goat), carrot juice, warmed black strap molasses, applesauce, olive oil, fruit smoothies, etcetera. It is well worth the money to buy drenching 'guns' or plungers made for your animal type or size.   The ones I use have metal tips with a rounded ball end for safety and are calibrated in cc/ml amounts on the barrel. They fully disassemble for thorough cleaning. They are MUCH easier to work with than syringes as the action moves smoothly as you push the plunger. I'm going to say that again- they are MUCH easier to work with than syringes- so please invest in your animals and keep a couple on hand. Syringes sometimes can stick and pop causing liquid to hit the back of the throat risking aspiration in the lungs. Also, drenching guns can handle herbs, especially powders, better due to their larger opening at the dispensing end. Please get training on drenching from an experienced breeder or veterinarian. I could try to explain this to you but it will be much safer for you and your animal if you can WATCH the process to learn it. You can get liquids into the lungs or sustain physical injury to yourself or your animal if done incorrectly.   Don't let me scare you though,   done correctly it's a valuable skill and with good equipment goes faster and is safer.   When drenching a cat you might consider giving it a 'blanket party'.   I take a long bath towel and wrap or more like carefully roll the cat up in it rather snuggly. Sort of like a cat straight jacket! That gives me only teeth to watch out for instead of teeth and four well armed sets of claws!   Bags are made for working with cats too or you can make one out of a tougher cloth or vinyl with a drawstring. Just put the cat in the bag (it probably sounds easier than it is!), draw up the string without choking the cat and now you can work on it easier.   Make the bag opening large enough to be able to get a fussy and uncooperative cat into it. Personally I prefer the towel method as I'm not sure how successfully I could get a cat into a bag after the first time.   You may have to keep cats kenneled in a large dog or cat carrier while working on them.   They tend to hide real well just before you need to work on them again.

Injections- Tube Feeding

The Accessible Pet, Equine and Livestock Herbal

Tube feeding would also be another type of drenching. Please get proper training before you need the skill and have the proper equipment on hand. You must get a feeding tube into the stomach, not the lungs, and you must use equipment that will not damage the trachea, nasal passages or other sensitive tissue. The equipment tubing also must not collapse during use. The age and type of the creature, and sometimes consciousness level, usually dictates whether we enter via a nostril or the mouth. We find ourselves stomach tubing an occasional newborn kid that is too weak to nurse but thankfully not often. We have also had to stomach tube an adult goat that had severe bloat and a horse many years ago that got into the grain. I VALUE this tool! If you don't think you can do it safely please hire your vet who will be well skilled in this procedure.

Bucket or Bottle Feeding

Milk feeding is a nice way to go if you have bottle fed, bucket fed, or lam-bar (buckets with nipples) fed young stock. Also for puppies, kittens, poultry, dogs, and even an occasional horse! I used to feed extra goat milk warm and fresh to my older horse in the winter when we lived in a cold climate. It would likely only work for horses that were used to it of course. Goat milk is the milk of choice if you are unable to obtain the milk of the species you are working with. If they have not been on milk for awhile I caution you to only use a bit as you don't want to get their gut flora or themselves in trouble with a fast feed change. While my baby goats are still young enough to be on their lam-bars, I mix herbs and tinctures in their milk as I want for their management, and then make sure that they all nurse well. It saves a lot of time and effort! When we milk raise pigs on our extra goat milk, all of my deworming herbs and anything else I want to give them goes right in their milk. Slurp! Done! If you are lam-bar, bottle, or bucket feeding, I place one or two inches of milk in the container first, then add my herbs or tinctures and mix well. Then I add the remainder of the milk I am feeding and mix again. If there are any dregs left after they drink I give that with the leftover milk to our chickens and our guardian dogs. They benefit from the leftover herbal nutrition that way too.

Tricky Bitting

For lack of a better place to put this tip, I'll put it here. Some horses don't seem to appreciate taking a bit in their mouth for riding or training. By putting a smear of black strap molasses, real raw honey, or real maple syrup on their bit, along with a small amount of cayenne mixed in it you'll accomplish a few things. One, the horse will learn that bitting is an enjoyable experience with an instant yummy nutritional award attached to it. Also, besides some of the other benefits of cayenne I have listed with that herb's information, cayenne also encourages salivation, which will give you a softer, more responsive mouth to work with. It doesn't take a lot of cayenne to produce this effect, a very small pinch should suffice. Mixed with the raw sugar base it will not have a lot of heat to it either.

Water Buckets

Water buckets are another good way of administering herbs. I especially like this when giving herbs the day of birthing. I make a hot infusion (tea), add it to their small water bucket containing a bit of additional hot water and sometimes black strap molasses. Nearly every time my dairy goats will suck it right down. It's certainly easier than drenching when you can get them to take herb powders, infusions, decoctions, or tinctures in this manner. If they don't suck it down then I make another batch that is more concentrated and drench it, mix it with feed, or use another method. Notice I didn't say stock tanks here. Unless your stock are drinking that stock tank dry every single day then it would be hard to gauge that all of your stock got the amounts they needed. Therefore I prefer smaller buckets appropriate for one day's worth of water so I can gauge and dose better.

Vaginal or Rectal Boluses

Boluses can be very helpful in reproductive issues. I will take a measured amount of powdered herb or herbs equal to that animal's regular dose and add gently melted coconut oil (using a double boiler). This is then stirred together until you have a pie dough type of consistency. Then form 1 inch long, finger shaped segments for a 100 to 200 pound animal size. Form them narrower or fatter for

The Accessible Pet, Equine and Livestock Herbal

smaller or larger pets or stock. These I place on waxed paper on a cookie sheet and put in the refrigerator. Once they have cooled I bag them and keep them chilled. I'll explain specific usages in the reproductive chapter. Rectal boluses can work well in animals that only defecate 2 times per day. For animals like livestock that shed manure several times per day they are not a good choice to work with.

Essential Oils

Essential oils are a nice tool to have. In general, many pure oils can be diluted at the rate of 15 drops per tablespoon of olive oil (or 5 drops per teaspoon) and then applied topically. For young stock I dilute even further in most cases. Remember that you cannot use just any essential oil. Some are dangerous during pregnancy, some can't be used with young stock, and none should be used with cats on a regular basis. Do keep them away from eyes and body orifice openings. Also keep in mind that some are considered toxic in any dosage and should not be used. It baffles me why companies even sell ones of that nature. There are always other choices that are safe which could be made. I remember looking at an essential oil blend last year that a gal in a spa handed me. I asked her if she knew that she shouldn't be using that one with pregnant women or really anyone. It contained mugwort. She didn't know. She bought it because of the herbs she did know, and because she loved its fragrance. It was being used with clients! In my opinion the safest oils to learn on and probably the most versatile and useful in the barnyard would be Eucalyptus globulus, Melalueca alternifolia (tea tree), and Lavandula officinalis/angustifolia or L. Vera (lavender). For livestock my preferred oil to blend with, called a 'base', is olive due to its nutritive values. Some oils can be applied 'neat' or directly onto the skin undiluted. I will discuss that a bit under particular issues, but for the most part consider that the exception, not the rule. Internal use of essential oils can be very dangerous or deadly. As mentioned earlier in this book accidental ingestion requires a call to poison control for a human and your veterinarian for a creature. ONLY use them orally if instructed by a person trained in aromatherapy and only use real essential oils orally that are therapeutic grade. I will use one or two drops of only certain oils that way on rare occasion for larger creatures, but really it is less effective most of the time than applying them topically. Please don't let this scare you. Let it educate you to respect them for their strength. Remember to always keep them away from children. I love working with them. Otherwise they would never find their way into this book to help you.

Chapter 6- Pregnant Creature Basics and Challenges

Every Fall we breed our dairy goats and are rewarded in the late Winter and early Spring with brand new bouncing kids. In this chapter I will discuss some herbal ways to increase the opportunity for a successful pregnancy and to help avoid some of the postpartum problems that really are most often rooted in faulty nutrition, toxic accumulation, or herdsmanship choices before or during the pregnancy.

Conformation

First let us consider some conformation whether it is a chicken, a dog, a pig or an ox. Conformation is the way a creature is built, body part to body part. No matter what type of animal, they need to have sufficient width in the pelvic structure to be able to birth the offspring in a manner that is efficient. They also need this width and body length to have the internal room needed to consume and process enough feed to support the pregnant creature and the growing baby or babies (or daily egg laying), especially during third trimester! This is also important to allow the cleansing organs (liver and kidneys) as well as lungs, enough room to be as little crowded as possible. Rump angles need to be considered. Rumps that slope gently downward from the hips towards the tail have vaginal canals that will work with gravity to encourage easier birthing and better drainage of uterine fluids for the two to four week period following parturition (birthing). Consider the strength of the feet, pasterns, fetlocks (ankle joints) and other leg, shoulder, and hip construction. This animal (now pregnant, and in dairy stock also probably still milking from what we hope is a capacious mammary) needs to be able to support the weight of the dam, the milk weight and growing babies to get to feed, water and shelter. Strength of face and width- both viewed from the front and also from the side; should be considered. A strong jaw, measured in part from the distance from the eye to the bottom of the jaw directly underneath the eye and from the mouth to the bottom of the lower jaw at the chin, is needed for consuming large amounts of feed in pregnancy support. Udder support in dairy stock is very important and will be covered in the milking stock chapter. Even in non dairy mammal stock, udders need to be at least considered.

An udder that doesn't function well won't support the offspring well for their optimum growth and health. A mammary that is well supported and attached that has productive tissue within will support the babies well, help them to grow well, and may grant you additional years of use for your brood animal.

Breeding Age- Dairy Goats and Other Creatures

A question I get asked a lot since I have a show herd of dairy goats is, 'How do I know when to breed my doeling?" Here are some things I consider when breeding my standard sized dairy goats. First, is the doeling healthy and gaining weight? I like my kids gaining a minimum of 10 (4.55 kilos) pounds per month to show me they are doing well. I also like them to weigh at least 80 pounds (36.4 kilos) and be at least seven months old. I need them to have a sound bone frame and need to be walking well (no leg injuries). In my herd, the doe kids born April and later may be iffy to use for breeding that year, as they don't tend to grow as fast as the earlier kids; although on our alternative raising program I can usually still breed them later in the season. However in my experience, the buck kids often are usable even when born as late as June, even July in the LaMancha and Toggenburg breeds. If they don't meet my requirements above, I hold off and breed them later as I watch them grow or hold them over until the following year. Note that holding them over a following year is expensive. In dairy goats, holding them over another year if they are ready to be used will lower their lifetime milk production numbers and may give you a fat yearling. You will have an additional year of feed, herbs, hoofcare time, and etcetera into them without knowing for sure if she is going to be a doe that you keep once she freshens and you can evaluate that udder. So I don't hold many over, and over the years have culled out lines that had problems in these areas. As to the buckling, as soon as he is able to mount does and able to settle them he can start breeding as long as he has good nutritional support. Even though this is specific for dairy goats, if you are breeding something else you will still need the answers to how old, what minimum weight and bone structure, at what age knee joints may mature in large stock (often 36+ months old in horses), and their current health including mobility to assess when to breed. You can ask these questions of a veterinarian or respected breeder and get the answers for your creature. In my horses I don't like breeding before they are 3 years old to give their body plenty of time to let knee joints finish fusing, to allow the dam to reach the majority of her mature body size before foaling, and to allow her to get to her 4th birthday when she will be more mentally mature.

When are they too old? There are a few things I consider when assessing my older ladies for breeding. They need to be sound in the legs and able to move well. They need to be keeping correct weight without any issues and in general exhibit good health. Now I do have one older dairy goat that has an old tendon injury to a front leg that healed straight at the knee due to the none flexible splinting we had on her. She sustained that FRONT leg injury while pregnant, and had no trouble completing the pregnancy or lactating and is even able to get on and off of milkstands by herself. If it were a rear leg injury with an incorrect heal, that would have ended her breeding career here. What age is too old? I don't have a preset age. In dairy goats we like to get 8 to 10 productive years from them, but I have had a 13 year old toggenburg and a 14 year old lamancha kid just fine and milk at those ages- and every year prior to that that I owned them. In the human midwifery units I've had age is not considered a risk factor in healthy child development. The factor we consider is NUTRITION! So, is your mare, cow, sow, dog, cat etcetera too old? You decide. If you do breed them and they have no more eggs to ovulate with, then their body will tell you they are done as they won't get pregnant. GI Soother by Fir Meadow has been used for situations where GI Tract damage has slowed the animal's rate of growth or ability to retain weight if that situation applies to your creature. Other supplements will be listed under the Brood Lady section.

The Stud

Let's think about the male part of the equation. Sometimes semi forgotten, we like to say he may become half of your herd or kennel, via daughters and granddaughters and any linebreeding you may later do if he has proven himself. So pay attention to his care! On the average, his semen develops and begins to mature approximately six weeks before the day you are breeding him to your stock. Be sure you are completely up to date on his nutrition and cleansing before then, as it is what your program was at least six weeks before you breed with them that is going to be the start of your new generation. An unhealthy stud or malnourished one can't provide healthy sperm to contribute to a stronger constitution (inherited body tissue strength) in his offspring. They will be more susceptible to health conditions as compared to what they could have been because dad couldn't provide his best. Address his deworming and herbal supplement programs and make sure he has the best quality of feed available appropriate to his needs every day. In our dairy goats our males (bucks) get their hay split 50 % as alfalfa and 50% as pasture, or a nice quality mixed grass hay when pasture isn't available. Make sure your stud animal gets the amount of protein they need, but don't overdo it in this protein crazy society. Too much protein can cause literal rotting tissue at the precipice- the area of skin where the penis will extend from for breeding. In goats that is referred to 'pizzle rot'. Too much of this going on can cause problems with your male being able to mount and breed and can render him useless. Our boys also get kelp mixed with the herbs that I want them having. Two months before breeding season we start giving them some grain again and feed that through the winter to get their weight a bit heavier than normal. I do this because of their tendencies to become anorexic during the rut when the does are cycling, which corresponds with wetter and colder weather. If they will still eat grain for me while in rut (most will), then I start adding olive oil to their grain if needed for weight gain or at least to try to hold them where they are, starting at 1 Tablespoon per mature standard sized dairy goat buck (100 to 200 pound dose) per day. I can work it up to triple that, slowly if I determine I want to do that for an individual. This adds additional nutrition and calories in an easy to digest form. For horses and other large stock, you can start at three to four tablespoons; for smaller stock, adjust down as low as ½ teaspoon total for small baby animals. I can sneak herbs in the oil as well and mix it with their grain. Do NOT substitute the olive oil for any other type of oil. Also make sure your olive oil is not rancid, which would cause it to be full of liver and cell damaging free radicals. Rancid oils will smell rancid. If in doubt throw it out. It's not worth liver damage taking a chance.

Your Brood Lady

Of course your female needs the same quality of care as her prince, and often she is already receiving better care and attention than the male. Some great prenatal herbs to start her (and him!) on long before you start breeding would be red raspberry leaf, carrots (shredded and mixed in food for pets), cold water kelp, squawvine, alfalfa, stinging nettle, dandelion, yarrow, and comfrey. Better Daze or God's Greens can also be used, both Fir Meadow blends, or Dr. Christopher's Vitalerbs can be used. These are great herbs for your poultry or ratites too. Fir Meadow's Layer Support herb mix is also available, so don't leave your birds out. Some types of poultry are 'pregnant' up to most days of the year, one day at a time! Herbs can be fed to them crumbled or powdered and mixed into feed, or as a tea added to their water. I prefer mixing the herbs with a wet mash feed for birds. Remember to start any new supplementation slowly, as it takes at least 10 days for the GI flora to adjust to new feeds. You do not want an acidosis or enterotoxemia (toxic reaction in the intestines) reaction which can be fatal. See the supplements chapter to review some wonderful supplements listed.

Consider that her nutritional needs WILL increase greatly coinciding with her third trimester when the babies will start growing rapidly. But please don't shortchange her first trimester- when the brain and nervous system is developing and body organs start taking shape. This time is probably the most sensitive to damage and birth defects from toxins. As the babies grow quickly, they will take up space once occupied by the stomach or rumen, making it harder for your broodstock to take in enough calories and nutrition to sustain the ever increasing needs of the growing babies and still maintain the dam. In our dairy goats, that means that I slowly restart the does on grain (increased energy food or carbohydrates) about six weeks prior to their due dates (third trimester is about 6.5 weeks from kidding). I also start increasing their supplementation including alfalfa. They are started on a small amount of grain, which I increase more each week until I have them at what I expect will be their milking ration at kidding. I have found this to encourage uneventful pregnancies. I don't, however, want them getting fat, so if their weight is good at this point I monitor them twice per week with a pinch test at the elbow and a feel on the ribs and spine to be sure they are not gaining or losing and can adjust their grain according to my findings. Sometimes while you are getting the hang of this it is helpful to chart this on a whiteboard. So many people say to start goats out with grain just two weeks prior to their due dates   but I don't find that matches up well with their third trimester physiology.   It also raises the risk of foundering your dam or causing other GI tract upsets as the grain has to be started and increased at a much faster rate to accommodate a two week 'lead feed' schedule. For any lady out there that has been pregnant, you'll understand this. You don't just start feeding yourself for your pregnancy or lactation 2 to 4 weeks out from birthing. We shouldn't do that to our creatures either. I'll discuss more below.

I also would seriously consider running some cleanses on the sire and dam before you breed. This would be ideally at least three months but preferably six months if they have never been cleansed before. This will pull many acquired toxins out of the system before you breed which will minimize what is in the system and being passed on to their progeny.   Releasing toxins at a faster rate than acquired and running them through the dam when pregnant is not necessarily a good thing for your unborn babies. This is especially true during the first trimester when the nervous system is incredibly delicate. Pets that eat processed food will benefit from a bowels cleanse for at least 2 months (twice as long or longer if they have bad breath, release bad smelling gas, etcetera), to remove old layers of food that is rotting along the digestive tract walls.   This putrid matter is drawn into the bloodstream via liquids that go in through the intestines, sort of a manure tea if you will. This is toxic to the whole animal and will settle in the weakest parts of that creature, lurking to cause cellular change and deterioration over time, which will cause dis-ease.   For stock that is eating green plants and hay for the bulk of their diet the bowel cleansing step can be passed over as the long stem (over two inches long) fiber will keep the walls scraped clean. If they are eating complete pelleted feeds or hay products that are short chopped or contain non black strap molasses then you will probably need to consider some bowel cleansing. For pets and stock you will then want to consider cleaning the liver and kidneys, and then the bloodstream itself and the cells, and address heavy metals. Those are covered in more detail in the following related organ and system chapters of Part ll.

Breeding Suggestions

When breeding your animals there are a couple of things you can do to try to encourage having a higher rate of boys or girls. One is timing. The sperm from your male determines the sex of the upcoming baby (ies) as well as the inner ph level of your female. The sperm which creates the male babies swim hard and fast but is not long lived. The sperm that creates the females tends to swim slowly but live longer. Keeping that in mind, if you breed as early as possible in the standing heat (the time when your female will willingly stand to be serviced), the boy spermatozoa will rush up first and then expire hopefully before the dam ovulates. This would increase the chances of having girls, as the longer lived female sperm should be in greater number in this case in the uterus at the time of ovulation. Reverse that if boys are hoped for. Breed as late in standing heat as possible, as the dam will ovulate just out of standing heat just in time for the boy sperm to be ready as the girls are still taking their time to get to the egg(s) (maybe they are window shopping)? Another thing you can do is to use raw apple cider vinegar and put it in the water or grain of your female broodstock. You need to start this approximately two months before breeding season to gain effectiveness and then keep it going in every day! One year, as I previously mentioned, I did this with my doeling pen, at the rate of about 1 cup of raw apple cider vinegar per 5 gallon bucket of water. I was simply amazed at kidding season to watch these doelings produce several sets in a row of twin and even triplet doelings with an occasional single doeling in for variety! The bucklings didn't start showing up in that group until later in kidding season, at which point my girls were no longer receiving the raw apple cider vinegar in their water. For people familiar to goats, boys usually are at least 50% of the crop, and getting twin and triplet girls is not nearly as common as having mixed litters or all boys. I have also heard of one person that would give apple cider vinegar douches to her goats before she would breed them. I have never tried it so I don't know for sure on the exact process or timing. If you have experience with that application, I wouldn't mind hearing the amount and procedure so that we can let people know about this option.

For those that do AI (artificial insemination) consider using virgin or extra virgin olive oil for your lubricant. All of the purchased lubricants out there for AI are synthetic. A friend of mine ran an unofficial test a couple of years ago. She took microscope slides and put lubricant on one, olive oil on another, and one more slide with lubricant that contained chlorhexidine. Then she thawed out sperm from an AI straw and put some on the different slides. The olive oil sperm were happily swimming for many hours long past the life span of the others. Why not? They were being exceedingly well nourished. Any olive oil that would be absorbed by the sperm or taken to the egg(s) would also help the start of those new babies. Not a bad prenatal start! Just remember that your oil can't be rancid, or you'll get the opposite, unwanted effect.

Is She Pregnant?

So how do you know if your dear lady 'took'? The first thing I look for is an absence of a heat cycle. This would be the next time they are due after being bred. In goats that works well, since they tend to cycle every 17 to 21 days, averaging at the 21 day mark. In mares it is usually every 21 to 23 days. In some species like pigs and dogs, if you missed their cycle it may be 6 months until the next cycle so that is not a practical plan for you. You will have to watch for other body signs or ask your vet if blood or urine work can be done on your species for confirmation.

The next thing I watch for in my goats (which have a 5 month gestation) is for their flank area to begin filling in at about two months pregnant. Instead of being well defined at the loin area they will start to fill that area in. This would correlate with 40% of the way into their pregnancy if you want to try to make this observation in other stock.

Ultrasound can be done, but I prefer not to expose the tiny developing nervous systems and organs to things of this nature unless deemed absolutely necessary.

In many types of animals blood testing can be done. Biotracking LTD, in Moscow, Idaho is a resource I send ruminant blood to when I need to know for sure on a doe I am puzzled about. I'll put their contact information in the appendix for you. Different animals require different amounts of days to be pregnant before a sample can be mailed. I don't like to puncture the animal's skin for any reason, but if I am in doubt on pregnancy status I will pull a sample. It is important for me to know how to properly feed a doe if she is or is not pregnant to avoid metabolic problems down the road. Biotracking is in the process of developing on the farm testing, so watch for that in the future. Other species such as pets, pigs, and equine have resources too. Do an internet search or talk with your veterinarian. We like working with Biotracking because we can draw the blood ourselves and submit it, saving us veterinarian fees. If you want to learn how to draw blood from your animal(s), most veterinarians will be glad to teach you how. Remember to keep it safe for your creature and you. We always use two people for the procedure. One person's job is to safely restrain the animal and the other does the draw. You do not want the animal to jerk causing cutting damage to the surrounding tissue or vein or artery you are in.

Therese Carpenter suggested an interesting technique (thank-you Therese!). I'd love to get feedback from you if you try this. If you take a thermometer and chart the daily temperature of your brood animal starting a few days before you breed her. Once you breed her, if she takes her temperature should stay elevated after ovulation. You can track her for several days past ovulation to watch the trend when compared to preheat temperatures. In her experience with a human it was only a fraction of a degree, but with a digital thermometer was able to be observed. You will need to take the temperature about the same time every day as outdoor temperature and stage of food digestion does affect inner creature temperature some. Often you will find differences in temperatures taken in the morning verses in the afternoon, so staying consistent will be important if you want to try and catch this. If there is a later edition of this book I would be glad to put information in here that anyone shares to help other breeders.

Hoof Care

Remember to keep up with foot care during pregnancy. In goats, we do not trim the feet the last month (last 20 percent) of pregnancy. If a doe resists or bounces, you could risk slipping an unborn baby off of its umbilicus, so the hoof care has to be up to date before then. However, do make sure it's current. The weight on those rear legs and pasterns is at its highest third trimester; you don't want to injure or weaken your lady's tendons or joints. There will be similar concerns with all stock, so consult with your veterinarian or an experienced breeder to find the appropriate time to avoid any extra procedures with your pregnant lady. That includes things like drenching herbs into an animal that is going to fight with you or shearing animals that can't be calm during the round up or procedure.

Exercise

Exercise is essential for your "mom to be". Exercise keeps her mind and her muscles (including uterine) more toned for the big day and making it more likely she will have her baby(ies) in the proper position for birthing. Exercise also causes her to breathe more deeply taking in more oxygen to nourish herself, her brain, and her babies. As is mentioned in other sections of this book, movement allows her body to pump lymph to enable cellular waste removal and encourages a more regular bowel. What pregnancy does not benefit from that? When working with our goats, we make sure they have to take a walk to get to their water at a location different from their hay. I also feed hay outside of the barn in outdoor feeders every day the weather allows us to do so. As long as it's not rainy, snowing or windy they have to walk away from their barn for their hay. If I get any barn potatoes lounging around, I first assess them to see if there is additional concern (perhaps a lung, pregnancy toxemia, injury or other condition). If they appear well, then I will take them by the collar and walk them to the end of the pasture. Then I let go of the collar as long as I know they will walk back with me (not run). Doing that also gives me individual time with my pregnant lady, which they always seem to appreciate and I gain a walk during the time of year where one isn't outside as often. Just this one 12 to 15 minute walk each day has been sufficient to gain improvements for my third trimester girls.

Social Issues

Congenial herdmates are important. If you find you have one animal being rough with the other pregnant animals, then get it out of there! It can have its own 'jail pen' which serves to protect her pregnancy as well as those in the remainder of the herd. In a past winter ('09 – '10) we had one goat being very rough with the others, but we didn't catch her at it in time and she had not previously been that way (but the previous year she was a 'new to us' goat and probably didn't have

The Accessible Pet, Equine and Livestock Herbal

time to elevate her position in the herd).   We had 5 dead kids that year with most of those slipped off the umbilicus. We also had one case of torn knee tendons in a doe.   We don't know if it was the same doe doing all of that, but we expect it was as the barn has settled down tremendously since she was separated out. She was the only one that hit in the manner that she did and we normally only have 1 or 2 kids born in that type of situation about every other year.   So watch your herd. Bullies can have their own princess or prince pens. They'll even think they are special. Temperament issues in breeding stock are discussed later in this chapter.

Male Performance

Breeding endurance in male stock can be an issue, especially when you have a herd situation where a few males are expected to service several females each and the females also decide to cycle at close to the same time period.   Use the supplements chapter to increase their nourishment well ahead of breeding season. Paying careful attention to their minerals and be positive that their parasite control program is up to date.

Be sure to rule out any possibility of a subclinical pneumonia or lung condition as well as any other infection in the body.   Those will sap the strength of your stud. A fever within 6 weeks of breeding can kill the semen. If that was the situation note the date in your records, as it may affect your breeding program.   In approximately 6 - 7 weeks he should be back up to settling females again. A semen sample can be taken after a fever or during the six week 'recharge' time and looked at under a microscope for sperm to check their motility and wellness levels. You are looking for normally shaped sperm (there are two acceptable shapes- one for females and one for males) that swim forward with purpose.   You should not see decapitations, deformities, swimming in circles or swimming like they are drunk. If I had a breeding male I was trying to get back on board, I would plan to double the amount of herbal supplements given to him to give him the opportunity to build back quicker. Comfrey would definitely be a strong consideration, as long as the liver on my creature was in good shape. I would also want my boys on Fir Meadow's Better Daze and cayenne if they hadn't been before this problem occurred.

Correct weight for breeding season is also important. If they are overly fat or moderately underweight their fertility can be negatively impacted. Adding cayenne to their diet will directly and quickly (often within a minute!) impact endurance with its high quality vitamin B, circulatory stimulation, and heart support. It's not a bad idea to feed or drench some additional cayenne on breeding days, as well as the morning of an artificial insemination semen collection. If they can be given cayenne at least 20 minutes before the event then the semen will also have time to be exposed internally and your little swimmers will also have more endurance. Not a bad plan.

Hemolytic Anemia

Sometimes animals will have what is similar to RH factor, or Hemolytic anemia, which can occur in humans. This situation makes one unable to raise the babies on the dam due to a potential life threatening immune reaction causing red blood cell death. The babies will incur this situation from drinking their dam's milk. If you have a brood animal with a history of this condition or if her dam or a sister had this history, I would consider doing several months of liver, kidney, metal and blood cleansing herbs before breeding her again. I would also remove any potential toxic exposure possible in feeds, grooming supplies, fly wipes, chemical dewormers, hoof dressings, fungicides, and etcetera. Please see the related body organ chapters for more in depth on cleansing.

Midwives working with humans have been able to encourage the body to heal itself well enough to have normal blood work in future pregnancies. After a cleansing program, do consider getting a blood test done to recheck the blood cell health before you breed. Some animals will take more cleansing than others depending on their toxicity level and their individual constitution.

Immunity

Immunity in pregnant creatures is an interesting topic. At approximately 2 weeks prior to birthing to two weeks after birthing, the immune system in your brood dam will take a dip. Try to minimize her exposure to changes, weather, feeds, and the like during this time when she is more susceptible to health challenges. Immune herbs you can have her on during this time would be Echinacea (ten days in a row followed by 3 days off), eleuthero for stress, shitake and maiake mushrooms, thyme in regular doses only, nettle, drinkable aloe juice (not the powder or fresh gel which is purgative), astragalus, ginger, cayenne, garlic and olive leaf. Raw organic honey is another good resource, added to feed, or gently warmed and added to their water. A good prenatal herb program also reduces the risk associated with this drop in immunity. Fir Meadow makes an MMune herb mix and Dr. Christopher has the Immune System formula as well. Fir Meadow Better Daze can also be fed at double the normal rate. These nutritious blends are also supporting your babies yet to be born!

Mastitis

Mastitis is discussed in good depth in the Milking/Lactating Stock chapter.

Miscarriages

Miscarriages are no fun when you have been anticipating the precious new babies along with your hopes in the genetics behind this new generation of your breeding program. If your brood stock is starting contractions before their due date, and before it would be safe to have babies on the ground, there are some things you can try. First I like to carefully get a ginger drench down them. I also like to make an infusion and soak cotton toweling in it and hold that up against the dam's abdomen if possible, resoaking it every time it starts to go below body temperature. Other herbs that can be tried to relax the contractions would be skullcap, chamomile (German), Lobelia inflata in small doses, ladies slipper, valerian, hops (not by itself in dogs), clary sage, and lavender. Or make a blend of some of these herbs. A tincture can be dribbled along the spine of any or a few of these herbs too. The other herbs that should be used without fail are to mix a three parts blend of false unicorn root (Chamaelirium luteum) with one part of Lobelia inflata. If the baby (ies) are still in good condition and still on their umbilical cord(s) then this blend can give the body what it needs to hold a pregnancy. Make a regular strength tea and serve per the dosing chapter every 30 minutes for two hours and then every one or two hours after that for the day. Then three times per day after that. Stall or kennel rest is a MUST! If the placenta was starting to detach then we have to try to avoid any further detachment and movement can cause that problem. Have you ever noticed how much movement there is in a third trimester pregnant belly when the dam walks? If I see any blood discharge at all or if I suspect I might as in situations where I see a pregnant animal fall hard or get hit hard then I also start giving cayenne orally to help the body stop any hemorrhaging and help deal with any shock. For uterine hemorrhaging shepherds purse can also be used, but I've always used cayenne with amazing results. Do note that if the babies are no longer viable or too weak to survive then this same blend will provide the nutrients needed for the dam to abort them. This saves the possibility of having to deal with a later c section to remove dead, mummified, or putrefied fetuses and reduces the opportunity for a uterine infection (metritis). I have used this blend successfully both ways- to help the doe's body save unborn kids, and to help the does' body clean out a baby that was no longer on its umbilical cord a month before her due date. The reader assumes full responsibility if using any of this information.

Pregnancy Toxemia or Ketosis

Pregnancy Toxemia or Ketosis is almost always caused by a glitch in management. Don't beat yourself over the head for it learn from it and move forward. This condition is called pregnancy toxemia if it happens during pregnancy and ketosis if it happens post parturition (after birthing). Two names for the same condition. It is caused by an energy imbalance in your pregnant animal; usually during third trimester. As mentioned before, as the babies start growing quicker the dam has less space with her rumen or stomach to process food, yet the babies are placing larger nutritional demands on her. If she falls behind in her carbohydrate or energy intake (what she can eat), then her body will begin to dissolve and use body fat for the additional energy. As this happens toxins stored in the fat, as well as ketones, are released into the bloodstream.   Your dam is already processing waste from herself, her rapidly growing babies, and now has been asked to process additional toxic waste released into her bloodstream from her dissolved body fat. At some point, she may not be able to keep up with these demands. These ketone or paint thinner type of substances accumulate in her bloodstream making her feel nauseated. The nausea causes her to partially or completely go off of feed further compounding the situation. If this situation is not handled, according to what I have read over the last decade, it is about 50% fatal.   From personal experience I don't think it has to be that high of a number. With good supportive herbal support there is a lot you can do as we have yet to lose a creature to it.   I have found that the animals that are most susceptible to this condition are those that are overweight (inner body fat also competes for space allowing even less room for food to fit in the GI tract), are finer boned, are heavy milkers, have a tendency towards higher birth numbers or weight in the litter, and those who have had the problem in the past.   If you have a pregnant mammal that is starting to fuss with feed or getting lethargic; besides ruling out possible problems with the feed and infections making her ill, you need to make sure you are not dealing with this problem. Some animals that are further into the problem will have swelling (edema) in the lower front legs which is common with kidney distress from trying to clean out the ketones from the blood, and some will have a sickening sweet chemical type of breath that you can sometimes notice.   There are ketone testing products that you can apply milk or urine onto to help you in your assessment. And of course, contacting a veterinarian that has experience in dairy animals is not a bad idea if you want a diagnosis. Dairy vets work with ketosis issues frequently so usually have developed good diagnostic skills for this problem. If I think I have an animal just starting to head this direction then I first will put some high quality sugar into it- for my dairy goats (100 to 200 lbs) I give 60 cc for the initial dose of any of the following: black strap molasses (least preferred), pure maple syrup, raw honey or agave syrup. I gently warm these in a double boiler if needed or in a canning jar placed in a small bucket of hot water, until they are runny but not hot. Then I give mine another 30 cc 3 to 4 times per day until I get them back to eating feed well again.   The other thing I do is start giving them liver, kidney and other cleansing herbs to speed up the removal process of the ketones which can also kill the unborn babies. This is a case where I WILL cleanse a pregnant animal. Some herbs that I like to use are milk thistle, dandelion, nettle, red clover, burdock root, carrot, cleavers, garlic, wormwood, or plantain. If your animal won't eat them (often they won't due to their nausea) then you will have to make a tea and carefully drench them. If they have any swelling or edema in their legs, then I like to be sure I am giving them nettle and dandelion. You can also put hot, but safe to the touch, fomentations on the swollen areas. Ginger is good to help with the nausea, as is peppermint. An excess of peppermint though can decrease milk production, so go light with it or only use it a few times. Fir Meadow also has a product called Keto-Mix that is formulated to cover many of the organ support and gentle cleansing needs for this type of an issue. The heart will be under additional strain during this condition, so feeding hawthorn berries or leaves or a tea, or Fir Meadow's Heart Support tincture, or Dr. Christopher's Hawthorne Berry syrup, and some cayenne supports the heart.

I see on the internet from time to time where people confuse this condition with milk fever or hypocalcemia (low calcium). They are NOT the same condition. Remember however, that a pregnant or lactating animal that goes off of feed, including her calcium feeds such as alfalfa, can set herself up for a bout with hypocalcemia and it can be concurrent with the ketosis condition, so be on the offense. See the Milking Stock chapter for more on this condition.

Problems with Cycles

Problems with cycles will be discussed in the Reproductive System section.

Temperament

Temperament is taking into consideration the personality and behavior of your creature whether they are cycling or bred or not. Many creatures can be corrected by cleansing and nourishing the cleansing organs, reproductive system, and endocrine system. A few creatures may just be bent on destruction and are not safe to work around. If after several months of cleansing and nourishing with efficacious herbs, exercise, sunshine, grounding out, EMF shields, etcetera, you find you are not getting anywhere at all, consider not using the animal again in a breeding program. Temperament problems can be heritable, but so can the toxins causing them, so see if you can break the 'family cycle'. Meanwhile, if you decide to work with them be ABSOLUTELY sure that your safety or someone else's is never at risk. While we are on this topic, please respect breeding/cycling animals for what they are, usually hormone controlled during that time. Even the gentlest stallion, buck, bull, ram, dog or female equivalents can have a temperament change or get very protective over their female when they are focused on mating. Ladies that are having their own menstrual cycle could experience aggressive behavior from a male breeding animal. Previously easy to work with animals can have a negative temperament change once they have accumulated x level of toxins, so be aware of any changes. Don't get stressed about it, just be wise and use handling precautions so that you never have a problem. I myself do not go into my bucks' pens that are one year old or older during breeding season. In the rare situation where I have to, I collar them and snap their lead to a strong post BEFORE I get in their pen so that they don't have free access to me.

Testicular Damage

What's a person to do? Your best sire has injured himself in the testicle region or scrotum. Whether they are torn, crushed, hardened or otherwise abnormal, herbs may provide just the support needed for his body to mend that sensitive area. The easiest way to deal with this in stock is to make teas to either drench them with or add to their water or feed, as well as using matching salves on the injured area if they will allow you safe access to their jewels; put on copiously two or three times per day. First give the body what it needs to control any bleeding or hemorrhaging. Of course cayenne given orally and cayenne powder can be placed on the damaged area if needed. In case of tearing or cuts, treat as wounds in the wound section, but also do the following which is also helpful in other testicular damage. Take three parts mullein and one part Lobelia inflata, and get it on the injured areas. If giving drenches, space them out a bit as large sips so that you don't hit up against the emetic effect of the lobelia. Continue herbing 6 days per week until they have normal appearance and tissue feel. Fir Meadow does make a GlandAide salve and GlandAide herb mix which can be used for this situation. Herbs to consider for inflammation would be marshmallow root, ginger, perhaps lavender, and then mullein for pain (or Fir Meadow's HerBamine tincture every 20 minutes until the body relieves the pain). If the Testicles have hard areas, I would also want to be using marshmallow root internally and externally for additional body support. For infection see the wounds section under the Skin/Tissue chapter.

Ultrasound

To ultrasound or to not ultrasound that is the question! If you feel you have a reason where you need to know the health of the unborn baby because of an incident or dam pregnancy history, then maybe an ultrasound is to be considered. For the most part though there are still unanswered questions on what the sound waves and additional heat may do to those tiny nerves in those tiny ears, tiny eyes, little brain and tiny nervous system. Do they compromise them? I don't know. Could they interfere with the electrical system running in the babies like a precisely set clock, sending information to and from little organs, cells, and tissues as they form and grow? Is it something that sets the stage for later seizure activity in creatures, a condition that is becoming way too frequent in our canine friends? I only know that it is not a natural procedure, so not one I encourage except perhaps in extenuating circumstances. We have had an ultrasound done in a doe that had kidded and torn a bit and was still having contractions due to the tear. We had her done to be sure we had not missed any kids in her. She was clear.

Weak Placental Attachment

Weak placental attachment can happen in the case of an undernourished animal, one that has been on several medications recently (or ever), a fall, or a hard hit or kick from a herd mate. In this case you will have to stall or kennel rest your animal for the remainder of its pregnancy, allowing only controlled walks after at least 2 weeks of good behavior and nourishment. Remember the rocking motion of a fast walk or a jog can put additional stress on that area causing more abruption (separation from the uterine wall). See the Nervous System chapter if you want some ways to encourage a quieter, more compliant dam. I also like to use cayenne in these situations in case there is any uterine hemorrhaging involved and the 3 parts false unicorn root and 1 part Lobelia inflata blend to help the body hold the pregnancy as mentioned in the miscarriage section. Wheat germ oil helps to strengthen placental attachment so is put to good use here. The easiest way to feed it would be to mix it with feed, adding black strap molasses if needed to aid palatability. I like using brands made for human use, as many of the livestock brands contain added synthetic vitamins as well as risk of rancidity. You will have to let up on the wheat germ oil at least a couple of weeks before it would be safe to deliver the offspring, as you do need the placenta to let go after the delivery. Comfrey given orally and fomented over the abdominal area or salved over the same area will also help the body repair damage at a faster than normal rate and can be used in conjunction with the wheat germ oil. Fed fresh, added to feed, or making a strong tea and added to their drinking water. Wounderful!, ReBuilld, or other salves containing herbs traditionally used to encourage mending can be placed at the abdominal region, as long as the dam lets you without bouncing around.

Chapter 7- The Pet and Livestock Midwife

The big day is here!   It may be just weeks (as in chickens), months (5 for goats and sheep), nearly a year (11 months for horses), or even almost two years if you have an elephant (if any of you reading this have one- I'd love to hear from you). Is it or are they boys? Girls? How many? Colors? Markings? Conformation? Finding all of that out is just hours or minutes away, and it's so exciting!   This chapter will provide traditional tools that I use when I attend my births.   I'll also talk you through some of the 'heart in your throat' situations that may be encountered. Always feel free to contact your veterinarian any time you feel you are over your head in a situation. I always call my veterinarians before kidding season to put them 'on alert' that they could get a call from me wanting assistance. I have two clinics that I work with, which gives me a backup if one is out of town or caught on another emergency. Certainly always feel free to pray. I pray before and sometimes during every kidding for guidance, wisdom, safety, calmness.

Supplies

Some supplies I like to keep on hand in food grade buckets or Rubbermaid types of containers with lids.   I always try to have more towels on hand then I think I will need. For me that is at least one bath towel for every kid expected, plus a couple extras and two more face towels more than I expect on kids.   On larger livestock that have single babies; that will be at least 2 bath towels and two face towels.   I like to have a natural brand dental floss, a sharp knife or sharp scissors, a nylon hay twine soaking in a distilled water and 10% grain alcohol mix which I keep in a canning jar with a lid.   To infuse herbs into the uterus I use a weak kid syringe with its tubing for the goat kids which would work with any stock that size or smaller, even pets, until you get to the smaller lizards and rodents. For larger stock, a ladies douche system with the insertable tip sanitized works. Syringes and drenching tools are helpful if herbs must be given orally.   Sterile latex types of gloves to reduce the chance of me introducing infection into the dam if I need to assist her or check things out vaginally.   A bottle of cayenne tincture, powdered cayenne in a shaker bottle with an easy to remove lid, eucalyptus essential oil,

The Accessible Pet, Equine and Livestock Herbal

lavender essential oil, Lobelia inflata tincture, olive oil, herbs for the umbilicus or Nav-All tincture and one or two sanitized stainless steel buckets with lids. Evening primrose oil can also be helpful at times. You also may want some type of obstetric chains, kid or lamb pullers, calf pullers, the aforementioned soaking nylon hay rope or whatever else is commonly used with your form of livestock. Do not forget to keep your veterinarian's phone number with your kit, a phone if possible, and a friend or two if you have some available that can help lend moral, spiritual, and/or physical support. My husband and I work as a team on our does. He supports their head and comforts and talks to them, and I work the back end unless I need emergency help with a kid or the doe then he may assist there as well. I do the pulling and digging and he does the hugging and talking. No wonder they usually like him best! That is except for Shekkinah. She has to lie on my lap or she won't push. Goofy goat.

Be mindful of where you are planning for your mammals to birth. What's the weather like? Will a clean pasture birth work? Do you need to have a stall or other area ready in case of inclement weather or in case of the need to tie your dam? Is the bedding clean and dry? If your mom had her offspring while you are grabbing a late dinner (a favorite trick of mares!) could the baby accidentally end up outside of the pen? Remove or reposition all water buckets once your mom is preparing to birth and anytime not under direct supervision if you are not sure exactly when she is going to go. Offer her water often, but you do not want to take any chance of her dropping a baby into that bucket and drowning. With my dairy goats I do leave a small bucket in with them with more of their parturient herbs in warm water, but I have the top of the bucket tied up several inches higher than the top of their rump. They can stand on their pen rails to get tall enough to reach their water.

Hatchlings

For babies hatching from eggs please let them do the work of hatching. Whether it's something getting squeezed through a birth canal, or a bird or reptile hatching from an egg, or even a butterfly coming out of its cocoon, the process itself adds strength and gets body fluids moving and lungs functioning within your newborns.

With our chicks the main thing I like to do is to give each chick one or two drops of cayenne tincture onto the side of the beak so that it drizzles into their mouth. BE CAREFUL to not get any close to the nostril openings or back of the throat. The cayenne will give your new hatchling added endurance, raise its core temperature, get its blood moving, provides B and C vitamins and heart support enabling it to be ready to take on its brand new world. You can do the same for chicks you receive in the mail to help them perk up and deal with stress or for any that have been chilled. Repeat every 15 minutes if needed. You can dilute the tincture with a bit of water if you would like to make the tincture less hot, but remember to increase the dosage in that case. Be careful not to choke them. Just getting it in the mouth will allow it to absorb through the linings directly into the capillaries and will move around that way. GI Soother herb mix by Fir Meadow has a lot of neat herb stories for new baby birds when mixed with their mash.

Preparturition Herbs

For the mammals it's not quite that simple, but here we go! In the dairy goats we can cheat a bit on figuring out their kidding time. They are one of the few animals that do not have a lot of muscle cover over the tendons on both sides of the tail head area. This may also work with some dogs, especially the racing varieties, but then dogs usually are off of feed with bloodshot eyes when they get close, so are giveaways that way. If you do not know how to feel for the tendons have someone teach you. Generally within 24 hours those tendons begin to relax and within 12 hours they get very soft and hard to find. The birth canal is now able to open wide enough to deliver those babies. You should not have to go into a second 24 hour period once those tendons start loosening. If you do, call your veterinarian or an experienced friend for guidance, as a baby is probably out of alignment to start the process. This process is true with all stock but may not be palpable in other types. Once I have determined that my pregnant mom is going to deliver that day, I like to get uterine stimulant herbs into her. I find that the herbs will not start her labor, but they will work with her body so that when it is ready she will have well timed, efficient contractions and usually fast and efficient expulsion of the afterbirth- often within 20 minutes of the last kid being born! That's not the same as the hard, stressful contractions that the hormone labor inducing drugs will cause. I've seen labors done both ways and I certainly prefer the herbal route. I think my does would agree with that if we interviewed them. Of course, I use the Fir Meadow mix called "Ewe-ter-N", but one can also pick and choose from the following herb list of parturients: red raspberry leaf, fenugreek, blue cohosh, squawvine (Mitchella repens), black cohosh, Lobelia inflata and shepherd's purse. Placing my selected herb or herbs into a canning jar, I pour hot to boiling water over the herbs and put on a lid. Then I can pack it down to the barn or kennel and let it cool to serving temperature while I'm checking on the new mom to be. Mixing raw honey or black strap molasses to it, or sometimes just serving it in a small bucket, I find that the broodstock will most often drink it right down. It can be drenched as well, but remember to do so carefully for your stock and your unborn baby (ies) safety. You can't have the dam struggle or she could slip a baby from the umbilicus. We also find that we have less kiddings with bad presentations (the babies not being in the correct placement for an easy birth). Probably the toughest test I've had was the year we had a handicapped yearling goat ready to kid. This doe had no exercise for most of her third trimester except for the two to three times daily when I would lift her to her feet so she could stand for a few minutes and I could massage her limbs and rump. Normally I like to have the herbs into them a few hours before labor. We got the herbs into her as she was starting her hard contractions. Within 10 minutes she had delivered a large strong healthy single buck kid without any abnormal assistance and then passed her afterbirth per normal on the herbs. For those of you that aren't used to goats, it is common to dread the 'single buck kid out of a yearling' birth. They tend to be large and hard for the first time birthing doe to get out. And here was one from a doe in just ten minutes that had not had any exercise for well over a month! Needless to say we give Ewe-ter-N for every birth.

Normal Birthing

Once the doe starts kidding I glove up just in case I need to assist and to give me better traction holding onto slippery baby legs. For disinfectant I like to use a grain alcohol like vodka or an Everclear type of alcohol diluted in distilled water. Remember that iodine is toxic, so even though it is popular I won't use it. Ditto that for rubbing alcohol. That product is very dangerous. Please don't use it. I don't even own any. I also will put 15 to 25 drops of lavender essential oil into a cup of olive oil in case I need a safe herbal lubricant. A canning jar to hold your oil of lavender made sterile by dumping boiling water in it then turning that jar over to dry on a fresh towel. Protect these from contamination by barn air, dust, knocking them over, etc.

First we should have the water breaking to lubricate the birth canal and then once we have a few pushes I like to just do a quick feel just barely inside to see if I can feel a hoof, or a nose, or whatever else might be coming at me. Of course 'nose and toes' with the toes leading is ideal and what I like to feel. If I find I have nose and toes, or toes for rear legs with flat hocks and I feel that the legs belong to the same kid I do help my does at this point. I will grab onto the feet with a towel over my shoulder and gently but firmly pull with the doe's contractions, and I always pull towards the dam's hocks to stay consistent with the angle of the rump. It doesn't have to be a race with a nose and toes forward presentation, just consistent progress. Until that umbilical cord gets pressed in the birth canal, that baby is still receiving oxygen via that life giving cord and on a face forward presentation that won't happen until after the head is out of the canal. As soon as I have the nose exposed I immediately start wiping the face clear with a towel-before it's even born! I want the nostrils and mouth and then head completely free of all amniotic fluids so that there is no chance of any being breathed down into the lungs when that first gasp for air comes. They may not always look alert immediately so don't let that alarm you, but they should start waking up after being that far out within about 10 seconds. Sometimes they are alert long before then. I've had kids pull their feet and legs out of my hands before we even had a face exposed!

If it is a rear feet backwards birth, which is common in goats and sheep you will want to assist your dam. I determine this by feeling up from the feet up the leg. If they are knobby like round knees I look for a nose which should have been there before I get to the knees! If I feel sharp, flatter, angled joints, then I have the hocks and have a rear facing birth. If it is any of the larger livestock that normally have only one baby you may need to call your vet or another experienced breeder for assistance as the vet may want to try and turn the baby in the womb. It is quite difficult to get a large livestock animal born fast enough without it aspirating on amniotic fluids. You may be encouraged to walk your stock around to keep the baby safely in the womb until help arrives to deliver with assistance. In these rearward cases the umbilical cord will get pinched before you have the face of your baby out to air. In the goats and in sheep we will deliver them backwards but will work with the dam to get them out as fast as absolutely possible and try to do it without putting the dam at risk. Remember that you will pull them towards the dam's hocks. I like to have a towel to hold the kid's legs with to allow me to get a better grip on them and sometimes I will gently rotate them a bit from side to side a few degrees to help them slip out a bit easier. This is a situation where it does not hurt to load up your weak kid/lamb syringe with the olive oil and lavender mix and insert some just inside the cervix so you can have the lubrication help you move the baby out faster making it less likely to tear your mom. I have extra towels ready as well as my husband to catch the kid and strip the face as fast as absolutely possible before it draws in its first breath. This is a time when you definitely don't want them waking up too soon. We always try to keep the kids held by the rear legs face down or on the ground on a towel with the face downhill in these situations with the other person stripping fluids quickly. We also use the herbs in the breathing problems section below as soon as the face is clear of fluids.

Newborn or Kid Care

Once we have the kid out and lying on a clean towel if everything looks normal we let the dam help us clean it (you can do this if your dam is negative for conditions that would pass via birth fluids such as CAE in goats discussed in a later chapter). I give all of my kids a bit of cayenne tincture onto the gums for quick heart and circulatory support and also provides quickly absorbable quality B and C vitamins. We then treat the naval with herbs for traditional antiseptic support. Since we handraise our dairy goat kids, we then place them in a container with a blanket covering them to await siblings or go to the newborn kid raising area.

Aftercare of the Dam

I always give the doe a cayenne drench after kidding. I take 1 teaspoon of the powdered herb, mix it with about 20 cc of water and drench my standard sized doe with it. One of my crazy does actually sucks it out of the syringe! Remember that cayenne will never harm her, only protect her if she is in early shock or has a bleeding condition from birthing that you are unaware of. I also like to milk my does or draw some milk from each half (or quarter if you are working with a cow) after the last babies are born. This helps contract the uterus down so that there is a smaller cavity to fill with blood if she is hemorrhaging. My does also relish hot raspberry tea with black strap molasses after kidding and half of their normal grain feed. Remember that cayenne, the raspberry leaf and the black strap molasses are going to provide much needed b vitamins and easy to absorb minerals at this point as well as boost the heart and bloodstream. If it is cold or cool out, I will always blanket (or goat coat) her and the kids after the birth. Your dams will lose a lot of body heat while birthing making it easy for them to get chilled. If your babies will be raised separate from their moms or if they are weak or it is cold they too will greatly benefit from a blanket until after they are dry. I only remove blankets when they are dry, strong, and the weather is suitable. If it's night, then the blanket stays on until around noon the following day in stable weather. If you have dam raised babies, your dam may not allow you to leave the blanket on. If that is the case, you will want the baby dry and having nursed before you remove the blanket. You will also want a deeply bedded area if it is cool at nights, to help keep it warmer to give it a good start. Even a straw bale broken up in the pasture will be used by dams and babies as a bed.

We like to clip the dam before she births, if she will let us without her bouncing around. Otherwise we try to clip her after we milk her and after she drops her afterbirth. We use a number five or 10 blade. We clip around her vulva, below her vulva, the mammary, and the area in front of the mammary. This helps keep her much cleaner as she spends the next two to four weeks discharging after her birthing. That discharge should be a red color with some consistency to it. If you find that her discharge is watery/runny, purplish, brownish, or has a foul smell, consider that you may have an infection going on and support the body both intra-vaginally with uterine boluses and/or vaginal injections and orally with antiseptic herbs. Clipping also lessens the opportunity for mud, bedding, or other things to cling to it, reducing the chance of mastitis as well as reducing the filth that the babies might be nursing on if dam raised. I like using Fir Meadow's HerBiotic and fresh garlic mixed with olive oil when we have a discharge I'm not comfortable with.

Breathing Problems

Breathing problems are scary to say the least. You have the baby you have waited for and it's not breathing or not breathing well. The first thing I do is sprinkle just a tiny bit of cayenne onto the nostrils to encourage sneezing out blockages and get a few drops of cayenne tincture onto the gums, followed by about 5 drops for a goat (10 drops for a foal or calf, 1 or 2 drops for puppies, etc) of Lobelia inflata tincture to help the bronchioles dilate. I also may put just a tiny smear of pure eucalyptus essential oil onto the nostrils which will also expand the lungs and encourage sneezing out of any blockages. If you can swing the baby by holding its back end or rear legs firmly, the gravitational force can also help remove fluids. I find the baby nose suckers made for humans, that are sometimes recommended, to be of little use with a true problem. As yucky as this sounds, I have been known to mouth to mouth and nose my goat kids (which are TB and Brucellosis free) and suck fluids firmly but gently out. It doesn't sound so appetizing, but is definitely better than a dead kid and you can get material out fast. You can also very, very gently blow fresh air back in. It must be gentle, as you do not want to push any blockage further into the lungs. I have had to breathe for two kids that were not yet born but had their heads out in situations where we had such a tight fit that we could not get the kids out fast enough to allow for their rib expansion to breathe. In those cases I had to breathe air into them several times while working to still get them out. One of them, "Dinky" aka "You R Free", is still on the farm. She is very spoiled by my husband and is now three years old with a Best in Show win! For one that is on the weak side, I also take a towel and rub fairly rough along the rib cage to also stimulate breathing. Don't press too hard, but do press firmly and rub well to get some friction going. This is especially important on a c-section born baby that didn't get squeezed through the birth canal. You'll be hitting body reflex points to nerves all along there encouraging body systems to wake up.

You can also rough rub the scalp (do NOT do this on a human baby, as you could damage the soft spot that is not skull protected) including the brain stem area and hit many reflex points there. And if you rub the sternum (breast bone) firmly, but not so hard that you damage it, you will work the Solar Plexus area which is the nerve bundle that communicates to the organs in the core of the body. So you just thought those dams were only drying their kids with those rough tongues, but now you know they also practice body reflexology.

Dystocia or Incorrect Baby Presentation

Please remember it is always okay to call your vet or an experienced breeder if you feel you have a situation that you don't want to try and handle by yourself. This is one of those. If your vet does come out, ask them if they are willing to teach you what they are doing as they are doing it and what they are watching for to make decisions. Many will be glad you asked! After any difficult birth I always give my dam cayenne orally and infuse some intrauterine (into the uterus) in the case of any bleeding I am unaware of. I will also infuse with antiseptic powdered herbs mixed in olive oil. Some of those choices might be garlic fresh pressed and mixed in olive oil, goldenseal, myrrh, cayenne, lavender, rosemary, black walnut (never in equine or camelids), cloves, sage, peppermint, and thyme. The olive oil will protect the uterine walls from some of the stronger (hot) components of some of these herbs. You could also infuse Dr. Christopher's Infection formula, or Fir Meadow's Udder Blast, Nav-All or HerBiotic formulas. I want at least 60 cc's of oil with at least 1 tablespoon of herbs mixed in a dairy goat size (100 to 200 lbs). Scale up or down for larger or smaller livestock or pets. Much of this they will lose when they deliver their placenta, so you may want to re-infuse another dose afterwards.

Uterine contractions will be caused when you reach inside of your animal to the cervix area. Don't let this alarm you, in fact I use that information to my advantage hoping the doe can push that kid closer to me if I'm having trouble grabbing onto it. In larger stock, like horses, you need to be careful to not get your arm between the mare's pelvic bones and the shoulder or other hard area of the foal. Horse and cow contractions are strong and one at the wrong time could result in a broken arm or wrist on your part.   Also beware of animals that may kick. It is best with the large stock to have more than one person present for the birth.

Once we have strong contractions I like to see feet presented within 15 minutes on my dairy goats.   Many times it's just 3 to 5 minutes and in first fresheners (first timers) it may be 20 minutes.   After that time frame I lube up and sanitize and go in to the cervix to see what I find.   Please note that if there is not a hard part of the baby, like toes, nose, knee, or something else actually pressing on the cervix from inside of the uterus your dam may not dilate properly nor start strong contractions. If this happens and you are not comfortable handling it, call your vet. If you have mucous coming in any amount and you are not sure how to read it, call your vet and let them know how long you have been seeing the amount and color of mucous or amniotic material coming out.   For the dairy goats, mucous coming out generally goes along with or just precedes the strong contractions. You do not want a 'dry birth' to deal with if the dam should push out the placental fluids before the delivery of the baby. Dry births make it SO HARD to get the babies out, even with lubrication, and make it quite likely that the dam will be damaged or hemorrhage. In today's world you might even be able to take a photo of what you are seeing and email it to your vet so they can see exactly what is happening.

You will want to make sure that the baby or babies have their withers (upper shoulder area) and spine lined up with the top of the birth canal.   If I get one that is a bit sideways or worse,   I add a bit of olive oil lubrication and try to firmly but carefully twist them by holding their legs so that they are upright which will reduce potential injury to your dam or baby during the birth.

Breach Births

Breach births are labeled a bit differently, depending on the stock.   If it is an animal type where multiple babies are common, such as in goats and sheep, then a true breach would be a baby coming rump first without the rear legs.   Those are difficult.   If your dam has a wide pelvic girdle giving you a wide rump on her, you may be able to deliver it that way as I have, though I wouldn't consider it my favorite presentation to work with!   In this case, it's nice to have a weak kid/lamb syringe to fill with olive oil and 15 drops of lavender essential oil and see if you can work it along side the kid to the cervix or into the cervix and apply the oil to give you more lubrication. Donning latex or rubber gloves to give you more traction and some towels to grab the kid with, you will have to try to reach and grab onto the hip bones and pull those downward towards the hocks (whilst praying under your breath)! You will need to get the baby out fast and be ready to start stripping the face immediately. When I am able to, I prefer to carefully push the baby back in and gently try to retrieve the back feet. Whenever I am going into the uterus for a body part (head or feet) I try to work slowly so as to not risk rupturing the uterus. I also try to cup my hand over the toes or mouth to try to prevent any cutting or tearing the uterus or cervix as I position body parts. I was taught this (you guessed it) by my veterinarian when we lived in Washington state. If you are not comfortable doing this, call a breeder or veterinarian that you trust. Please have this prearranged with your friend or breeder so that you know it is ok with them that you call on them. Now if it is breach as in rear legs first, which it is called in cattle and horses, you will want to consult with another breeder or veterinarian before you try to get it out on your own. They may want to try to turn the baby in utero instead of trying to deliver it that way. ALWAYS have cayenne ready to give to the dam in case she tries to get shocky or weak or you have any reason to believe she could be hemorrhaging. I give it to every doe after they kid as a safety measure. A note for you on dairy goats. They do not handle rough or aggressive handling when birthing. If someone is helping that is used to working on sheep or cattle, per se, the level of force, pushing, and pulling and digging inside that one can get away with on those livestock will kill a dairy goat. Dairy goats don't handle pain well and can get shocky pretty easy if treated roughly during kidding. She may make it through the actual event but you'll have to watch her carefully for the next 3 days to keep her progressing well. Bringing her small brush bouquets of different edible plants and herbs for treats (remember not to overdo it) as well as overall herbal support (see supplements) and cayenne is never a bad idea. BetterDaze and kelp are nice recovery supplements in this situation along with HerBiotic vaginally and orally combined with raw garlic mixed in olive oil.

Dry Births

Dry births have been mentioned. That is when a brood animal is allowed to lose too much of their intrauterine fluids before the baby(ies) have been born. Remember your olive oil and lavender essential oil (olive oil only for cats) and relube that uterus. It will nourish the dam and the babies while it's in there, giving them all added strength at a time it's much needed. Also get the dam onto small amounts of wheat grass juice and/or raw freshly juiced apple juice (2 ounces for 100 to 200 pound animals) as the babies will be fairly low on oxygen if things have gone to this point. As the wheat grass and apple juice enters the bloodstream it will oxygenate the dam and the oxygen will pass through the placenta to your babies.

Palpating for Additional Babies

Feeling for additional babies is fairly easy to do with goats. I'm not sure how easy it is on other creatures, so you will have to tell me! The first thing I consider when deciding if a kidding (or lambing when I've helped with those) is finished, is the attitude of the dam. Most of them will not start eating or drinking until they are finished birthing all of the babies. Many will be distressed if one has not been delivered. Sometimes they are too weak at that point to move one more out. The other thing I do is feel for more, in this case, kids. I will stand behind the doe, roll back my sleeves, and then reach around her with my hands coming together just in front of her foreudder attachment. Usually any unborn kids will be down at the center near the foreudder waiting to be born. I then feel with my hands by lifting up gently on the doe. I am feeling for hard knobby knees, hocks, heads, or feet. If you are confused feel on another doe that has already kidded and then compare what you are feeling. As mentioned before this is not failsafe, but is usually reliable. I once had a very tiny, less than three pound quad baby, that was further back into the uterus near her dam's ribs and I missed her. Her mom delivered her on her own later that day but she didn't make it. I had even checked inside of her uterus since I was already inside to untangle the other three kids and still missed her. I believe I only checked one horn. Goats have two horns or sides to their uterus. You have to check them both.

Tangled Babies

Tangled babies always make birthing interesting!   These are cases where you may have two legs, but each leg belongs to a different kid (dog, hog, and cat births are spared this issue)!   Or you may have the head of one and the leg of another.   If they don't seem to be coming out rather easily, then you will need to glove up and lube up and do some investigating. Feel up that leg to the elbow and then along the neck to the head to be sure the leg goes with the head.   This will also help you sort if you have two legs of different babies.   Once in awhile we also experience the situation where two babies are head to head at the cervix (still completely inside the uterus), with both of them vying for position to be born first.   You will need to push one back carefully to get the other first.   If I have a choice I try to deliver the smaller one first which I can pick out by feeling for face or leg size. If I am having a hard time getting a baby pushed back far enough to fetch the littermate, then I will try to get the backend of the doe higher than the front to use gravity to slide them back further into the uterus, which frees up room near the cervical area. By the same token, if I am delivering a kid that is harder to get out or if I am having trouble reaching the kids well in a deep bodied doe, then we'll stand her front end on a straw bale. This again lets us use gravity to help us move the babies towards freedom.

Spine or ribs first I have only encountered a couple of times.   You may never see strong contractions start with these, as there is no hard part of the baby like toes to push from the inside of the cervix telling it to dilate fully.   Once you are gloved up and lubed up and go inside and you start feeling through the cervix, you will feel the individual ribbing or individual vertebrae or dorsal process (the bones that come up off of the vertebrae to form the withers).   When you are carefully running your finger along the baby creature, try to imagine in your head what you are feeling.   The next course of action will be to see if you can locate a leg, then foot, and hopefully two feet.   If you have front feet (feel for knobby knees) then you also need to try to find the head to make sure it comes with you when you pull the feet.   You do not want the head turning away when you start pulling or you'll have a more difficult situation on your hands.   Because of this potential issue, if I can find hocks and then the toes that go with them I'll deliver them backwards in this situation, if I think I can do it quickly.   You will have to carefully move the baby to get the rump end or face end towards you.   If you do not have space to work with, please call your veterinarian.   Sometimes goats do get too full of kids to be able to deliver them vaginally. Also some goats do not have rumps wide enough to work with these situations well, or they are too overweight resulting in a smaller birth canal and a smaller uterine cavity due to the inner body fat competing for that was to be used to expel the kids. Real short and steep rumps also can have an improper angle to allow kids to enter or move through the vaginal canal. This is another reason while I'm picky in my breeding program to breed for those wide, gently sloping downward rumps. It really does matter!

<u>Having a head or neck turned</u> can be, in my opinion as a livestock breeder, the most difficult births I've encountered.   It seems that they have been that way in utero for some time.   Many times when I get the head turned to line up with the feet, I'll pull a bit just to find that the head returns back to be alongside the body instead of forward.   When I experience this I don't keep trying to turn the head, but I take my nylon hay twine that has been disinfected in a grain alcohol and distilled water blend, lube it, and take it in with my hand by holding the center of the rope tightly on the tips of my fingers.   This leaves both twine ends outside of the doe.   I am then trying to get the loop over the top of the kid's head with my fingertips and around down to the base of the rear of the skull.   I then move my hand to under the jaw, trying to keep the twine taunt, and twist the rope five or six times (no more as you do NOT want it tight on the throat area) as I hold it and try to guide the nose back in line with the front feet. Then I will grab the rope and pull it taunt with one hand while the other grabs my kid's feet.   By keeping the rope tight I can oft times guide the face while pulling the front feet and rope with the other hand simultaneously.   It's a bit of a coordination thing, but has helped us deliver several kids within minutes that we may not have been able to any other way.   Try not to jerk, but rather try to pull firm and always pull towards the hocks of your brood animal. Since you are pulling forward with the pressure at the rear base of the skull, the throat area should not be receiving pressure. I have found the lamb pullers that are plastic handled with a cable to work if I need more assistance if the kid's head IS lined up with and at or through the cervix, but if I have to go into the uterus very far at all, the puller doesn't reach or give me the flexibility I need.

<u>Head and no legs</u> in large stock is cause to call your vet or another experienced breeder for help if you haven't experienced this. They will want to try to get the other leg without damaging the dam. Also, when we have had this happen, the baby tends to be alert and breathing through the mouth and nose, so we can't push them back in. In smaller stock (again referencing goats as that is where my primary experience is) delivering them head first can be quite a challenge. If you don't think you can get them out, call your vet. If you are confident you can, remember to lubricate that cervical area with olive oil, as you will need more lubrication if it's a tight fit. If you can add some evening primrose oil to the olive oil at this point with your anti-inflammatory and antibacterial lavender essential oil, you may be able to talk the cervix into opening a bit more. The lubrication at the cervix area is very important to minimize tearing the dam or injuring the neck of your baby. You can also give a few drops of Lobelia inflata tincture orally hoping that the body will use it to further loosen the tendons/joints to allow a bit more precious space to become available. Then I grab around the skull right behind the ears; NEVER putting pressure on the throat, and pull carefully but firmly, and as always, towards the hocks of the doe. If I need to carefully rock the baby a bit side to side to help unlock its shoulders from hanging up at the cervix or doe's pelvis. In these cases I also add more lubrication on both sides of the kid. Because the front legs are under the kid it will make them wider than normal at the shoulder area. In rare cases, the front legs can be broken in this type of a birth, though I have not personally experienced that. We also tie our dam's collar to the kidding pen fencing before we start working on one of these. In our experience, she is not going to be comfortable with this and will try to walk away from you. Once I make enough progress to grab the neck, being careful to not damage or jerk the trachea, I will continue to rock the kid back and forth a bit to try and get the shoulders to clear the pelvic girdle. This is another good time for more lubrication. As soon as I can grab the elbows which are the bony joint near where the leg connects to the body, then I will hook one of those and pull from there with one hand and the other pulling from the skull right behind the ears. After you get those shoulders through the rest goes normally. If the kid is stuck with its ribs compressed it will not be able to expand its lungs to breathe well. You may have to do some mouth to mouth and nose breathing during the process to keep your kid going. We have had to do that with two over the years. If at any time during the

process you get uncomfortable, please call for assistance! Prayer for wisdom certainly counts for that, too. Unless you have a doe with an extremely wide pelvic girdle these are hard to deliver. Thus my preference for WIDE rump structures on any brood animal. Your kid will likely be weak. Definitely have cayenne ready for it and the dam when you get the baby, out even if the other kids aren't out yet. Remember that your dam may have an internal bleeding injury from a birth like this, but you may not know it yet.

Head and one front leg is another cause to consult with your vet or an experienced breeder if you are not comfortable with this presentation, especially in large stock. In goats and sheep these can be delivered normally, but they are tighter than the standard nose and both toes birth. When I am presented with one of these, I will pull a bit to see if it seems like it will be easy going. If there is no movement or very little progress, I glove and lube up and check to be sure that the head and leg do go to the same baby. If they do, then I may add some lubrication and deliver as a normal delivery. In this position they will be wider at the shoulders than if both front feet were out, but you risk more injury or possible infection of the dam to go into her uterus just for one leg. However, if after lubrication and pulling and some gentle rocking from side to side you still aren't getting anywhere, and you know for sure that the head and front leg do go together; I might push them back in a bit and gently go in for that other leg.

Dead Baby(ies)

If the baby creature is dead before the birth it may not be correctly positioned. They seem to be harder to work with to get into position. You also may not get correct contractions going if the baby does not have something pushing on the cervix to encourage it to open. I can usually tell if I have one of these by feeling over the eye socket. If I have a bulbous eye we probably have a live baby, but if it sinks in at the socket it's usually not good news. If you can't deliver these as above after lubrication, etcetera, you may need to get professional or more experienced help. Herbs you can use to help the dam help you move the baby would be Dr. Christopher's famous blend of three parts false unicorn root to one part Lobelia inflata. Be sure you use the herbs together in the correct parts for this one.   You can also use emmenagogue herbs such as raspberry, blue cohosh, black cohosh, fenugreek, squawvine (partridge berry), and lobelia or the Ewe-ter-N blend by Fir Meadow.   Give every half an hour until you have progress.   As long as your dam is not in distress, you can continue with the herbs. If she was full term, check in with your vet and do not go more than a day over (half a day in goats) without again contacting your vet, as the baby will be decomposing and setting up your dam for a major infection that can go septic (systemic) putting her life at risk. While I would be working with this process, I would also be giving antiseptic herbs or products. As mentioned under Dystocia, I would give my dam cayenne orally and infuse some intrauterine with distilled water or olive oil in the case of any bleeding I am unaware of. I will also infuse with antibiotic powdered herbs mixed in olive oil.   Some of those choices might be fresh pressed garlic, goldenseal, myrrh, cayenne, lavender, black walnut (never in equine or camelids), cloves, sage, peppermint, rosemary, and thyme.   The olive oil will protect the uterine walls from some of the stronger components of these herbs.   You could also infuse Dr. Christopher's Infection formula or Fir Meadow's Udder Blast, Nav-All or HerBiotic formulas.   I want at least 60 cc's of olive oil with at least 1 tablespoon of herbs mixed in for an animal the size of a standard sized dairy goat (100 to 200 lbs). Scale up or down for larger or smaller livestock or pets.   Much of this they will lose when they deliver their placenta, so you may want to re-infuse another dose afterwards.   If the baby was dead, I would want to keep the herbs going in to the dam starting at acute dosing for a day, then followed by at least two days at the chronic rate. If the baby was decomposing, I would want to continue herbs for 10 to 14 days minimally.   This would be oral and vaginal or intrauterine administration, or vaginal blousing along with oral doses.

Discharges

Normal discharge after birthing is known as 'lochia'.   This should start as a somewhat runny reddish tint changing to a more reddish crumble consistency as they are postpartum. You may see this for up to three or four weeks and it is considered normal.   If you see off colors, running watery purple, brownish or other colors, or off smells, you will want to support your animal orally and vaginally with antiseptic herbs as found under bacteria in the Immune System chapter. I would work with the first day as an acute situation and then adjust the following day according to what you observe. Don't let these go another day without doing something! Certainly you may always employ the expertise of your veterinarian to obtain a diagnosis.

Failure to Dilate Completely

If you know for sure it is time for your animal to birth and they are dilating enough to let birth fluids out, but not finishing the process, here are some things you can try. I would give them the Ewe-Ter-N tea by Fir Meadow LLC, you can also start giving them every 30 minutes: Lobelia inflata (very small doses), blue cohosh, black cohosh (though I like blue cohosh better), squaw vine (partridge berry), fenugreek, or raspberry leaf. I like teas for drinking or drenching best in these situations, as the herbs are much more quickly absorbed. Besides, if you could even get your dam to eat anything in this situation it would not be ideal, as her body would then have to deal with digestion and lose energy and focus needed for birthing. You can also take Lobelia inflata tincture and infuse some of that to the cervix, as well as drop some along her loin area. You can take evening primrose oil, squeeze several capsules out onto your gloved finger tips, and place that on the cervix and give oil from a few capsules orally too. In addition to the herbs, I also relube my gloved hand and gently but firmly go into the cervix and try to firmly spread my fingers. This is a good time to have a clock to watch, as even just a minute may feel like forever, but it may take five or more minutes to start getting the cervix to open if it will. The key word is firm pressure here that is not hard enough to tear the cervix. Often I can get them open this way. If I'm already in this far, I then use my fingers to feel what we have going on. Usually this will be a malpresentation. Sometimes it will be something as simple as the top of the head first, which requires a careful push back to get the nose forward, then locate the front feet, and line them up to come out.

Heart- Weak or Stopped

If the heart is weak, or if it just stopped, your **Cayenne Tincture** will come to the rescue. Get it on the gums, then drop a bunch on the rib cage and take a towel to do some rough rib stimulating by rubbing back and forth firm and furious. Make sure they are still breathing once you attend to the heart. These are scary; we've had a couple after prolonged births that we've been able to restart. One was after it was already born and on the ground. The good news is they can restart if you can catch them quickly.   Now you see why my 'every baby animal' protocol is to get some cayenne on those gums and some given orally, even if they are alert. That helps MY heart!

Hemorrhaging or Bleeding Dam

If you remember reading about Wiese earlier in this book, you already know what to do!   That's right, grab your **cayenne tincture** and give it to the doe orally- I will give 2 or 3 droppers full or even upwards of 18 cc's to a standard sized dairy goat. I don't have time to play with this situation. A horse or cow could take 30 to 60 cc's and smaller stock less.   In this situation it is more important to get some down them right away then to take time to find your syringe to get a completely accurate measure if you can't find it right away.   Get some in orally and intrauterine (dilute with distilled or sterile water, if you want, before giving it that way), then go find your syringe or drench gun if it wasn't in your birthing kit. I'll bet it will be from now on (grin). Then monitor your dam and keep her movement minimal, as walking or worse creates a rocking motion to the body cavity which could encourage a hematoma (large blood clot) to slip back off before it's on solid, which blocks further blood loss.   Here is a trick I thought of this past year while out of town after a doe of ours had hemorrhaged.   If you think you have the possibility of a hematoma (large blood clot) and you want an 'internal bandage' to try to help hold it in place, you can mix 1 part slippery elm bark powder with 1 part of olive oil, and add some HerBiotic, Dr. Christopher's Infection formula, or antiseptic herbs at double to triple the oral dose for that animal size. Now infuse this into the uterus. The body will use the olive oil and the slippery elm to nourish and encourage faster repair by the body, as well as help hold the hematoma in place. As the body uses up the herbs to heal itself, they will be dissolved. You can continue to give the cayenne orally as needed, but at least three times a day for a few days. Continue with oral and vaginal antiseptic herbs for at least that long also.

If I suspect a problem, I also like to milk my does immediately after they kid. Milk letdown releases the hormone oxytocin within the bloodstream, which encourages the uterus to contract down. That makes less uterine cavity size to bleed into, allowing them to clot faster and any resulting hematoma to be smaller with less blood loss to your dam. Blue cohosh would also be helpful here, as it encourages the uterus to contract down. Though I don't do a lot with homeopathy, Caulophylum (blue cohosh) can be used. However, you can't use homeopathics at the same time you are using herbs or you cancel the energy of the homeopathy out. Since I will certainly be using cayenne at the same time, I prefer to use the herb blue cohosh in tincture or infusion form.

After that, a person may want to consider using some comfrey poultices at the abdominal and loin areas or salves such as The Complete Bone and Tissue formula by Dr. Christopher or Fir Meadow salves such as Wounderful! or ReBuilld to encourage the body to repair itself faster. You can also feed comfrey orally if you have some on hand, but remember to never feed it to animals with serious compromise to the liver. If you got this book prior to breeding your animal and did some prenatal liver maintenance, then you should be ready to go with the comfrey. Comfrey salves applied externally are fine.

You will also want to think about giving your dam wheat grass juice (30 to 60 cc for a standard sized goat or sheep) or powdered herb (one to 1 1/2 teaspoons each time) three times per day and one tablespoon of black strap molasses three times per day, to help her recover from her blood loss quicker. Dandelion, nettle, marshmallow root, and/or yellow dock root would also be good herb choices here. Dr. Christopher's Vitalerbs and/or Fir Meadow's Better Daze are beautiful blends for support. I would continue for at least two weeks straight, then if wanted afterwards you could go to twice per day, six days per week for two to four more weeks for a six week total, if the blood loss was severe. After all of this herb support, she may even feel better than she did before she was pregnant!

Hypothermia

A couple of winters ago, I got a frantic phone call from a dear friend. The temperatures were in the low teens (Fahrenheit) at her farm and her Nubian doe had kidded before five a.m. She had pulled two kids off of the ground with their bedding frozen to them and iced fur and had run them to the house. As one would expect there was not much life to them, but they were still alive. I suggested she start getting a pinch of cayenne into both mouths to give their hearts a wakeup call. Tincture would have been ideal, but we worked with the powder. After they started coming around a bit, I had her mixing the cayenne with ginger half and half in a bit of water and syringing it down them. First they got it every 15 minutes, and then hourly after the first hour. They soon were able to take a bottle of colostrum. Ginger is used to stimulate circulation to the brain and legs at the same dose as the cayenne. If you can get started on any possible frostbitten ears right away with body temperature comfrey poultices, Dr. Christopher's Complete Bone and Tissue formula, or the Fir Meadow Wounderful! or ReBuilld salves then you may be able to save ears as well, even if they have already turned black. Keep the salves going on hourly at first, but do NOT rub or pull the areas just gently dab the salves on. If it's cold out you may need to warm the salves a bit on your own hand or by setting the salve container in some hot water to soften it. You can also soak the ears in body temperature yarrow and/or ginger tea to draw circulation out fully to them before reapplying the salves. Animals should be blanketed loosely to help them retain heat once you start them on the herbs. You might also consider giving them some mullein tincture or Fir Meadow's HerBamine tincture to help them cope with some of the pain as they start warming up. You can give more every 15 minutes until they seem comfortable.

Prolonged Birth

Our goal here is to try and keep the dam as stable and comfortable as possible and to keep the unborn babies safe. A nice midwife tea recipe mixes a tablespoon of raw honey with a teaspoon of fresh pressed lemon juice and ¼ teaspoon of cayenne in a cup of hot tea water cooled to body temperature. This "shock tea" would be

The Accessible Pet, Equine and Livestock Herbal

for average human, goat, or sheep sized creatures. For large stock you might triple those amounts, and of course reduce it for smaller stock. Any time you feel the led, or at least every 20 to 30 minutes, give your creature some more. This will help her with shock and help her gain some more endurance. If she is dealing with pain consider additional mullein, or even add it to her 'shock tea'.

During labor, the dam's contractions cause reduced oxygen flow to the unborn babies. If you can give fresh wheat grass juice, an ounce at a time (30 cc's) to a standard sized goat,(give more or less for other sized creatures) you will increase the oxygenation rate of the blood. As the dam's blood passes near the placenta it will impart additional oxygen to the babies. Give it every 30 minutes, unless you feel led to do otherwise. Remember not to overdo it, or you could get an acidosis or enterotoxemia problem going with the dam. If you have the luxury of making the wheat grass juice fresh EVERY TIME before you serve it you will get the best results. It deteriorates quickly after it is made. Freshly juiced apple juice, especially from apples robust with flavor or sharp tasting (like Gravenstein or King), also can supply oxygen. Store bought apple juice will get you nowhere in this situation.

To help support her in her delay additional Breathe Tea, raspberry, lovage root, fenugreek, fennel, blue cohosh or squawvine can be carefully drenched or offered as a tea to see if she will drink it on her own.

Retained Placenta

Oh how I hate these. Have I ever told you I hate these?! If your dam is on a good herbal prenatal program, you should greatly reduce your chances of having to deal with one. Also getting them on good parturient herbs (birth promoting) such as raspberry, squawvine, black cohosh, blue cohosh, fenugreek, or Fir Meadow's Ewe-Ter-N creature herb tea will minimize dealing with these. Most of our afterbirths are delivered within 20 minutes of kidding and some in only ten minutes. Occasionally after having to 'dig' for kids we will get one that is retained. As a breeder, I consider them retained at 1 hour, although many veterinarians have been trained to let them go 24 hours. Maybe a cow can handle that, but not a dairy goat. She is apt to get shocky and an infection, perhaps also milk fever if she goes off of feed.   When I recheck my doe at an hour, besides the normal cayenne and antibacterial herb plan (remember I was probably inside retrieving kids) I will continue with the Ewe-Ter-N or parturient herbs every hour. I also will take a ½ or one gallon plastic container with a handle (I get milk jugs from the neighbors before kidding season in case I will need them) and fill with one pound of water for a standard sized dairy goat.   I then take hay twine (the forever farmer's friend!), sanitize it, and cut it in 1 foot lengths.   I tie it to the handle of my jug, then stand behind my doe and also tie it as high as I can to the afterbirth.   As soon as I get about 6 inches of movement I will retie the jug with a new section of twine at the top of the placenta again.   I do not untie the old rope until the first is completely tied and the weight is supported by the new rope or the placenta can slip back into the dam.   I repeat this as needed.   I've seen them come out in minutes this way and sometimes hours.   Any placenta that starts getting close to the ground gets tied in a knot so that it cannot get stepped on and torn.   We want all the gentle and firm weight we can get, but not enough weight to prematurely tear the placenta in half or away from the uterine wall.   In some creatures, like cows, the buttons of the placenta can be manually detached from the wall, but this is not the case in goats.   Once it does come out, proceed with antiseptic herbs and anything you might want to do in case of bleeding (cayenne and/or shepherds purse).   If a placenta was hanging on for more than a couple of hours, then I will do several days of oral and vaginal bolusing of antiseptic herbs.   I also try to get some intrauterine herbs in before the cervix closes back up by using my sanitized weak kid syringe.

Sometimes a placenta will tear and you will lose part of it into the creature.   Now it is in there to rot at body temperature.   I have had a couple of these and was able to successfully breed those girls that following fall, so it's not the end of the world. But you do need to support your dam or you could lose your brood animal's life or fertility.   Try to get a uterine infusion in before that cervix closes. I like double or triple the usual herb amount in this situation.   At least one month of strong antibacterial herbs such as goldenseal (don't use goldenseal this long term by itself), cayenne, myrrh, garlic or Dr. Christopher's Infection formula or Fir Meadow's HerBiotic formula.   You can also give immunity enhancing herbs such as echinacea (use 10 days in a row, then 3 or 4 days off, then back on), Dr. Christopher's Immune formula or Fir Meadow's MMune formula. Mullein is a great herb to support the lymphatic system, as it now has to carry out this entire mess one cell at a time. Some citrus fruit, juice, or peels (organic preferred) will also help them clean this mess out of their systems and provide some additional whole food Vitamin C.

Shock

Although discussed above, we will mention it again in case you are paging through your book in fury trying to locate this information quickly. **Cayenne**! You can use a tincture or the powder, mixed with water if needed and given orally (drench) to a conscious animal. If unconscious then get it on the gums- the tincture is best but even some powder on the gums and tongue until you can mix some more powder with water will help. Remember to keep it away from the back of the throat so you do not drown your animal or get fluid in their lungs. If the unconscious animal can be stomach tubed, knowing for sure that you are in the stomach and not the lungs, then I would put another dose down that way. If you can't stomach tube and can give an enema, then I would enema cayenne mixed with water into the animal via the anus. Remember to lubricate the tip of your applicator and be gentle with the rectal tissue. You can give more, as led, every few minutes until you get a response. Remember, though the cayenne is hot it will never damage any tissue. A hot anus and sigmoid colon is preferable to an animal dying from shock! The water will moderate the heat anyhow and it will still be taken up by capillaries and race to the heart. You can also place cayenne tincture on the chest and ribs area and massage some in. Remember that as some animals come to they may flail with their legs and neck, so use care that you are not struck by a flying horse or other creature hoof or head. Work on them from beside their spine rather than their belly side. Also keep an extra long lead rope on so that if they try to rise you again can stand out of harm's way if they strike with a leg or become unsteady and fall. You do not need a situation where you will need the cayenne going in to revive YOU. For additional follow up you can make the **shock tea** of ¼ teaspoon of cayenne, one tablespoon of raw honey to one cup of hot water cooled to body temperature. One lime or ½ of a fresh lemon can also be squeezed in if wanted. Make extra and you can have some too if you need a quick 'pick me up'. Continue hourly with the cayenne or shock tea until your animal is responding well and steady on its feet.

Slow Starters

Is your new baby starting out slow or having a hard time coming to?   This is another good application for some **cayenne**, placed on the gums and if your baby is conscious then give a small tincture orally and then every 15 minutes as needed. Ginger can be used if you don't have cayenne, but cayenne would be my first choice. Other choices would be rosemary, peppermint, a small amount of cloves, or even a small amount of Lobelia inflata.   These would be in herb form, not the essential oils. The herbs can be mixed with a bit of water for drenching if the animal is conscious. Also dipping the navel in Fir Meadow's Nav-All tincture has given us many stories of baby stock getting up and nursing sooner than average. That means you get to get back to the house sooner if you need or want to.

Umbilicus bleeding

Early last year my husband called me when I was out of town to announce that he had just used his cayenne powder to stop a newborn kid's naval from bleeding. He knows more about herbs then he realizes and this is exactly what I want you to do if you get one of these.   After that we carefully tie them off with some dental floss, being sure that there is NO intestine starting to hernia before we tie it off. We haven't had one yet, but you do need to check. You would do this by disinfecting your hands (Nav-All Tincture or HerBiotic works nice for this situation) and then carefully squeezing the navel from the lowest point working your way towards the tummy. You should run into any rounded tissue feeling as you approach the tummy. If in doubt tie it off lower- away from the tummy. Tying off any intestine by mistake will kill that baby.   We have had a couple of naval bleeders start up hours after they were born, so now we keep checking them several times during that first day and apply cayenne to the cord any time we feel we want to.   It seems that we also get one or two bleeders a year, usually because I accidentally jerk the naval if I have to sever one that is too strong to break on its own.   This is another reason why cayenne is always at my side during births.

Umbilicus Sanitation

So now your baby or babies are on the ground breathing, heart beating and their dam is stable. What a good herbalist you are! You have even checked to see if they are boys or girls and what their colors and markings are. Maybe you've already named it or them!   Now is the time to take a tincture or powdered herbs and attend to that navel. I often do this before each additional kid is born, if the doe rests in between kids.   Sometimes she doesn't, but will shoot the babies to me in rapid order. We do not use iodine at our farm.   A few years back I realized that anything I put on that naval gets pulled right into the bloodstream and circulates through my brand new baby I stopped using it. If you are perceptive you can smell the product via their ears or mouth within a minute after dipping. Inorganic iodine, after all, is poisonous.   You can take a powder of sage, goldenseal, thyme, rosemary, cayenne, myrrh or some combination and sprinkle or dip it on.   I personally like to use Fir Meadow's Nav-All tincture, which has been formulated with a traditional approach to stimulating circulation, the heart, the brain stem, the lungs, digestion, provide B Complex and C vitamins all in a safe herb form, as well as being antiseptic and anti-inflammatory. I like to apply whatever I'm using two to three times the first day or until the naval is dry.   The benefit with these natural choices is that if the dam should lick it off you are nourishing her rather than poisoning her.   Meat goat and mini goat breeders have been so pleased with this way of doing things allows them to get to the house and a hot shower faster than before their herb product use, as their babies are up and nursing sooner.

Chapter 8-   Raising Your Babies

Your long planned for and awaited beloved baby or babies are here!   Now the goal is to get them off to a good start and keep them growing well to reach that full genetic potential that you are excited to watch unfold before you!

Nourishment is so important for your new babies.   Colostrum, prepared and given by God to provide antibodies, initial nourishment and laxatives to start moving the meconium (the first dark tarry manure) is of utmost significance. Please be sure your babies get real colostrum and not some prepackaged, manmade product.

We always try to handmilk our goats an hour or two before they kid so that we are sure we have fresh colostrum on hand in case we should lose the dam during kidding or shortly after.   We also freeze excess colostrum which is usable for about 18 months in that state.   It's not as ideal as fresh, but it is infinitely better than any replacement product.   We make sure that our baby goats get at least one ounce per one pound of body weight the first twelve hours of life.   So a six pound kid would get a minimum of six ounces by 12 hours of age.   Having said that, they are usually consuming about triple that amount, but this gives you a minimum if you have to ration a limited supply.   Your veterinarian would be able to tell you the minimums for other creatures.   Sometimes you can purchase frozen colostrum from dairy goat breeders to keep on hand in your freezer for a backup.   That would be your second choice if you did not have colostrum available from an animal of your baby's species.

It is also important to know about certain diseases.   With some milking stock, some of those buzzword conditions would be Johne's disease, Mycoplasma, CAE, OPPV, TB, Brucellosis, and CL some of which will be discussed more in the milking stock chapter. Animals that have those diseases should NEVER have their milk used to feed young stock.   In the case of CAE in goats and OPPV in sheep, milk can be used but the colostrum must be safely heat treated at 130 to 139 degrees Fahrenheit with that heat sustained for a full 60 minutes and milk must be pasteurized at 165 degrees F for 15 seconds to destroy the virus.   Some diseases don't pasteurize out but CAE does, as long as it is done correctly.   The CAE would

The Accessible Pet, Equine and Livestock Herbal

only be a concern for milk going to other goats and sometimes sheep. The pasteurized or heat treated milk will now be a dead product with the life energy, some nutrients, and the enzymes killed; however, this is still preferred to spreading those serious conditions to the next generation and you can supplement the milk with herb powders such as Dr. Christopher's Vitalerbs or Fir Meadow's Better Daze to help compensate for nutrient loss. Not all diseases will be symptomatic, meaning that an animal can have the condition, but not show any symptoms of it. There is testing available for those diseases. Some of it is pretty accurate and some not so. Do more research if this interests you.

Just as the babies need real colostrum, they also need the milk provided by their dam. A bag of formula (replacer) that contains a couple of dozen nutrients, often synthetic, is no match for the possibly hundreds or thousands of nutrients contained within their mother's milk. Many of those nutrients probably haven't even been 'discovered' yet, so how would a skilled scientist or nutritionist even know to put them in? It doesn't mean they aren't there and aren't needed. Another thought of interest. Each day that your brood animal is nursing her young one(s), her milk changes just a bit in nutrient type and load to match with what will be needed for a baby the age of hers. Replacers can't do that either. Immunity, longevity, and productivity are often negatively impacted in the future use of that baby. That could be part of the reason that in cow dairies we often see a three year turnaround on their milk string. A cow will be used for three years then sent to butcher. The same cow, raised naturally and not having Johne's disease may milk into her middle to late teens on a small farm. I think it would be an absolutely fascinating study to read the eyes of cows (Iridology and Schlerology) and goats and compare those that were replacer raised to those that were dam or raw whole milk raised. I think the results could prove interesting. If for whatever reason you don't have the dam to feed the baby, or she is not producing enough for the baby's needs, you can supplement with a disease free source of raw dairy goat milk. Many orphaned animals of probably every type imaginable are and have been raised this way and do well on this diet.

We also make sure our babies have safe access to fresh water from about three days of age on and free choice alfalfa hay. I personally don't add any grain to their menu until they are close to weaning, but then our babies have all the milk they can consume twice per day. In a dam raised other species or fiber or meat goat situation, you will need to start supplementing with some grain mixed with herbs once your animal type is past their peak production. We feed milk for a four month minimum, though some kids do wean themselves before then. Incidentally, because we show and often sell kids before weaning age, we do handraise our kids. Since many of our hand raised does get in the 175 to 190 pound range, have longevity (8 to 14 years), and most having above average productivity for many years, we are fine with handraising as long as we are able to give the babies attention every day. Afterall, they think YOU are mom if you are feeding them; they need time with mom for emotional stability. It doesn't harm my or my husband's emotional stability either to be greeted by a pen full of happy kids (grin). If you are unable to give your hand raised babies some individual attention, may I suggest that you probably have too many. Please remember this attention needs to be appropriate for the creature. Larger stock does need to learn personal space and respect or you will have problems with that mini livestock to draft sized animal, so you need to establish that fact with them while they are quite young. There are excellent training videos and methods out there. My rule of thumb with my horses is that if it is not cute at 1000 pounds then it isn't acceptable behavior at only 100 pounds. Thankfully the goats outgrow their spoiling once they are working (in milk).

It's always a good practice, to clip around your dam's rear leg area as well as near and below her vulva. If they are long haired, clipping around the mammary will reduce the debris that sticks to them, whether that be post partum vaginal discharge, mud, or bedding. This will reduce the likelihood for mastitis and lessen the amount of bacteria your babies suckle off of their dam if they are dam raised.

Separating male from female babies is something you will need to consider. Find out what age that is for the type of animal you are working with. In dairy goats bucklings can sometimes be fertile as young as one month old and can accidentally breed some doelings nearly that young; or their dams if they can figure a way to do it and she comes into heat. Doelings bred too young may carry the kids full term, but will usually die during the birth; not being mature enough to go through the process. Our kids get separated out at about three weeks of age, if not sooner, to their own boy and girl pens.

Know the history of your stock. If purchasing stock for the first time learn about them before your purchase including asking questions of informed people; including veterinarians, about where to look for stock. Some health conditions are very prevalent in various areas of the country and in certain breeds of stock. If a breeder gets upset or sidesteps the questions about the above mentioned conditions or others that are important for your species, find another one to work with. Why purchase a headache condition to deal with? If you have these conditions, please educate people about them. A new friend is much better than an underhanded stock sale.

Issues with Young Pets and Stock

No one wants to have problems with their babies. Sick or injured babies can have a heart rending effect. Have hope, as there is often many things you can do for them.

In emergencies you are going to have to make infusions or decoctions or use tinctures and drench them. You can carefully enema herb teas and or use some of the safer essential oils diluted and/or salves with them externally. In chronic issues, you can put powdered herbs or tinctures in their bottles. If they are dam raised and the baby is a problem to work with orally, then you can put the dam on the oral program you want the baby on at the dam's dosage. Baby will get the nourishment through the milk.

Bleeding

Bleeding is not fun to encounter, but if you raise young animals eventually you will run into this. Just like children, their activity levels and lack of life experience can find them getting into situations that cause bleeding. But by now you probably remember that you are going to grab your shaker bottle of cayenne and pour it onto the injury. Also give some tincture, or some herb mixed with water orally, so the body will even out its blood pressure system wide. If there is serious bleeding, apply pressure over the powdered cayenne, and if it doesn't start to reduce in 3 minutes or if it is spurting (artery), call your veterinarian as the tear could be to a vein or artery that is larger than is able to clot and hold. Usually the bleeding will stop or largely reduce in as quickly as ten seconds. You can repeat with more cayenne if needed. Remember to wrap the area with a pressure wrap if deemed beneficial. If one of our goat kids breaks a horn bud (area that we have disbudded or removed horn) and it's dripping blood, then we will apply cayenne powder; then a clean paper towel over that and then duct tape over that. Then we put them where we can monitor them and where herd mates can't remove the wrap! If they are shocky, the cayenne helps with this problem as well. The cayenne is antiseptic so I don't usually use sterile wrapping for an exterior wound, but the fresh paper towel does need to be clean. You can use a nontoxic plant leaf for the dressing before you tape; just layer it over the cayenne. Mullein leaf is nice for this; being large, velvety soft, and easy to tear. Comfrey is nice too, but needs the main rib removed and then be gently blanched in hot water or steam so it is not stickery on the injury. I do know of people that have also used their disbudding iron to cauterize a bleeding horn bud. I prefer to start with the cayenne, as it is less fearful for the young creature than the hot iron.

Damaged Bones and Tissue

Broken bones, damaged (even severed) tendons, or other injuries can be disheartening. Have heart though, as young stock usually heal better and faster than mature animals and can heal themselves completely! See the Skeletal chapter for more detail on this. Do be sure that if something is out of alignment or doesn't look right, and you are not comfortable with working with that situation that you employ the services of a veterinarian. Setting bones on your own can be dangerous- if they are compound (coming through the skin) or broken apart inside, a vein or artery can be torn when you try to reset. Not a good thing to say the least! Dislocations need to have more than a salve applied; they need to be put back in place by someone understanding the anatomy of the animal so that you minimize the chance of damaging nerves, veins, or arteries. If joints are involved, sometimes they need to be pinned to hold them in place well enough to give the herbs time to support the repair work by the body. But after your veterinarian's help, herbs will become a good friend for your creature and enable their body to heal the situation faster. See the related chapters in Part ll of this book.

The Accessible Pet, Equine and Livestock Herbal

Coccidia or Cocci

Coccidia are a single celled parasite that can affect several types of livestock as well as poultry. There are different species for different types of stock, but are all handled the same way. They can affect and sometimes even kill mature stock under a lot of stress, but they can kill young animals quickly once they become established. One oocyst (egg) licked off of fence, barn wall, or feeder can mature into an adult that can put hundreds to thousands of more eggs into the environment via your stock's manure. If you have chickens or cats that wander around, consider this. They may walk through your livestock pens and then walk on the feeders, feed, or hay stack spreading coccidia eggs from their feet to the feed. Even if those hay bales sit for six months before you use them, the oocysts will still be infective, as they can be for seasons. Coccidia likes wet weather and are most prevalent then, but later in the year when it's hot they can take hold of the lowered immunity of heat stressed stock; because most stock will have some level of coccidia in their GI tract at all times, waiting for a large immune system reduction to take hold. They have an approximate three week life cycle from their being ingested as an egg to becoming an egg bearing adult. Meanwhile, as they grow and feed they chew up the lining of the intestinal tract, causing hemorrhaging and diarrhea in serious cases. It is this hemorrhaging that usually kills the host. The thing is that by the time you see and smell the characteristic cocci colors and odors, and possibly see some blood mixed with the feces, you already have quite a bit of intestinal damage done; leaving the animal in immediate danger. Ginger and cayenne are your friends for coccidia assistance. They must be high quality herbs or you are putting your babies at risk due to the speed needed at which to get this situation back under control. We mix a Fir Meadow product, called GI Soother, in lambars (buckets with nipples) or bottles with their milk two or more times per week starting at three or four days of age. Use a pinch of an herbal blend per kid for young kids; with more for older kids. During wet spells which really cause the coccidia to proliferate in the environment, we may even give it every day and even double dose the amounts given, knowing the kids are picking up new eggs daily as they taste and lick things. This is the only product we use to keep cocci from being an issue on our farm. We have had clients that have had baby's systems re-heal from supposed permanent coccidia damage. The key is to not let it go that far. Raw milk babies appear to be more naturally resistant to coccidia than are pasteurized raised babies. This product and herbs also works well with poultry. Just mix it in some wet layer or chick mash and serve.

Colic or Constipation

Colic or constipation seems to be more common in the male babies than the female babies. For colic, when intestinal gas may have built up causing pain levels up to excruciating, you can take five drops of dill essential oil, mix it with 1 teaspoon of olive oil and rub it on the tummy or rumen areas. You can also make some double or triple strength peppermint tea (not the essential oil) and drench some orally, just a dose every 15 minutes as needed. In addition, you can also take the strong peppermint tea, soak a cotton washcloth or towel in it, and place it as hot as is safe onto the stomach or rumen area. We do not like to use peppermint essential oil with young stock or pets, as it is too strong for the system unless used in very tiny amounts. However, in severe cases of bloat I will put 3 drops of peppermint essential oil and blend it with one teaspoon of olive oil and put SOME of that on the baby animal's stomach area or rumen area and then cover that with a hot but safe to the touch wet cotton washcloth to drive it in faster (remember, this is an emergency). Ginger tea can be used to soak the washcloth in, as it will be relaxing for your baby. After the bloat emergency they can have some liver herbs like Milk Thistle, Dandelion or Fresh Start by Fir Meadow to help their livers compensate for the essential oil. Don't play with bloat. It is nothing to ignore. Get on it right away.

Constipation (sometimes called colic in foals), can occur anytime the baby eats more dry matter than it drinks fluids, causing an impaction in the intestine somewhere.   It can also be the meconium being too dry at birth for the baby to easily pass. As previously mentioned this tends to be a greater problem with the male creatures, but is not unheard of in females.   Therefore it is very important to watch each new baby to make sure it poops and pees well and from the correct locations.

For constipated babies there are a few things that you can do.   My favorite and most messy of course is to give an enema.   Those are mentioned in the Dosage and Administrations chapter in more detail.   You can use warm water with some olive oil added. Make sure and lubricate the tip of whatever you are using with more olive oil and be gentle with that tender anal orifice. You do not want to tear anal tissue or puncture thru the anal wall. You need not go in far; just to the opening or barely in. You can repeat this several times, as each time the contents will go further into the colon. Be sure and stand clear or don your hazmat suit and do this in an area that can become soiled. Don't forget to choose appropriate foot ware for yourself too You also can give bowel products and/or cayenne orally to encourage peristaltic action, but those are not as fast as an enema and if you have foal or other baby down colicking you don't have time to play with. The oral products can be used after the enema if you'd like additional support.

Olive oil can also be drenched or tubed in amounts appropriate for that animal to lubricate their intestines from the front end. Remember not to feed too much olive oil at a time when the animal is not used to it as it is very calorie dense and could cause an acidosis if fed too much at once. Five cc's (ml) may be all you need at a time for a 10 pound animal. 20 cc's for a 30 pound animal and so on. I have also been known to grab a baby buck kid and hop on my rebounder (mini trampoline) for up to five minutes of gentle hopping with him in my arms. The gentle action does help to get bowels moving. Don't go over the five minutes. Rebounding also encourages the organs to release toxins and you do not want a baby creature that is already distressed also having to work with a large load of toxins. Yes, if your baby is not from at least three generations of herbally cleansed and maintained creatures, then your baby WILL have inherited toxins in the organs. As mentioned before, even the rain carries toxins from the air down onto our pastures.

Diarrhea

Diarrhea has many causes and can be disheartening to fight when you don't know the cause. Fortunately we've been provided with some good herbs for this situation. I like to consider the GI tract, liver, and sometimes the blood in these situations. If I think it is parasite related, including coccidia, then I step up my program on those. This is always a great time to do a fecal. You can learn how too. Ask your vet. If I think (prayer is excellent for help with your sleuthing) they picked up bacteria from licking the facilities, nursing on teats that have been lying on soiled ground or eating dirt or manure then I focus on those. A toxin or mold could be involved and if I suspect that, I also start supporting and cleaning the liver, and bloodstream. For liver, kidney, and blood cleansing look at those related chapters.   In most situations I find that they are usually GI tract related and probably bacterial.   For those I whip out my GI Soother which I developed keeping a multitude of potential problems in mind, but you can also try goldenseal, slippery elm bark, cloves, garlic, cinnamon, sometimes cayenne, myrrh, rosemary, wormwood, blackberry leaf or root, raspberry leaf, strawberry leaf or thyme.   I find that most conditions start responding within two hours. I give the herbs orally every one to two hours.   Often my first dose will be a double or triple the regular dose. If I don't see progress within two hours then I start adding in additional herbs for the liver and for toxins and make sure that the herbs I am using are indeed efficacious.   I also start investigating the other animals, hay quality, their grain, any new possible plants in the hay or pasture, any possibility of a neighbor spraying chemicals and the like, to try and see if I can discover what may be going on.   If the diarrhea is very loose or has gone on for more than one half of a day, then adding probiotics and electrolytes of some type becomes necessary, as well as being certain your animal is staying well hydrated.

I have a homework assignment for you.   Ask your vet, vet technician, or an experienced breeder if they will show you how to do a skin pinch test so that you can learn to determine hydration levels in your creature.   It's a two minute education that will be helpful if you ever need it! Then give them some kind of thank-you for their time- a bar of handmade soap or ??   Your vet will be more inclined to help you if you are thoughtful to do something for them for the time they take to answer your question.   Remember that their education took a lot of time, effort, money and even sweat and blood. How many of you vets have had on the job injuries? Okay, you can put your hands down now. Folks, it was all of them! Show them your appreciation. If my animals need electrolytes, then I juice a grapefruit (do not use grapefruit for animals on prescription heart medications) and drench them. One half to 1 tablespoon is used for small creatures. 30 cc's for the 50 to 100 pound group, 60 cc's for the 100 to 200 pound group and 300 cc's (200 pound dose x 5) for the 1000 to 1250 or so pound group.   I consider having herbs on hand for diarrheas a "must have" in my tack box for shows as well as in my barn. These herbs work well for poultry and ratites, too. For the easiest use with them, one can dampen or add a bit of olive oil to their feed and mix the powdered herbs with it.

Enterotoxemia

Enterotoxemia is a long fancy word for a toxic response (toxemia) to the entero organs or intestinal tract. If you have ruminants it is a term you have probably at least heard of, but it can happen in any creature, even humans. In humans it is relabeled as a Herxheimer Reaction where it can be a quick bacterial or intestinal flora die off. It is sometimes referred to as 'overeaters' disease though I have not heard that term on the west coast. Typically what happens in this situation is that an animal gets either <u>too much</u> to eat of a feed they are used to (like a grain raid or even too much milk on a baby). In addition, they can get <u>too rich</u> of food that they are used to; which can happen when switching from mediocre quality hay to high quality hay or changing to a higher grain quality, or eating a moderate to large amount of a plant they are <u>not used to</u>. Sometimes that happens when a helpful neighbor throws prunings or weeds over the fence, or perhaps a tree will lose its leaves in a big drop and the creatures greedily gobble them up. These are the same situations that cause acidosis, but acidosis would be a milder form of digestive system upset causing diarrhea. These scenarios can cause a situation where the intestinal flora are overwhelmed and begin to die off in large numbers, causing a toxicity that will reach the blood stream and then circulate throughout the animal nauseating and impairing it. When I have seen it, the animals are lethargic and disinterested in feed. They often will bloat. They will have diarrhea, often severely so. They may even be vomiting and unable to regulate their body heat; going hypothermic. Younger stock and smaller stock are more susceptible to overfeeds, but it can happen with any age or size of stock. There are also Clostridium types of bacterium that can cause enterotoxemia. Those need to be addressed with GI supporting herbs and antiseptic herbs in large doses (double or triple normal doses).

They can die quickly from the situation, so speed in supporting them is important. Don't let it go half a day (or even two more hours) without doing something; DO SOMETHING NOW! The great thing about these herbs is if you suspect you may get a situation because you caught someone eating more than what they should (like a grain raid), you can often head it off before you have a major problem. Thus causing just a speed bump in your schedule instead of having to take the time to work with a major event. I use the same herbs that are listed above for diarrhea, plus kidney (uva ursi, dandelion, and nettle) and blood support herbs (wheat grass, red clover, chaparral, burdock root). For bloating I'd add a strong peppermint tea drench and put 5 drops of peppermint essential oil with 1 teaspoon of olive oil and spread that over the stomach or rumen area. If it were a very young animal (under 8 – 12 months old or the equivalent of a 6 year old human) I would only use 2-3 drops of peppermint essential oil with the teaspoon of olive oil. This is a pretty strong oil to use on young ones, but if you think the bloat is bad enough (they getting tight or close to it and in pain) then I believe this situation warrants its use. For a large pig, I would double that essential oil recipe (10 drops and mix and use two teaspoons of oil). For a cow or horse, I would triple it. If you let enterotoxemia go too long, the kidneys will be painfully and severely damaged to the point of losing the animal. They also need to be kept hydrated with electrolytes (I like FRESH grapefruit juice). You also will want to consider blanketing a real sick animal, as their ability to regulate body heat is not done well if they get this sick. Once they are a ways into this situation they will try to go hypothermic as their body shuts down. Try not to let them get that far. In those cases supply outside sources of heat, as well as adding oral cayenne and keeping up on the other herbs. I also would add bowel herbs at this point (see the GI Tract chapter) in case their digestive system tries to shut down due to the pain and stress. If I had this happen here with my goats and they were going symptomatic, I would double or triple dose the first herbs; then give regular doses as often as every 15 minutes the first hour. Then I would give regular doses hourly after that. If I wasn't sure if I was going to get a problem (before they are symptomatic) then I would double dose the first dose, give another single in 30 minutes and then every hour for the remainder of that day. The best part is that if they really didn't need the herbs, they won't be harmed.

Thankfully I've always been able to catch them in time with the herbs. I use ClostridEaze herb mix by Fir Meadow and of course have it on hand in my milkroom ready for creature support if I need it.

Emotional Problems

Developing emotional problems from bottle raising orphans is nothing you want to encounter. This is generally not a problem with the smaller stock as long as you still teach them to respect your space. However, with creatures like llamas or horses, as well as dogs; if they do not learn some respect and to grant you some personal space you can end up with one that can be a danger to work around as they try to treat you more like a herd mate then as their kind, benevolent master. Try to make sure they learn ground work and appropriate behavior early. If it would not be a cute or safe behavior in a 1200 pound horse, don't let them act that way as a 95 pound foal. I remember one time, years ago, when my blood bay Arabian colt went rip roaring by me, flew up his rear heels and clipped me in the gut. He was a whole six days old when he did that. I was able to grab him immediately and have a quick conversation with his rump. You can be sure most mares also would have corrected their young child pulling the same stunt on them. He was a compliant and willing to please young man, as he never did it again in the 23 years I had him.

In addition to whatever you choose your training work to be, I would make sure they have a good liver, kidney, and blood cleanse, especially if they were to display any unstable emotional or mental ability. Also consider giving them herbs to help support brain and nervous system function. Those will be in the Brain chapter in Part ll.

Learning the areas that the baby's dam would use to comfort their young one is also good for their mental security. In foals, you will find their mothers nuzzling them with their muzzle along the bridge of their nose, including the area between their eyes. I use that on adult horses to my advantage if I want them to mellow a bit and gently scratch and rub them there. My goats also relax with that same location and also when I hold and gently work my hands along the sides of their jaws. All animals have these areas, observe and learn where they are and take advantage of them to both help your creature bond with you and to relax at times they may be less than secure.

External Parasites

External parasites can be a problem for animals of any age, but they can take down a young one extra fast. On a regular basis inspect for ticks, fleas, areas of missing hair or irritated skin which could indicate mites among other things. Infestations can cause anemia, underweight, can transmit disease, can lead to secondary infections, can start an autoimmune disease, and if left unchecked, can cause a creature to perish. Some of these issues will be discussed in more detail in the Epidermis chapter. Specific external parasites issues will be discussed in the Parasites chapter.

Floppy Kid Syndrome

Floppy kid syndrome is something that can occur in some goat kids. It may be an electrolyte imbalance, or possibly an electrolyte malabsorption problem. As far as I know; scientifically we are not for sure yet what causes this. Some people also call it 'wobbles', as the young kids, usually ten days to three weeks old, will start to exhibit incoordination and wobble as they walk. Left unchecked they usually die. I do wonder if there is not possibly some genetic involvement, as some lines and farms seem to experience it, while others do not. My tendency would be to put them on GI tract herbs such as slippery elm, cinnamon, cayenne, and ginger, as well as electrolytes. Grapefruit juice- FRESH SQUEEZED or juiced, not the store bought junk from concentrate in a bottle, would be my electrolyte choice. Adding a stalk of celery and a touch of wheat grass juice (5 cc's) when making the grapefruit juice would make it even better. On a non herbal approach people successfully deal with this with a pepto bismol type of product and baking soda combined.

If I had this in my herd can you guess what I'd do? Yes, more cleansing for at least three months after I had the kids stable for a few days, starting slowly and building them up to full dose. Liver, kidneys, blood at amounts appropriate for a small kid (pinch doses rather than teaspoons) and try to reduce the chemical exposure of the herd. I would want to have any kids that experienced this on a cleansing program for a few months before breeding them to try and break the cycle. I would also want their sire and dam on the same program to try and break the cycle at the parent generation.

Internal Parasites or Worms

No matter where in the world you may live, this is a problem that has to be addressed in every creature. I once had a person tell me that they knew it was time to deworm their animals when they saw diarrhea. At that point you have a heavy infestation and internal damage already in progress. Don't wait for signs like that! Be proactive with your Offensive Herbalism™. Babies are especially susceptible to them; not having immunity to them at any level yet. They also have habits of eating dirt and manure to populate their intestines with flora and licking fencing and barn walls, etcetera. To reduce the facility contamination level try to have your babies raised in an area that has fresh soil and bedding. Areas, pens, dog runs, or corrals to be used can be planted in mustard and then tilled into the ground to help purify the soil. Fencing and stalls can be scrubbed and then sprayed with diluted essential oils- 60 to 80 drops of pure essential oil per quart of water. I like thyme, oregano, cinnamon, eucalyptus, lavender, ginger, and/or peppermint for these situations. Fir Meadow makes a nice Dis-N-Fect blend of essential oils that can be used in this manner. Make sure there are no cats around to breathe the spray and then you need to allow for at least a couple hours of airing out before putting stock back in. Running a fan in the area after disinfecting it will speed up the process of clearing the air. I will discuss more specifics in the Parasites chapter.

Pasty Vent

Pasty vent in young birds can be handled with the same herbs used for diarrhea including Fir Meadow's GI Soother herb mix. Also adding non gmo organic cornmeal to their mash helps reduce the gluey-ness of their droppings. Beware of store bought feeds for young birds. Most are antibiotic filled. We take our goat grain without the sunflower seed shells (they can have raw sunflower shell-less seeds in their mix), run some through the Vitamix if needed, add herbs if wanted, and raise our chicks on that. You will have to adjust this recipe for birds like pheasants that require a higher protein content to thrive. Young birds also also benefit from sprouted grains, legume sprouts (alfalfa, clover, etcetera), alfalfa hay, kelp, grass & herb clippings, and access to insects or a bit of raw goat milk. Fir Meadow's Layer Support and/or Better Daze make very nice young bird supplements that are easily mixed in their mash. God's Greens can be used to increase the whole plant protein content in their diet.

Pneumonia

Pneumonia including pleurisy (inflammation or fluid filling of the pleura just outside the lungs) is just plain evil to deal with. Be watching for it in your babies, especially during the wet and cold times of year and during times when the temperature swings from day to night are 30 or more degrees. Have your veterinarian teach you how to listen for healthy and unhealthy lungs. I actually put my ear right on the rib cage and listen that way. A stethoscope can be used too but you need to invest in a higher quality one to cut out the background noise. This is no time to have background noise distort or cover what you need to listen for in the lungs. That puts me back to the pioneer method of using my ear on the rib cage! I personally listen for any noises outside of heart noises, as was taught to me by my veterinarian. If I hear anything else, then I have just cause to be suspicious of an arising issue or one that is already established. If in doubt, I listen to animals that I know are healthy and then compare again to the one in question. Also look for any combination of lethargy, fluffed out hair, fever, disinterest in feed, head hanging lower than normal, ears drooped in eared breeds, rapid shallow breathing, nasal discharge, fever and not hanging out with the herd. We have dealt with this successfully with this and similar problems with herbs, even severe problems. You do have to be tenacious and keep on top of it every 2 hours at first if you want to have a shot at turning them around. Lung conditions are nothing to play with. If you feel intimidated, please feel free to contact your vet and hire their assistance. See the Respiratory chapter for specific lung information.

Here is something of interest to note. I have found through observation over the last few years that goat kids that have been vaccinated are much harder to save and are much quicker to perish than the kids that have not had vaccinations. Whereas in a vaccinated kid, often you only get hours to work with them in difficult respiratory challenges before you are too late; in the unvaccinated you literally have days, as long as you catch them early and get to work. I believe the immune system stays compromised once they are vaccinated and it seems to run consistent with my observations and education. There are good books written on this subject by people that have devoted parts of their career to studying these issues in depth, so I won't go into detail about it here. I hope to do some studies on this topic later with my iridology skills. If you practice iridology, it might be something of interest to you too. Consider comparing eyes of unvaccinated creatures with the irides of those that have been vaccinated. I'll bet we'll see some interesting data. I plan to develop more educational materials later on this and related topics.

With herbs and herbal tinctures only, we have saved kids with severe respiratory problems that were at the point of not responding anymore, but still alive as their bodies started working with the phytochemicals and utilizing them. Of course we have lost kids, too. The same was true when we used drugs- we saved some and lost some. Respiratory challenges are hard, require fast work, and will be described in the Lung chapter. The earlier you catch it, the easier it will be to work with. I have already said that, but I can't emphasize that enough. Please don't ignore possible respiratory challenges in your pets or stock. You will kick yourself if you do.

Structural (Skeletal and other) Problems

Structural problems are an issue one often wouldn't think about, but they happen. If you think a baby isn't moving correctly on all four limbs or carrying its head correctly, do some careful investigating. Do both sides match up at each joint? Are they the same size and in the same location side to side? How about the head and neck? Are they being carried correctly? Is there swelling somewhere? Do you feel heat to the touch that doesn't match the temperature of the rest of the animal? I've had two of these this past year. The first was a dry (non milking) yearling doe that had gotten stuck under a hay feeder. Once she was out, it was evident she was walking stiffly. After giving her a few days to walk it out, as well as giving her anti inflammatory herbs like lavender, ginger and marshmallow root it still hadn't changed. She did not appear to be having pain with it, just a 'hitch in her git along'. So I carefully felt along both sides of her spine from fore to rear with my fingers. Then I softly went over the top of the spine with my flattened hand and sure enough, at the loin area, one vertebra was raised a bit out of place as compared to the others. So the next few days at chore time, I would take her out and carefully massage the muscles on both sides of her spine in that area to encourage them to relax. Typically in these situations, one or more muscles will remain tight not allowing the bones to shift back to where they belong. Within a few days it went back into place on its own as the knotted muscles relaxed. I didn't use any essential oils for this situation, but I could have used lavender, peppermint (not for real young stock) or ginger mixed with olive oil to also encourage the muscles to relax, as well as applying Lobelia inflata tincture and/or Wounderful! Salve to the skin in the area. Please do NOT do this if you even have a slight suspicion of a fracture or a crack. That must heal FIRST. Get a veterinarian's diagnosis if you need to know what you are dealing with.

The other situation I was faced with was a two day old kid that wouldn't raise his head correctly, but would stand with his head halfway down. Nothing was wrong with his attitude, and his plumbing and appetite were all fine, though it was hard for him to nurse. So I began feeling his spine. Sure enough, we had a raised vertebra in the neck, probably caused from the birth process, as he was one we had to work on extra to get him breathing again. I carefully massaged both sides of the neck for several minutes and then firmly, but gently held the lower jaw with one hand and his chest with the other and pulled the jaw firmly but gently forward (traction). After three cycles of this, with him showing me no evidence of pain the whole time, it went back into place and he was able to raise his head to a normal position all by himself. If you see pain symptoms, consult your veterinarian to be sure a fracture isn't involved or a nerve pinched. If the neck is fractured and you manipulate it, you may very well kill your animal. Or use herbs to support the body for a fracture diligently for at least three weeks before trying to ask a vertebra to move through massage. This is also a good plan if you don't know the cause of the displacement. Sometimes you can also employ a human or equine chiropractor. Expect them to require x-rays before working on a back or neck, however. Pinched nerves will return to normal once any out of place bones have found their way back to their correct placement.

Tetanus

Tetanus, also known as 'lockjaw' is another issue that babies can be more susceptible to. First we consider that herd management such as tail docking, disbudding (horn growth suppression), and castrating can make the types of

The Accessible Pet, Equine and Livestock Herbal

anaerobic wounds that tetani bacterium like to reside in. If equine animals have been on the property in recent years, that will also account for higher levels of the bacterium in the soil and perhaps on fencing and such. Due to their playfulness, younger animals tend to more often get cuts and scrapes and pokes than older stock. This is an emergency situation, as if left untreated it progressed to being fatal. Fortunately, God has given us good tools for this problem.

Whenever I do herd management such as disbudding horn buds, I will put herb powders like myrrh or goldenseal or thyme or olive oil mixed with garlic onto the area being managed. In horn buds I just pour the powdered herbs right in and then give a small drench of the herbs mixed with a liquid for better palatability. I personally use Fir Meadow's HerBiotic herb mix since I keep it on hand in the barn. If you would like a cooling effect, you can add peppermint or eucalyptus powder to your herb blend. Dr. Christopher's Infection formula can also be used orally. Do NOT put herb products on including salves that are aimed at helping the body to heal; you may just undo your herd management! I don't know about you, but there are some things I prefer to not do if I didn't have to, let alone having to some management chores a second time.

Should you actually get a tetanus problem in progress, I would use a twofold approach. I would get the antiseptic herbs (or HerBiotic) into your creature orally every two hours, with the first dose being a triple dose. I would also get that wonderful friend, Lobelia inflata as a tea or tincture and give it orally in case the animal is starting to lock up or even if the animal was already locking up. Remember to use the Lobelia i. in smaller than other herb normal oral doses, so you don't get its emetic effect. Personally I'd want to run some of the tincture along the entire spinal column too. Make sure that cayenne is also a part of your support program for your creature. Continue the herbs for ten days to make sure the body is well supported for a long enough amount of time. You would not want a relapse! Also keep your creature warm, dry, comfortable and in a quiet and somewhat darkened place to take stress off of the nervous system. After the first day, if the creature is acting normal I'd move to chronic dosing at three times per day. If you are able to get the body to unlock without dealing with the cause- helping the body to chase and conquer the bacterium, they will relock and still be at risk of dying.

Umbilical Hernia

Just like in people, sometimes creatures are born with these and sometimes they appear sometime after birth. At times dogs are known to get overaggressive with their puppy cleaning, jerking an umbilical cord in the process and causing a hernia. Whatever the cause, the body often can be encouraged to heal them by adding nourishing herbs to the area so that the body can strengthen the musculature responsible for holding the intestinal or other tissue back in place. I like salves the best for this. If it's not too cold out, carefully shave the area with a 10 blade clipper to get better skin contact and put a healing salve on. Herbs to consider would be comfrey, nettle, dandelion, white oak bark, horse tail, oat straw, carrot, or any other high calcium/mineral herbs. Fir Meadow's Wounderful! Salve is a nice choice here, as well as Dr. Christopher's Complete Bone and Tissue formula for oral use.

These types of tissue weaknesses are often ultimately the result of a calcium deficiency to the area. See the Supplements chapter for suggestions for diet changes to prevent this from happening again. If the hernia is in a shape that risks the intestine getting pinched off you may have to consider surgical intervention due to the extreme danger to the animal's life and possibly not having enough time for the herbs to get the body to repair the condition.

Hernias in upright living beings, such as humans, can be held in fairly easy with supportive belts, wraps, or medical tapes as they mend. However, in creatures that walk on four legs, we have an additional hernia enemy to deal with. That would be gravity, which allows the hernia to droop down rather than be held in. If you can use some type of support system or wrap over the area that will not be chewed on or consumed by other pen mates then you can consider that along with salving. Tapes don't work well in this situation as you have to pull on the hernia to remove them, which could make them worse. Also be sure that no other creature or herdmate can get caught in the support and that it can't get caught in something.

Undescended Testicles

The Accessible Pet, Equine and Livestock Herbal

Undescended testicles can be worked with in the same way as damaged testicles mentioned in the Breeding chapter. Brew a tea of three parts mullein and one part Lobelia inflata and serve it to your animal in a bit smaller than normal amounts, so that you don't come up against the emetic effect of the Lobelia. Continue this daily, at least three times per day, until the body uses the nourishment to heal the problem. Sometimes the body will correct this problem after the first dose!

I attribute this problem to a phytochemical nutritional deficiency. If it were not so, then the herbs wouldn't be able to assist the body in correcting the problem. Can nutritional deficiencies be hereditary? Of course! So remember to cleanse and nourish the sire and dam also to break the possibility of their contribution, or rather, lack of nutritional contribution. I like Better Daze for this type of supplementation, as well as cleansing the body organs. You can also reread the Supplements chapter to pick our herbs that interest you in your own program for your beloved creatures.

White Muscle Disease

White Muscle Disease can either be a Vitamin E deficiency or a selenium deficiency. Both or either deficiency can give the same symptomology, according to resources I've read over the years. It may be recognizable at birth or it may show up as a collapse, and possible death, in a perceived healthy baby. This may happen once the baby's growth gets ahead of their muscles' ability to keep up with them (remember that includes the heart muscle). Babies that are not as spunky or coordinated as normal should be assessed for this problem. Sometimes babies that have a hard time controlling their tongue as it grips the nipple on a bottle or their mom would benefit from additional E and selenium sources.

Of course the best support for this of course is avoidance by having your sire and dam well supplemented before breeding and during pregnancy. Wheat germ oil is probably your best source of Vitamin E along with some high selenium herbs including catnip, milk thistle, sunflower seeds, Hibiscus sabdariffa otherwise known as 'Jamaica" (ha-my-kah) in Spanish. Do not mix up the hibiscus with any hibiscus, it must be sabdariffa only and makes a red fruit punch color of tea. Other

Hibiscus species may be toxic. Couch grass or quack grass is also a high source (and here you've been complaining about it all this time). Kop-Sel, a whole herb copper and selenium supplement by Fir Meadow, can be mixed with milk and bottle fed or drenched. In animals too weak to swallow, you will want to either stomach tube their herbs into them or give them via anal injection/enema with a very warm, properly made infusion. If I had that problem here, I would be giving tinctures or teas of the appropriate herbs along with health food store wheat germ oil given at double the amount appropriate for the creature size. I would also want my creature on cayenne and hawthorn berry, leaf, or bark, Heart-e tincture by Fir Meadow, or Dr. Christopher's Hawthorne syrup for heart muscle support. Better yet, keep your broodstock, male and female, on a good prebreeding and prenatal diet, as discussed earlier in this book.

Chapter 9- Working with Milking Stock

You just can't wait to freshen that cow, goat, milking sheep, water buffalo, camel, or other stock that you plan to milk. Information in this chapter will also be helpful for those who have breeding stock that they don't milk, as many of the situations apply to any lactating creature. Though I consider milking my goats a joy and welcomed quiet and thinking time, milking too comes with its challenges.

Regular Milk Schedule

The following are some things to consider to help make chores go with less health hitches. First, try to establish regular milking time, ideally every 12 hours. I realize there may be some dairy people reading this that milk cows or other stock every 8 hours, you are already on a regular consistent schedule for your creatures. If you are milking that often be sure they get their herbal supplements every milking to support them in their increased productivity as they work overtime for you. Udders that are allowed to get overfull from a failure to milk on a regular schedule can obtain tissue damage from the increased pressure caused by being too full. They can also be more susceptible to mastitis if the pressure causes tissue damage, sphincter muscle damage, or an orifice to open. They may leak. They may not be able to walk as gracefully and more easily catch the udder on fencing, brush, hitting a milk stand or bench when loading up, and the like. They may decide to relieve themselves by self sucking (self nursing). Many of these issues can be avoided or reduced by keeping a regular milk schedule.

Udder and Teat Preparation

Another thing to seriously consider is cleaning the teat; including spraying the orifice end before you milk and after you milk with some type of sanitizer. Then you will want to dry the teat end with a paper towel after spraying. This is so that the moisture running down the teat that is partially sanitizer, partially debris and bacteria does not drip down to the teat orifice. Once the orifice opens in the teat, bacteria will begin to rush up the teat to enter the mammary gland. At our farm we try to get them sprayed as soon as they get on the milkstand, as they may begin to relax those orifices in anticipation of being milked. It may not be enough to let milk out, but enough to let microscopic and opportunist bacteria in. I prefer using a warm spray, especially in the winter to also encourage the orifice to open. A spray bottle sitting in a small bucket of hot water is sufficient for warming. As mentioned earlier in the book, microwaving your herbs or herb product to warm it is NOT an option.

You can choose from several essential oils and put 60 to 80 drops total in with distilled water and/or raw apple cider vinegar in a one quart sprayer. Scale down in size if you are not using that up within a week. Oils to consider would be: thyme, eucalyptus, peppermint, lemon, grapefruit, tea tree, lavender, or ginger. Though some of these are hotter oils, they are being greatly diluted and are not a problem in this application. Lavender is probably the most soothing of the group that I listed, and also has benefit as a cell proliferant and relaxant to the livestock. Lemon and grapefruit are helpful if dry skin becomes an issue. You can make a mix of two or three choices with lavender and/or lemon as part of your blend. Some of these essential oils should not be used in pregnant stock by themselves, but again, with this much dilution for this purpose they are fine. Fir Meadow has a blend called DisNFect that is a combination of essential oils that traditionally disinfect, encourage milk production, cleanse from toxins, balance hormones, encourage tissue strength, and grounding choices to encourage relaxation of stock (and you since you are going to breathe some in also). These same oils or blend can be used for sanitizing equipment or home milkroom counter surfaces.

Essential oils can flavor your milk if they are sprayed on the udder before the doe is milked. They enter the bloodstream quickly and will be being run through your milk. I personally do not disinfect my udder, but my teats only which can then be dried with some paper towel. If my udder needs some help I will wipe it with a dry paper towel so that I don't get any moisture dripping down the udder and along the teat while I'm milking by machine or by hand. If an udder needs support I put that on after I milk. If you spray essential oil blends into your inflations between goats for disinfection, then you will want to also dip them in a warm water wash to reduce the amount of essential oils that you will suck into your milk which will also flavor it. Somehow thyme milk just does not appeal to me!

After we finish hand stripping the udder, we then lift each teat and point it towards us and spray all around the teat end and up at least the bottom inch. It often takes a few minutes for the orifice to close after milking, so this practice of 'post spraying' lessens the opportunity for bacteria to take hold. If the spray can be cool or cold, the cold 'hydrotherapy' treatment to the sphincter muscle that closes the orifice will be encouraged to close much faster.

Udders that are dirty should be washed and dried off. Keeping hair shaved off of udders and in the body areas near the udder with at least a size ten blade (five blade in winter) will keep udders cleaner as less bedding and debris sticks to the udder and tummy. If the udder is clipped and appears clean then you only need to dry wipe it with a towel. You can use your spray sanitizer to 'spot clean' if desired.

When is She Done Milking?

I sometimes get asked how I know when the animal is done milking. After massaging and softly bumping the udder once or twice to encourage any additional milk being held to be dropped, I will continue to hand milk until the stream is greatly reduced. At that point I will feel the udder again by lifting on the bottom portion. It takes practice, but you'll learn to feel for a 'water balloon' feel that shows you there is still more milk to ask them to drop. If not, then once I have the much smaller milk stream, I sanitize with my essential oil spray mix and let that second spray air dry. You can dry it with a fresh paper towel if they are immediately heading out to cold weather or you are adding an herbal salve. Use your judgment for your situation on that. We like to have hay ready for the goats in their feeders to head to after being milked. It keeps them standing and eating instead of lying down to give the teats more time to soak in their salves to dry.

Udder Conformation Considerations

Conformation comes into play with mammary systems. On a dairy goat scorecard, the udder is 35% of the 100% score. That's over one third of the card! If the goat or cow in particular (they tend to have the largest udder capacities in relation to size of the creature) does not have strong and long lateral ligaments (the side tendon attachments where the mammary connects to the body wall), and strong medial suspensory ligaments (what halves or quarters the udder), then that udder is not going to stay well supported and in its place over the years.

I also look for an udder that is wide at the top rear, known as the escutcheon (es-cut-chun) arch. More support is gained by how far down the rear leg the mammary skin attaches to the rear leg. In general, the further down, the better. This along with the lateral and medical attachments is what keeps this udder from swinging and sagging as it works. As the animal ages, the likelihood of gaining a pendulous udder- one that hangs below the hocks is greatly increased. That pendulous udder can be bruised by the hocks as it rocks from side to side as the animal walks. It can also make easier contact with brush, the corner of a milkstand, trailer, etcetera, increasing injury and mastitis risks.

The width of the udder attachment can't physically be wider than the pelvic frame, so attention to rump width coupled with escutcheon arch width gives you a better indication of udder width potential. Ideally we like them attached smoothly from the front of the udder to the body wall without a shelf or pocket. This is also adds more mammary for milk capacity.

Teat placement on the udder, so that it is attached at the lowest point of the udder and pointing downwards (plumbness) increases proper drainage which decreases mastitis opportunities and the time needed to handstrip the last bit of milk, as your machine will be able to milk the creature down further.

Once milked, an udder should be relatively soft inside if it milked down well, rather than full of meaty connective tissue which robs space from what could have been milk producing tissue. There are no herbs to change the tissue types. Your breeding program will do that over time if you select well on your herd sires.

From the side view, we like an udder that extends approximately 1/3 in front of the rear leg, 1/3 covered by the rear leg, and 1/3 behind the rear leg. This again is another thing that indicates correct capacity and udder placement, helping it to stay more out of harm's way. An udder that bulges quite a bit more to the rear as viewed from the side is one that can be easily urinated on. The tissue on these udders will be a battle to keep healthy with a chronic urine scald issue and will be more prone to secondary infections. The milk producing tissue under those areas can absorb the urine and put it in your milk. If you get one of these, you will want to keep an herbal salve on the rear udder after every milking to protect the skin from damage, and the milk from taking on any urine flavor. Make sure you clean the udder every time before applying your salve. MammarEaze salve by Fir Meadow is a nice salve for this situation. Antibacterial herbs and tissue regenerating herbs should be chosen if making your own formula.

Bone Type and Strength for Milking Stock

Flat but strong bone is important to me as well. I don't mean coarse or round bone, as they should still look feminine, but moderate to strong none the less. The bones on your dairy animal are your mineral storehouse or 'banking system' if you will. Starting as a young calf, lamb, or kid, the feeds she intakes will ideally be rich in plant minerals which she will be using for her growth as well as putting some into the 'bone bank' every meal. If she is fine boned, her bank won't be able take as big of a deposit of plant minerals as a young female with a moderate to larger bone and frame would. Once she is milking and needs to withdraw deposits and during late third trimester of her pregnancy, she can get into trouble with milk fever or even lose strength and ability in her fetlocks and pasterns (ankle areas and just below) as they show the effects of demineralization to support the third trimester babies or milk production. If she has sound bone, with a proper plant feed program this should never happen. Please review the Supplements chapter, especially the information on alfalfa, comfrey, and kelp.

If you have a classification (dairy cows), linear appraisal program (dairy goats), or conformation/inspection inspection programs for your creature I encourage you to partake of them. If you can't participate with your animals, see if you can get permission to audit or observe one. I have learned SO much over the past decade and it has greatly improved my herd. It is cheaper than showing. For $250 I can have about 28 to 30 of my dairy goats appraised with the appraiser spending a full 8 minutes per goat going over the great, the good, and any ugly that they notice that I haven't because I see them every day. Or I can spend $200 to $250 (or more) by the time I consider entry fees, pen fees, supplies and diesel and get a 10 second opinion per judge per goat on perhaps 4 to 6 goats that I bring to the show that day. Yes, I do show and enjoy it and also learn a lot, but for me it does not replace appraisal. If you have registered stock and want a wonderful tool to help you improve your herd, consider it. If you have unregistered stock, see if you can watch one. Who cares if your beloved creatures are registered or not, that doesn't change your opportunity to develop better and more productive generations by learning more. Mine happen to be registered, but I am still breeding for that elusive 'perfect' goat. Will it happen? No. But can I try? Certainly! It still produces better quality genetics for my herd and to share with others. Isn't that the goal of a breeder?

Dairy Goat Milk Amount Suggestions

I get asked often what it is I like to see a standard sized goat milking. Gone are the days of the 'gallon' per day milker considered being a good milker. The animals have been improved upon much since the 1970's and earlier where these quotes seem to abound from. These highly productive animals are still able to maintain their longevity and productivity if they have the conformation and feed to support it. I have had two LaMancha does now that have milked 6 successive years at levels over 3000 pounds per year. They have done this staying in condition and having successful show careers at the same time. Your girls can do it, but it takes the whole goat conformation, genetic potential (breeding for milk genetics), and husbandry program to put the pieces together.

I am not speaking from decades of experience as some of my colleagues in the dairy goat industry can do, but I am able to speak from over one decade of experience of having been on official milk test (DHIR) for the entire time, as well as viewing milk records from around the country on the various breeds. This gives one the opportunity to see what a milk record on a particular day in what stage of the goat's production may produce for the year. It also teaches an observant person what builds of animals and genetics it takes to make them. In addition, it allows you to be able to track does and lines year after year for long run records and can give you some insight on what you may be able to expect their daughters to produce or if a particular buck is influencing your program in good or bad ways. I can feel the ribbing and skin on a kid and look at its conformation (as can many breeders) and have an idea of whether she is going to milk well, milk average, or milk worse. From my milk records I also know what my butterfat and protein levels are month to month and running totals, and how feeding or breeding programs can adjust that.

We breed most of our kids at 7 to 9 months of age as long as they are growthy, healthy, of sufficient bone, and weigh 80 or more pounds. Otherwise mine have a tendency to get overweight their yearling year and then I also have to wait until they are two year olds to evaluate the udder and milk production to see if I am going to keep them. If their udders don't turn out, that has given me a doe that was expensive to raise over that additional year, that I now have to sell at a home milker price. That is not cost or time effective for us. Look at feed prices. I'm not sure it's cost effective for anyone today that actually feeds their animals correctly. I don't mind holding one or two over as dry yearlings if they were late babies but still meet my conformation goals, but not more than that.

Having said all of that, assuming the goat has sound bone, strong feet and legs, a strong topline (back), and sound mammary attachment, this is what I like to see for production. Their peak is their highest 24 hour production in pounds, usually somewhere between two and four months into their lactation. Some lines will hold their peak for two months. Those animals are probably going to out milk the ones that shoot up high but then fall fast and are worth a lot to a home or commercial dairy situation. For general purposes, eight pounds equals one gallon of milk and two pounds is equal to a filled quart jar WITHOUT any foam. The industry standard in the United States is to quote milk in pounds and tenths of pounds and it is this format that you will see in official records. A full lactation is considered a 305 day lactation or two months, with the last two months corresponding with third trimester in a dairy goat. For a yearling, I like to see them peak at a minimum of five pounds per day, as I know that as a two year old that same goat will likely double her production. I sure don't mind yearlings that milk in the seven to eight pound range at peak as I strive for well above average production with my girls. As long as they are well fed, their bone is sufficient and the mammaries are well attached it's not a risk to them to milk like that. I like them to milk at least 1500 pounds of milk that first year, with at least 52.5 pounds of butterfat which allows them to earn their milk star and allow their sons to be in advanced registry or AR. My two year old first fresheners (if I have any) I want peaking at 9 to 10 pounds or more of milk, with an 1800 or more pound lactation. My two year old second fresheners, I want milking at least 10 pounds at peak with a 2000 pound or better lactation. Having said that, most of my two year olds hit 12 pounds or better that second year with at least 2200 pounds of milk and I know other breeders whose does usually doe the same. From three years old on, I want them milking at least 12 pounds per day at peak, with at least 2200 pounds of milk and higher for the lactation. My preference though is that they milk 14 pounds per day or better and I like breaking 2500 pounds of milk. I have found with the LaManchas if we have a fourteen pound per day milker at peak and if she can hold that peak for at least two months in a row, then we often can hit the 3000 pound milk level, which is kind of like hitting the 'milk hall of fame' for a dairy goat. In Toggenburg dairy goats, if they hit somewhere between 12 and 14 pounds per day and hold it for two to three months they also have a good opportunity to hit the 3000 pound 'hall of goat fame' level, as they seem to hold their milk level more steady when the cold fall and winter weather hits. No wonder, having been developed in the Swiss Alps! Older does (6 and older) will often begin to decrease in production, but I have and have had many that work hard and even increase in production through 7 or 8 years of age before they begin to taper down usually corresponding with a reduction in the amount of kids they have per litter. In general, does that product triplets or quads will out milk does that produce singles or twins, as their bodies know they have to feed more kids. We like getting triplets on our farm.

Show records and appraisal scores are nice and often they work into a good milker if you do well with those, but the proof is in the bucket. The most milk we have had from a LaMancha on test day is 20.2 pounds (twenty and two/tenths of a pound), and she tested 20 pounds the following month. However, this is probably a once in a lifetime goat; as a high ninety something percent will never produce like that. Please remember though, if you have a two year old or older dairy goat lady milking twelve pounds or more per day at peak you have a very NICE milker and one to be proud of! These higher lactation amounts are not all that common overall. With breeds like Nubians, I would still want to see the five pounds per day minimum as a yearling, as I would with any of the other standard sized breeds, but they usually aren't going to peak as high as the numbers I have given you as they mature though I know a couple of herds with animals that do. Nubians tend to specialize in butterfat production, as do the Jersey cows. For miniature breeds like the adorable Nigerian Dwarf, we would be looking at about 1/3 of these amounts. They are another high butterfat breed. The short eared LaMancha is often a balance between the higher production of the Swiss breeds and the butter fat production of the butterfat breeds. It is that butterfat that gives you a smooth, yummy tasting milk that has higher product yields.

Equipment Sanitation While Milking

Make sure you sanitize your milking equipment or hands in between animals so that if there is a bacterial or mastitis type of problem going on that is not yet detectible (subclinical), that you are not passing it on from creature to creature. Remember also that the most common mastitis forms are the staph bacterial forms. Staph normally resides on the skin, both your hands and your creature's udder skin. You can spread staph bacteria from the skin of one goat or your hands onto the teats or near the orifices of the next milker without proper teat and equipment sanitation. You can sanitize in the same way that you did the teats earlier in this chapter, with a diluted essential oil blend and by wearing gloves. Any known mastitis infected animals should be milked last to reduce exposure to uninfected herdmates.

To wear rubber or latex gloves or not is a personal issue. I personally want my skin coming in contact with the essential oil spray as well as any salves I may be applying to udders so that I also receive some benefit. In the days when I used to use diluted bleach sprays and chemical teat dips, I definitely did not want that coming in contact with my skin and always wore gloves in that situation.

When you have finished milking and are ready to clean your milking equipment, adding lemon or orange essential oils to your soap (5 drops per teaspoon works well) and then scouring with that really helps cut the butterfat and clean nicely, as well as helping to disinfect. If you are in a great need to disinfect due to udder health issues, then oregano, clove, cinnamon or thyme essential oils would be among the first I would consider also adding. Please wear gloves when working with these stronger essential oils. Vinegar mixed with soap and the citrus oils makes a very nice and effective way to cut milk stone and make your stainless equipment shine. You can mix the essential oils with the vinegar and soap and clean for both simultaneously, but now you know which product is doing which job for you by me separating the instructions for fat and milk stone. Milk stone is the mineral and protein deposits that appear over time on your equipment from applying hot water to it. It will provide a hiding place for bacteria, so you will want to keep this from building up and dulling your equipment.

Safety and Nourishment of Herbal Preparations

A neat thing about using herbs on udders is that if you are raising your babies on their dams they can nurse the herbs I mention in this section, unless otherwise noted. These herbs will not harm them, but rather nourish them. There also won't be any milk withdrawals unless you have an udder health problem like mastitis.

Butterfat and Protein Assistance

Butterfat and protein content is important, as the well being of your babies depend on the milk having enough substance or 'solids' to grow on. For cheese or other product producers the solids directly translate into income in the amount of product they are able to produce.

The fat is used for the developing brain as well as to provide a protective cushion around the internal organs, a subcutaneous layer to help your creature regulate body heat, and a bit for each cell for a back up fuel source.

The protein is broken up into amino acids in the digestive process and is used to build and rebuild tissue along with the minerals. Your breeding program will have some effect here, as protein and butterfat levels tend to run in family lines and there are some breed tendencies. Herbs can also help to an extent.

Alfalfa is an excellent protein plant source because it combines its higher mineral content. Other higher protein plants to consider will be tree barks, plant and tree root herbs, mullein leaf, chia seed, nutritional yeast, and several grains, even grass seeds that they browse on in their pasture! Other sources include spirulina (70% protein), watercress, oat straw, beans, peas and shepherd's purse seeds.

Butterfat can be encouraged by allowing your stock to eat the stems from their hay, barks, and roots such as slippery elm bark powder and marshmallow root powder as well as having browse/brush access where possible. Even cattle will eat some browse if they have access to it. Chia seed is another nice supplement for fat, as are calendula seeds and sunflower seeds. Soy probably should be avoided unless you can get whole soy bean that is organic, so that you don't run into GM (genetically modified) soy that is prevalent.

I don't personally use herbs to work the content of the milk of my goats as I do that through genetics. That way I know for sure what my breeding plan is doing or not doing from generation to generation. If I needed to supplement an animal because the babies needed richer milk this is what I would do. These supplements will be helpful whether it is a ewe, a mare, a bitch, a sow or any other brood animal that you are working with.

Congested Udders

Congested or engorged mammaries are udders with inflammation to the point that they are not able to easily release milk from the milk producing tissue. Just as a swollen leg can decrease blood circulation to a foot, swollen mammary tissue makes it difficult for fluid to move through the mammary, down the cistern, and into the teat canal. Engorgement causes can be injury, some disease causing organisms like CAE in some goats, mastitis, and sometimes it is a postpartum event. I am beginning to consider that it also may be more of a problem in some genetic lines than others, indicating to this iridologist that the weakened mammary tissue that is more susceptible to this problem may be passed on from generation to generation.

If it's an injury, you would treat it as any other wound. Some favorite herbs for this would be using comfrey, lavender, mullein or rosemary along with some ginger or marshmallow root. You could also use Dr. Christopher's Complete Tissue formula salve, or Fir Meadow's ReBuilld or Wounderful! salves for the injury, and A-King Arthur herb mix or DCongest Salve for the inflammation.

If it is postpartum or disease caused, herbs of choice would be three parts of mullein mixed with one part of Lobelia inflata. You can also use peppermint, eucalyptus or rosemary and you might be able to try plantain, though I haven't used plantain for this application. Adding to that some valerian, scullcap, or some lady's slipper will give you something that helps your goat relax to encourage let down as well as herbs specific to trying to break up the congestion. Fir Meadow's DCongest salve is a great choice as can Dr. Christopher's Sen Sei salve. The Sen Sei works best if applied over other herbs or salves you want to use to help drive them in better. Poke root tea can also be applied to the mammary to stimulate lymph movement. Do not let babies suck on a quantity of poke root or it may cause them to vomit. Poke can take hours to cause this response, so there is no way to monitor how much is too much with oral use. If you are dam raising babies, then use other herbs or just the herb tea wash. Essential oils of the plants listed above can be mixed in a blend of 5 drops essential oil to 1 teaspoon of olive oil and rubbed and massaged on. You can apply these to the udder hourly if needed. If babies are nursing, then stick to just the rosemary and lavender essential oils and leave them off of the teats as the others would be too strong to want young stock or pets to nurse on. You can also take hot and cold packs and do some hydrotherapy to try to get the cells to plunge out any waste they are trying to hold onto and it helps to force lymph to move. Heat is applied for approximately 12 minutes at a time, then cold for about 4 minutes. Try to gauge how long by the animal's comfort level. Then alternate back and forth for an hour if you are able, then every 3 or 4 hours afterwards as needed. The contracting and relaxing caused by the heat and cold will encourage fluid movement.

If you have an animal that is prone to this year after year, I would really consider doing some good cleansing work for the liver and kidneys and blood for at least 4

The Accessible Pet, Equine and Livestock Herbal

months if not longer before breeding again if possible to see if you can get ahead of it. I would also apply salves for several months to encourage the mammary gland to strengthen. Fir Meadow's GlandAide, Wounderful!, or MammarEaze salves can be used for that, as well as the udder injury herbs listed above. Remember to do some extra herbal nourishing and gentle cleansing on the next generation as they grow up to try and break this trend if you notice a heritable tendency.

If your animal is congested, don't forget to rule out the possibility of foul play in the form of a renegade spider, bee or other creature injury to the mammary. Generally you will see just a portion of the mammary affected as opposed to a whole half or quarter as in mastitis or the entire udder in a congested udder. See the Poisonings chapter for some hints on how to consider working with that issue.

Dry, Chapped, or Cracked Udder Skin

Dry, chapped, or cracked udder skin is at the least uncomfortable for your broodstock, and at the most may make her more susceptible to mastitis as the bacteria can breach the skin barrier better or hide in any skin tags or abrasions, which usually don't get cleaned as well. A few years ago I had one doe come into milk so fast after freshening that she literally split some of the skin on her teats. Try to milk that without her jumping! Poor baby. I applied Fir Meadow's Udder Luxury shea butter blend and in just 12 hours her udder used the blend to seal those up. Udder Blast by Fir Meadow, which is used for intramammary infusions, can also be used on the skin for damage. Just remember to pour out what you need without contaminating the inside ingredients if you still want to use some in an udder later. Comfrey, lavender and rosemary of course can also be used. So can olive oil, coconut oil, and aloe vera. With aloe use either the drinkable kinds or the gel from the plant. Don't use the sunburn products that have drying and irritating alcohol and other junk in them. I prefer a salve or shea butter blend so that I also can seal the crack with the natural plant fats in them and it stays on the mammary longer that way. Chickweed and calendula are also good herbs in your herbal 'toolkit' to remember for this purpose. Don't forget to lavish your hands with these as well!

Drying Up Milkers and the Dry Period

Drying up milkers and the dry period's function is important to understand. I encourage people to dry each milker up for a dry period of at least 2 months every year. If they want year around milk it is better to stagger breedings over the season so that the dry periods of each animal hit at differing times. The dry period is used primarily by your broodstock to slough the largest amount of worn out intramammary cells to do the greatest amount of mammary repair work if needed, to fight to an even greater degree any bacteria that may be present, and to allow your milker time to rebuild her body reserve mineral and fats banks. These tasks are difficult, if not impossible, to focus on while she is lactating and many times pregnant at the same time.

Animals that are 'milked through' without getting a dry period are more prone to mastitis the second season. They also may start doing a very large cellular slough come the following fall, well before it is time to actually dry them up. This slough can really elevate the SCC (somatic cell count). At that point without further lab work you won't know if you have an actual mastitis or a large cellular slough. It is the body's way to trying to catch up for that missed dry period the previous year. I believe longevity is impacted. Please don't send me notes telling me Susie Q milked into her tenth year even though she was milked through several times. My answer to that is how do we know she wouldn't have milked into her twelfth or fourteenth year? My guess is also that the lifetime milk production probably would have been higher. Another factor to consider is that the sphincter muscles do not get time off from their work of keeping the teat orifice closed in the presence of milk. This also increases the possibility of bacteria getting by that sphincter to get into the udder. Have a dry time off also allows them to rebuild and increase strength in that area. Mind you, real heavy milkers never dry off 100%. I have a couple that always have a tad bit of milk in them, but at least we aren't asking their bodies to make more which still allows them to rest and renew system wide.

Drying your milkers up can be accomplished by reducing her grain and alfalfa or other milk producing feeds and supplements, as well as using herbs. As I decrease the alfalfa a bit I increase the amount of quality non high protein grass hay. Herbs used to help encourage milkers to dry up would be peppermint, sage, white oak leaves (don't overdo the oak leaves as they are very high in drying tannins), and parsley. They can be made into an infusion and added to their water, you can apply a fomentation to the udder, or salve can be put on, such as Fir Meadow's DriMamm Salve, which can be used on the udder of any species. Best results are obtained from giving a tea or dry herbs orally at the same time as using a salve or fomentation. This is also the time that I dry treat udders that had problems during the year by doing a combination of putting on appropriate salves such as Fir Meadow's MammarEaze salve and sometimes infusing and leaving appropriate herbs into the udder after the last milking of the season as mentioned below in mastitis. This is what I do to replace the modern 'dry treatment' infusion full of chemicals.

So how do I dry up milkers? Nearly every person you talk to is going to have a different way to do it. The method I use depends on each individual goat. So here are some ideas you might use as you then consider the needs of your individual milkers. First, I start by considering the above herbs and feed changes. Then, if a milker isn't milking very much (1 or 2 pounds every 12 hours for a standard sized goat) I will just quit milking her and observe her every milking. Many times they will just dry up then. Then in one week I milk them out, dry treat if I want, and monitor them to be sure they don't refill. It takes the pituitary gland an average of seven days to recognize that the 'kids, calves, lambs, puppies...' are no longer hungry. At that point it usually shuts down the milk factory. However, if I have a heavy milker, or one that is not yet below one half of her lactation peak, then I will make some feed changes, add the herbs, and leave a bit of milk- perhaps a pound, in her when I milk her, to try to get her to back off of her production. So if an animal's peak was at 12 pounds, she would still be at 6 pounds of production or more per day for me to use this method. If she is milking moderately, but under half of her peak, then I will drop her to one milking per day. This is assuming that the "under half of her peak" production does not include any lost production from mastitis or udder damage that year. If that is the case, then you need to factor in what you believe they would actually be producing and consider if they are indeed below half of peak production so you don't harm the good half by letting it go too long. This whole time I'm monitoring each udder every milking to watch out for tightness, leaking, skin redness and shine (too tight!), or for any indications of mastitis including feel of the udder and appearance and smell and texture of the milk. Sometimes it is hard to get animals to back off on production when they have been bred to milk, but you can if you keep at it. Just keep it safe for her udder. Last year I had a milker that was milking 10 pounds per day having freshened 9 months previously. She was my dry up challenge that year. This year I have a yearling that has been pushing over 8 pounds every test and has just now dropped into the six pound range for fall. She is this year's dry goat challenge. I also like to take them for daily short walks under the oak tree branches that hang over our fence line. Those oak leaves do help cut production, just don't let them overdo it so you don't run into an acidosis problem. I also like to feed them some grass hay (not the high protein hot stuff) right after milking before I give them their alfalfa. That also helps them to cut production.

Some people advocate cutting back on their water intake as that will cut back on their milk production. I never agree with an approach that can compromise the kidneys, heart, and every cell of the body including your unborn babies. "First, do no harm."

Encouraging Milk Production

Perhaps your girl had a rough start with a tough kidding or maybe she is just recovering from an illness. Have you been showing her in milk, uddered up? Or you just don't think she is milking her genetic potential. Here are some things you can do.

First, remember, that you cannot force her to milk if her diet is not correct. Please review the Supplements chapter. Also if she is still ill, or has an underlying undiagnosed problem or unresolved parasite issue, then you will be hard pressed to ask for more milk and you shouldn't. But if you know she is now well and she is being fed properly as evidenced by the condition and production of other members of your herd then you can try some of these herbs.

Alfalfa is tops in my mind for milk making, so much so that I can see a difference in production sometimes from bale to bale if I have different cuttings from different places in my barn. Other herbs of value are comfrey leaf, kelp, blessed thistle, motherwort, fennel, fenugreek, red raspberry leaf, goat's rue, nettle, and dandelion fed at the chronic rate. Fir Meadow also makes a nice MilkMaid herbal product that can be mixed with the grain or mixed with kelp and/or black strap molasses and top dressed on the grain.

Holding Milk

Holding milk or unwillingness to let her milk down can happen from time to time. You have them cleaned, you have the machine or your hands and bucket ready, and no milk will come no matter what you try! It can be orneriness or stress, and besides those choices, goats can willfully hold back milk if they don't like the person that is handling them, or are afraid. We have herbal secrets for this issue as well.

First consider good milking protocol. Using body temperature or a bit warmer sprays or cleaners, and having body temperature hands or equipment when you touch her helps her relax more. Also massaging the udder some with warm hands encourages milk let down. If she's still trying to hold it, then you can give her some of the following choices. They can be fed orally, rubbed along the spine with a tincture or fomentation, or placed on the udder tissue with a tincture or fomentation. Your tinctures will be absorbed quicker and used faster. Valerian, hops, lavender, scullcap, ladies slipper, clary sage, or Lobelia inflata are some great choices. Blue cohosh can be used to encourage a natural oxytocin release within the animal, which they must do to let milk down. Remember to go slow and careful with any oral feeding of Lobelia inflata so that you don't come up against its emetic (vomit) response. Fir Meadow's Mel-O herb mix can also be used as well as Dr. Christopher's Relax-Eze. Essential oils that can be considered, diluted with olive oil and added onto the udder would be lavender, German chamomile, Roman chamomile, geranium, and clary sage. You might try some of these herbs for you as well, or take in a nice deep breath of your essential oil choices. If you are getting tense or upset because your milker is not cooperating with you, it will give her more of a reason to be tense because she will sense that something is wrong or endangering her safety. So make sure you aren't contributing to the problem. Remember love.

Ketosis

Ketosis is a problem where the carbohydrate intake does not keep up with the animal's nutritional needs. This is not the same condition as milk fever or hypocalcemia, but a milker with ketosis that goes off of feed can end up with milk fever as an additional problem. See the section on Pregnancy Toxemia in Chapter 6. Ketosis and Pregnancy Toxemia are the same problem, at different times in the dam's production cycle. Look for Milk Fever later in this chapter.

Leaking Mammary

Leaking mammaries at the teat orifice can be caused by mechanical damage to the sphincter muscle or teat. A milker can also sometimes have a hard time holding her milk when she is overfull. Occasionally waiting on the milkstand or in the parlor in her anticipation of being milked gets the best of her and she'll release. I've had one that just decides it's time to let her milk down whenever she feels like it. Stinker! Leaking mammaries are more prone to mastitis, as the orifice being opened and milk running out makes a nice nutrient rich body temperature milk freeway for bacteria to race up to gain entrance within the mammary. If your milker anticipates and tries to let her milk go right after she is loaded up to the holding pen or parlor, see if you can't arrange a way to milk her first and get to milking her before she starts to drop that milk. If she is leaking due to a weak sphincter or teat damage, then comfrey salves, Fir Meadow's Wounderful! or ReBuilld salves, or Dr. Christopher's Complete Bone and Tissue formula can be given. Oral herbs can also be given to increase the body's ability to heal from the inside. A favorite cytophilactic (cell proliferant or cell promoting) essential oil to use here, diluted in olive oil, would be lavender or patchouli. For milkers that are just letting go because they think they can just do that, I would place them on some liver and cell cleansing, and get them onto some nervous system nurturing herbs, and support herbs in case there is a tissue weakness. You can read more about that in the body system chapters later in this book.   I once had a doe that would leak through a small pore at the top of her teat near the udder floor.   Some good tissue nurturing salves such as Wounderful! or ReBuilld by Fir Meadow or Dr. Christopher's Complete Tissue Formula can assist here.   Lavender or patchouli essential oil, diluted in olive oil, may also benefit.   See the Epidermis chapter under Wounds for more information.

Mastitis

Wow.   Whole books can be and have been written on this topic as well as multitudes of detailed research papers. I'm going to try and cover a lot of ground in a few sentences. Fasten your seatbelts!

Mastitis is a word that really just means inflammation (itis) of the mammary gland. It is nearly always caused by a bacterial infection in which the bacteria multiply at a faster rate than the immune system can keep up with. This causes symptoms at some point.   Because there are literally hundreds of bacteria and then mutations of those, symptoms will be different according to the bacteria types.   Some symptoms can be: less milk in one half or quarter (or all if infected in all of them, which is not as common), swelling, heat, and fever to the animal, abnormal milk smells, abnormal milk texture including some types of clumps and/or strings. Even abnormal sounds coming from the udder can be involved with some serious forms of mastitis.   The appearance of udder bruising can also be extremely serious. Sometimes blood in the milk, making pink milk, is mastitis and sometimes it is residual bleeding from a milker coming into milk so fast with so much pressure that she blows some capillaries. That can also happen if they are overuddered from milking late or uddering them up too full at shows. Blood also sometimes shows itself from an injury to the udder.   The udder may feel like it has knots in it from the body's attempt to wall of bacteria into a sort of 'jail cell' to protect the rest of the body from it.

Subclinical mastitis means that there is an infection that is active but no symptoms are shown yet.   There are tests, both lab work and home test systems like CMT kits that can be done to determine if a problem is going on.   I usually can tell in MY herd with what we normally get (staph types) by udders going uneven because

223

of less milk production in the affected side.   Personally, as an herbalist, I will support the body no matter what the cause of the mastitis.

First I want to give you an herb list of what I like to use in any form of mastitis.   I like to give herbs ORALLY and treat the first day that I find the situation as ACUTE, even if it has been a chronic issue. See the Dosaging chapter for more information on that.   I also like to put salves onto the mammary and give an intramammary infusion, placing an herbal oil blend into the mammary gland itself. That too is discussed in the Dosaging and Methods of Administration chapter. Remember when working on an intramammary infusion NOT to use herbs that are traditionally used to curd milk as in cheesemaking. Two of those would be nettle and comfrey.   There will be more no intramammary herbs; I have not run tests on the hundreds of herb choices out there.   So be certain of what you are putting in that mammary so you don't cause a greater problem. Having said that, herbs I like using with mammary issues are goldenseal, myrrh, cayenne (diluted only and in a blend), thyme (diluted and in a blend), oregano (diluted and in a blend), lavender, mullein, marshmallow, and Lobelia inflata. Not all of these are antiseptic, as some I am using for additional support.   For instance, the marshmallow root is used to help the body combat any inflammation caused to the tissue but really isn't considered antiseptic. In pregnant animals never use goldenseal by itself. In fact, I never use goldenseal by itself, but always pair a high Vitamin B complex herb with it; like cayenne or catnip. I love plant synergies so will seldom use just one plant or one essential oil by itself anyways. Essential oils one can consider to dilute and place on the mammary would be rosemary, lavender, thyme, oregano, and German chamomile or yarrow.   Fir Meadow herb products used for mastitis support have been Udder Blast infusion (use in 30 cc amounts to really saturate the mammary) and HerBiotic oral herb mix and salves. Dr. Christopher's Infection formula would be good to use orally as well.   Vitamin C is popular for working with mastitis issues, but I won't use a vitamin isolate. Most of the Vitamin C out there is made from its chemical sidekick, ascorbic acid, which is not plant extracted Vitamin C and certainly is not whole herb. For a good quality C, may I remind you about our wonderful multipurpose herb, cayenne.   Rosehips and fresh squeezed citrus are also good sources. You are looking for that characteristic tangy citrus zing in those.   In cayenne it will be overpowered by the other phytochemicals in the plant.

The Accessible Pet, Equine and Livestock Herbal

If your milker does go uneven, it is going to depend on the level of damage to the milk producing tissue and how fast you were able to get going on herbal support, as to how long it will take to watch the body even that udder up. Some people have gotten back even udders in their stock in just days. The mammaries that sustained greater damage usually take the remainder of the year including the dry period to repair. Remember, the dry period is when the majority of intramammary cells are sloughed and replaced. For those that use a good quality salve, consistently during the year and dry period, such as Fir Meadow's MammarEaze or GlandAide, are supplying nutrients the udder tissue will use to repair itself. The Epidermis/skin chapter will give you some herb ideas if you want to do your own thing.

E. coli mastitis usually comes on fast and is something that has to be dealt with immediately or the life of your milker is in imminent danger. A friend of mine had this diagnosed in a goat once. She was told that when she milked if she heard farting type or air releasing types of noises from the udder that they would want to go after this form of mastitis aggressively. The source of this most often would be getting manure on a teat end with a concentration of E. coli on it and then having that bacteria run up into the udder. I would work with them as mentioned above, and do it aggressively via oral, intramammary, and dermal (skin salve or diluted essential oil) routes. Remember that E. coli is in the digestive tract of every mammal and human. It is when it gets into places it is not supposed to be, or when it gets over populated where it is supposed to be, that a problem ensues. Prevention of course would be to do the best you can with having clean bedding and clean milker preparation to minimize the risk. I know that some animals will lie in the dirt anyways, as I have a couple of them; but a clean "bedroom" where most of them hangout just makes good sense.

Gangrenous mastitis is scary and is another true "handle this immediately" emergency. Thankfully, I have not personally dealt with it here on the farm, but have coached other people through what I would do should it show up here. Any time you see black or blue types of bruising to the udder get diagnostic help from a vet to be sure if you are dealing with this, or just an udder injury. Hours lost can make a difference on your results in this situation. Giving herbs hourly, and salving and milking hourly has pulled some of these animals through. I would not hesitate to give my animal double or triple dose herbs for the first 3 or 4 hourly treatments to get things moving faster for them. Myrrh, goldenseal, Echinacea, mallow, plantain and marshmallow root are special herbs of interest in this case and I would double and triple dosages a blend of them with cayenne added for punch and more antimortification benefit until I had a few hours in. If the milker is in pain, then a large oral dose (triple or quadruple) of mullein tincture or infusion would be of benefit to her. I would also make strong infusions (teas) of the herbs and soak a washcloth or dishtowel and try to keep putting that on the udder nonstop or at least starting out with hot, but safe to the touch, udder fomentations (tea cloth on udder) and then switch to very good quality salves. You can then place a hot, but safe temperature, cotton washcloth over the salves to drive them in deeper faster. The fomentations need to be made fresh often with new strong herbs, as the hydrotherapy is as important as the herbs to aid the body in moving the toxins and polluted lymph out. Remember to alternate the 12 minutes of hot with 4 minutes cold water cloths to help plunge the bad material out. It will be a long day but well worth it if you jump on it fast enough. You can also use Fir Meadow's HerBiotic herb mix and salves for this situation. Do even better and apply Dr. Christopher's Sen Sei balm over the top of the HerBiotic salve, especially if you have to leave for a bathroom or stretch break so that the herbs are supporting the body at a high level while you get your break.

Remember that your male animals can also get mastitis. Sometimes they can even make milk! I've owned one milk buck and now have a second milk buck on the farm. We didn't milk them, we dried them up. Remember, all mastitis means is inflammation of the mammary and boys do have teats that can get infected. For the boys, I use oral herbs and salves and perhaps an infusion ON THE SKIN, not in the teat gland. We never like to open teat orifices on animals that have not had them opened, during their dry periods, or on young creatures that have never been in milk. To do so increases the risk of additional bacteria moving on in. The exception would be an e-coli or gangrenous situation where we will want to get that bacteria moved out of the body quickly. In that case you will milk them in an area that you can completely sanitize or be able to scrape up the bedding and dirt and burn it. You do not want that potentially infective material hanging out around your farm.

Strep and Staph mastitis types are treated per the directions above, even Staphylococcus auerous which is resistant to all currently known chemical antibiotic udder preparations and can really wreck an udder.

Chronic mastitis is when one has an ongoing problem with mastitis that hasn't been resolved. In these cases, when handled herbally, I like to use the first day to give herbs at the acute stage dosage, and then move into a bit more aggressive approach for the next three or four days of four times per day then down to just every milking (at least two times per day) if I am seeing progress, until a few days past any symptoms. Then I use a salve, such as MammarEaze or GlandAide afterwards to nourish that mammary for reparation until I see a normal appearing udder.

Udder knots from mastitis are disheartening to say the least. Here you have bred for this beautiful soft productive mammary, and now there are knots in it that the body formed to put walls around the bacteria in order to protect the rest of the udder from further infection. These knots are at risk of rupturing if the udder gets tight, such as early in the season when the milk really starts coming on or if they are uddered up for a show. Once ruptured, they release the bacteria causing a mastitis rerun. Sometimes they form in a teat, causing problems with milking. I was told by many when I was early into goats that once you had those, you were stuck with them. I have great news for you, however; as I have learned that is not necessarily so. My favorite thing to do with them is to make a blend of three parts mullein and one part Lobelia inflata, as taught to me during my herbal education and start putting that on the mammary. Fir Meadow's salve, GlandAide, is also used for this purpose. The knots will be broken down internally by the lymph system on a strong milker and then taken out a bit at a time, or those knots will abscess through the udder skin as the body pushes them out if the milker's system wouldn't be able to handle it. At that time I use HerBiotic Salve or antiseptic herbs or herb washes to clean the area and keep it from getting infected as well as continuing the GlandAide salve. You can even put dried powdered herbs mentioned in the Skin chapter onto the abscess. You can try putting lavender essential oil, diluted, around the area to discourage flies. For that matter, diluted lavender can also be put on the area as an antiseptic and to encourage the body to heal on a cellular level. Wounderful! Salve, ReBuilld Salve, or MammarEaze salves or Udder Blast could be used topically as well.

For animals prone to mastitis I would also consider liver, kidney and blood cleansing, as well as immune system herbs.   Dr. Christophers Immune formula, Fir Meadow's MMune formula, or herbs as explained in the immunity body system chapter can be used.   A MammarEaze type of salve can also be used six days per week each milking for Offensive Herbalism™ on the udder by the body to nourish that gland.

Milk Fever or Hypocalcemia

I've only seen this once on our farm. Believe me, you don't want to see it twice! Our first kidding season,   we had a doe kid three weeks before we had planned on kids arriving.   The first thing I learned from that was to write EVERY breeding date down.   Some goats (as well as other creatures) re-cycle even though they are already pregnant from the first breeding. They won't often ovulate that second time if it's a full cycle, but they'll sure talk you into taking them for a walk to the buck! Anyhow, we had not started her on full feed alfalfa hay soon enough. She was fine boned, a heavy milker, and was full of kids for her size causing her to deplete her calcium and supporting minerals.   Our guardian dog first alerted us to something wrong.   We went to the barn to find a goat staggering with her back legs lacking coordination.   After we carried her into the barn and figured out what was going on we went for supplies from the vet.   Fortunately we caught her early, before she was down, so were able to just work with oral products. This of course was before I was an herbalist.   I have also seen friends dealing with it at shows with heavy milkers that went off of feed due to the stress of the show or transport. Anytime a heavy milker goes off of feed, especially her alfalfa, this issue should be watched for.   Milkers dealing with Ketosis or Pregnancy Toxemia, as already mentioned, sometimes will end up with milk fever from being off of their high calcium feeds like alfalfa, but are still milking at some amount, putting them into a deficit or into hypo-calcemia mode.

Once they are down it is a veterinarian emergency unless you are really comfortable with working with your herbs. Realize that if you are not fast enough with your vet products, vet help, or your herbal nourishment, whichever you choose, you can lose the animal.   If you choose your vet, choose one experienced with dairy animals. They will probably administer an IV and if the calcium products are given too quickly the heart can be stopped.

Here is how I would approach this herbally should I ever see it again on our farm. For something like this where time is of the essence, I would want to use teas, tinctures and/or juices. Carrot juice with some additional cayenne and hawthorn for heart support is a good starting place. If you add a touch of horsetail (shavegrass) herb it will boost the bioavailability of the calcium to a higher level. Oat Straw, comfrey, white oak bark and raspberry leaf tea, made very strong, would be another viable addition. I would carefully drench a pint (two cups) for the first dose of carrot juice blend to a goat sized animal. The cayenne will drive the herbs to the heart fast which will be suffering from the lowered calcium in the bloodstream. I'd be giving more fresh carrot juice (with the cayenne!) every 15 minutes, then switch it to every 30 minutes then every hour that first day as I noted improvement. The oral herbs will not overdose your animal with calcium and stop the heart as intravenous products can do. But again, use common sense so you don't head into an enterotoxemia problem. If I had a good blender, like a Vitamix, I would also be mixing the above mentioned herbs or herb powders with the carrot juice along with the cayenne after I got the first dose of cayenne/carrot juice into her. Ginger root juiced and added (1 square inch chunk for a standard sized goat or ¼ to ½ teaspoon of strong ginger powdered herb) will encourage circulation to the extremities if the animal is down. Make sure your animal, if down, is not lying on its side! Leaving it there can cause a severe case of bloat, problems with the lungs, and of course decreased circulation to the whole side. Use hay or straw bales or whatever is needed to hold that animal so it is upright, with the spine pointing towards the barn roof. Also shift your animal from side to side at least every hour and massage the areas they were lying on to keep circulation going. Blanketing an animal that is down to retain its body heat is important, even in the summer, as it will probably be unable to regulate its body heat if it is in this condition. Offer warm water with black strap molasses in it for the additional mineral content. You can also keep a pile of kelp granules or powder in front of them so that they can self herb themselves for mineral support once they are feeling a little better. Remember how important the alfalfa and other calcium herbs listed in the supplements section are, stay away from breeding frail boned animals, and feed your stock well and likely you will never see this problem. In animals that are higher risk due to smaller bone frame, higher production, or have a family history of the problem, Fir Meadow has a Hi-Cal blend available to use as a daily supplement. Dr. Christopher has a nice Herbal Calcium formula as well. These products can be used for your egg laying poultry and ratites as well or use Fir Meadow's Layer Support blend. Please note that if you ever feel cold teats on your milker (all of the teats, not just one of them) one of the things to consider is a hypocalcemia problem coming on. Give some of the suggested herbs along with ginger, cayenne and carrot juice at a double or triple dose and check her again in a couple of hours. Her teat temperature should have returned to normal.

Milk flavors and Withdrawals on Herbs

If you remember some of your herbal basics, you'll note that there are no milk withdrawals from herbs as long as you stick with the rules- no toxic, poisonous, or habit forming herb use. They are nourishing and improve the milk quality. Now having said that; there are some plants that do flavor milk to make it less than enjoyable. I feed my herbs when I milk, or right afterwards which allows 10 to 12 hours for the herbs to clear. In a healthy animal that's well beyond the 4 hours needed to break down and clear out the herbs from the body. If an animal is sick enough that it is requiring the hourly or several times per day herbs, then you won't want to use the milk anyhow.

Sometimes you can have a milker that just has an off flavor to the milk and it isn't mastitis in their case. Check to see that they have fresh bedding (milk can pick up bedding odors), that they aren't urinating on their udder, that your milking equipment is clean and sanitized, and that they didn't get into some wayward plant or toxin somewhere. If it's breeding season and the male of the species wears smelly perfume for the ladies, as in goats, then keeping the males in their own pen away from the females will keep the musk odor out. Also be sure you are up to date on your parasite elimination program. The toxins and waste put into the animal's system from internal parasites can ruin milk flavor. Moldy or otherwise damaged feed certainly can a negative impact milk. If you still have a milker that insists on having unique flavored milk, I would seriously consider doing liver, kidney and bloodstream cleanses (sound familiar?), as well as adding lavender, rosemary and nettle to the diet, and see where that gets you in a few months. Red raspberry can also be added to the mix, being another gentle supporter of tissue restoration and gentle cleansing. My suspicion, in these situations, is that you are tasting some waste product or chemical that is inside the body.

Nervous milkers

Look at the above section on holding milk to find some support for your nervous lady. These can also be used if you have a nervous new mom not letting her babies nurse. Make sure she has been grounding out as mentioned in the Husbandry chapter. Unreleased electro-magnetic field (EMF) buildup in the system can also be hard on their temperament. Do you wonder why office workers can come home so tense? This is certainly a factor and influences your creatures too. If I had a family line of these, I would also start working them through the organ and blood cleanses for several months, to see if I could break the cycle, along with some nervous system herbs to nourish them such as blue cohosh, Lobelia inflata, black cohosh, hops, blue vervain, valerian, scullcap and rosemary. Fir Meadow makes a Mel-O herb mix and also a Think tincture, and Dr. Christopher has an excellent Mind Trac formula. In addition, I would consider some reproductive system nourishment which will be covered in that chapter. I might also consider getting and putting some EMF shields in the barn, pet area, tackroom and/or milkroom. A resource is listed in the appendix.

SCC Counts

Somatic cell counts are, simply stated, the white blood cell count within a milk sample. Generally we use these numbers to give us an indication of what the inner mammary health is as related to bacteria counts. In theory, the higher the number, the higher the amount of bacteria as reflected by the higher white blood cell count. You will find that in practice, the counts will vary according to the individual animal or sometimes family lines, with the time of year, with additional injuries, with anything causing a lull in immune system health, with a heat wave, and even when animals are cycling during breeding season. Vaccinations, of course, will also increase a SCC reading as the immune system, body wide; is faced with an animal protein and chemical challenge put straight into the bloodstream.

What I do with my animals is watch the trend and know where my animals are at. If an animal, in one month, has a reading that comes back higher, and I can't attribute it to a cut on the foot, or them being in heat, etcetera, then I start checking the mammary for its health.   As a precaution, even when I can attribute it to something besides mastitis, I will use antiseptic salves on the udder, such as HerBiotic or DisNFect essential oil blend that I further dilute (yes, 5 drops in a teaspoon of olive oil) to be on the safe side.   Do your homework though as if you have mastitis problem going, you do need to go after it, pronto!   Remember that late season udders are starting to shed more cells within the mammary, so expect your counts to go up some then but still watch for jumps in the numbers which could indicate mastitis.   Even if you are not on DHIR (official milk test) you can check with your veterinarian university lab to find out where SCC tests can be sent to or run an internet search for DHIR labs. Your animal doesn't even have to be registered for you to send a sample in to have the SCC count read.   Contact them ahead so that you can obtain milk sample vials to keep on hand.   Those will be next to the red topped test tubes that can be used if you do want to send a milk sample to a laboratory to determine which bacterium you are fighting with your mastitis issue.

Self suckers

Thankfully I've never had one of these, but I've had friends with them.   These are animals that either can't handle the sensation of dropping milk or the pressure of a full mammary and learn to relieve themselves.   It is possible that the problem can be taught to other milkers so don't let this go. They are also more prone to mastitis from opening their orifice several times per day. If I had one of these, I would try to milk it three times a day if possible to keep pressure relieved on the mammary as well as using some of the herbs for the nervous milker discussed earlier.   For some animals salve can be applied to the teat with extra cayenne or hotter pepper applied, in hopes of keeping the busy face away from the teat. Petroleum jelly could theoretically be used with cayenne, but I would not want anything ingesting

The Accessible Pet, Equine and Livestock Herbal

it, nor would I want it on the teat end, potentially blocking bacteria there. However, the petroleum product will stay on the teat longer than a salve, which the body will absorb. Keep it away from the orifice! Remember that some critters like hot peppers, so this would not detour those. The beauty of the cayenne is it won't harm the tissue, just nourish, even though it is hot to the touch. Though for very hot peppers you need to exercise caution by diluting them with salve or olive oil before putting it on the teat, as the very hot ones can blister skin as can garlic applied without dilution to the skin. Remember to keep your hands out of your face and eyes if you apply this with your hands. Some people will also take a stiff plastic Queen Victoria collar and put it on backwards, making the neck of the animal stiff so it can't reach around to nurse. These are typically dog collars and are available from your pet veterinarian. Be sure that no herdmates can get tangled in it and that your new "queen" can't get caught on anything in her pen or stall with it.

Teat Damage

For damaged teats, whether bruised from being stepped on, cut or torn, we will treat them just as we will in the Epidermis/skin chapter, by applying appropriate herb powders, salves, or fomentations. Carefully handmilk these injured areas as they repair. The vacuum of a machine can often undo healing done since the last milking. I like to put a salve on my hands before I milk a damaged teat, so that as I milk the salve is being massaged into the teat (and my hands). Then I apply a thick amount to the damaged areas and to a one inch perimeter around the damage when I'm done milking and spraying the teat end.

Udder Growths that Continue to Grow Exterior or Interior

Interior lumps caused by mastitis are explained in the mastitis section. Interior growths for other reasons can be handled by infusing Udder Blast or other herbs as mentioned in the mastitis section with the addition of pau d' arco, chaparral, cayenne and diluted lemon essential oil to them. Salves should also be applied to the exterior of the udder so that more herbs can soak in. Fir Meadow has a Skin Happiness salve for this purpose, and certainly one can use chaparral and pau d' arco here as well. One should also consider doing liver, kidney, and blood cleanses with their animal. Expect to see some change within six to eight weeks if it is helping. If it isn't, then please consider cleansing to get to the likely cause, which we believe is a polluted blood stream. Fir Meadow and Dr. Christopher both have excellent cleanses. See more in the appropriate organ sections.

Apricot seeds can also be fed as a food supplement. Thirty seeds per day for a 100 to 200 pound animal split between two feedings. I have a goat that gobbles them up like candy. You also could grind them fresh in a coffee grinder and mix into feed with black strap molasses. Taste one, they are nasty! As my editor mentioned, you'll never mistake one for an almond! I do eat one or two when I serve them to my stock though, since we all have some cancer cells in our body at all times. Apricot kernels feed vitamin B17 to healthy cells. To unhealthy cells that want to grow incorrectly, they will support the body in its efforts to go after them. Garlic should also be a part of the diet when apricot kernels are used to increase their use to the body. Apricot kernels are a regular part of the diet of the Hunza people, one of the longer lived peoples on the earth at this time.

I also like using fresh squeezed lemon or lime juice both orally and in preparations for abnormal growths. The nutrient profile and cleansing abilities of these two gifts should never be overlooked. I also like adding black cumin seed oil to topical preparations which has a reputation for assisting in these types of matters.

Please reconsider the idea if thinking about purchasing an escharotic. An escharotic is sometimes labeled as 'black salve' or salves for malignancies. Though they do contain combinations that can be very helpful to the body, they can also be excruciatingly painful as they do their work. Since we have other good tools, I personally don't have a reason to use them. Just to note, the Dr. Christopher Black Salve is NOT one of these. It's a wonderful drawing salve, so don't mix them up.

I would also make sure I had my creature on a good supplementation program per that chapter. For a nice herbal supplement blend in these situations consider Fir Meadow's Better Daze.

Udder Pox

Udder pox looks like pimples on the udder. They are often caused by unsanitary conditions. Before you get ready to tell me about how clean you keep your stalls, remember that some animals just have an affinity for lying in fresh manure or more specifically onto fresh urine. I think sometimes they do these things just to keep us busy! Occasionally an animal with an udder that bulges too far to the rear will pee on her own udder. Besides washing and drying the mammary (4 drops of lemon or rosemary or lavender essential oil on a cotton washcloth dipped in warm water is a nice way to go), salves or diluted essential oils with olive oil can be placed on the mammary tissue. Herbs to consider would be: goldenseal, sage, rosemary, thyme, oregano, myrrh, and lavender. Essential oils in the same herbs can be used if diluted at the standard rate of 5 drops per teaspoon of olive oil. There is no goldenseal essential oil that I know of and if there was I would expect it to be one expensive oil! If the animal is pregnant then the thyme, sage, and oregano should be diluted even further- 5 drops per tablespoon of olive oil before applied to the udder. Remember sage should be used on a limited basis only if you want to keep your milk production up. Nice salves are MammarEaze or Wounderful!, both by Fir Meadow. Dr. Christopher's Infection formula can be used as well. There is black walnut in the Infection formula, so if you have a camelid or equine you will not want to use it due to founder possibilities. If a creature were to get a repeated problem here, I would consider (can you guess??) organ cleansing and boosting her immune system with immune herbs as discussed in that body system chapter. MMune by Fir Meadow or Dr. Christopher's Immune formula can also be used.

Udder Sanitation

Shaving udders with a 10 in cold weather to a 50 surgical sized clipper blade to get extra hairs off help reduce dirt sticking to the udder goes a long ways in keeping udders healthy. Dairy clips, that include taking a number 5F skip tooth blade in cold weather and a 10 blade in warmer weather to the belly, insides of the upper rear legs, and from the rear surrounding the udder and tail sides will also reduce dirt and debris from sticking. Washing and drying udders if needed before milking then washing and sanitizing teats as mentioned above will decrease the amount of bacteria available for mastitis or udder skin issues. If you are hand milking then these steps will also allow you to keep your milk cleaner.

Uneven Udders

Uneven udders can be rebalanced as the tissue heals over time. Udders with minimal damage that you were able to get after quickly may rebalance fast, otherwise consider that it may take the rest of that milking season and the dry period when the udder rejuvenates itself. See the mastitis section above.

Warts on the udder

Warts are viral nuisances. If they are long, you can take sanitized fishing line and tie them off tight to cut the circulation to them. They will fall off, but that still doesn't get the virus part. In this case salves or essential oil blends are the easiest to work with, using them twice per day. Black walnut (not for equine/camelid use), pau d' arco, oil of garlic and lemon balm are some choices to work with. Fir Meadow has a Wart Wort salve that can be used in these situations. It does have black walnut in it, but can be used on camelids and equine if applied to the wart or warts only. If my animal had a habit of acquiring these, you guessed it; more organ and blood cleansing as well as immune system support. I would also make sure that they were not potassium deficient. If I thought they might be, I would add more dandelion leaf and flowers or tea to their diet.

Chapter 10- Failure to Thrive, Rescues, Senior Creatures

Once in awhile an animal just isn't doing well.   Sometimes there are contributing factors, but they just aren't responding as they should.   At times I get contacts from rescue outfits or from people that have acquired a creature that should be considered as a rescue. Of course, whether we like to think about it or not, the longevity that we hope our beloved creatures will have, means that they will become seniors at some point and may be in need of some extra care and attention. You will find the more generations of drug free and cleansed animals that you raise, the longer your life spans can go. So the more likely they are to stay healthy and functional to the end- abundant life, not just existence.   I think every animal deserves to just pass on to their Good Shepherd in its sleep while dreaming about what the next day's adventures might be.   This chapter, I hope, will help you accomplish that.

Cleansing

I will address cleansing in more detail in the body sections chapters of Part ll, but have to at least mention it here.   If this animal has never had a good cleanse of the bowels (if a canine/feline and some equine), and the liver/kidneys, and bloodstream, then it's not too late to address that.   The entire health of every cell depends on the garbage sites of every cell being able to dump out any withheld toxins which impacts the overall health of the entire creature. If this animal has gone through courses of cleansing then consider giving periodic tune-ups for 1 to 2 weeks at a time; unless you know of a reason why you should clean them longer. I like to cleanse seniors quarterly. Your payback? An animal that feels better and looks better will be more efficient with their feed use, allowing for a possible cut back in the amount of feed costs needed to sustain them. That should also reduce additional care for issues than it otherwise would need giving you more time to enjoy their companionship.

Cleansing (Healing) Crisis

Although I talked about healing or cleansing crisis in the Herbal Foundations chapter, I want to reiterate it here. Remember that as you cleanse your animal there is the likely hood that they will experience aches and pains and cold or flu like symptoms. They may all of the sudden develop abscesses if quite toxic as the body starts feeling well enough to move old putrid stuff out of the cells. Some of them will drop weight (sometimes a lot) as the old cells and accumulated filth are sloughed faster than new cells are rebuilt. This is very common in animals with a lot of toxicity or with long standing chronic illness. In these situations I suggest they be supported with additional blanketing if needed (often it is), good dry bedding, warm black strap molasses water to drink, additional light cleansing herb tea/infusion in their water such as raspberry, nettle, or dandelion. I also watch for improvement in their attitude and ability as a sign that even with the weight loss they are still headed in the correct direction.

There are a few things that seem to predispose a creature to a greater crisis. If your beloved animal falls into one of these categories; you might start with half dose with chronic situations to allow their systems to start their cleanses slower so that they have less toxic waste to deal with at a time, reducing the severity of the crisis. You will definitely WANT to cleanse these animals instead of leaving their cells bathing in their toxic waste waiting to turn into whatever serious health issue.

Animals that have been on an extended time period of one or more medications are one group. Creatures that have been shown 'on the circuit'; whether locally, statewide, or nationwide so thereby have been exposed to more toxins in travel, grooming supplies and additional vaccinations. A third group is the first generation offspring of the above two groups. The last group may be a surprise to you, but I am finding this to be so in my work. Equine, feline, and canine creatures in general seem to experience a greater healing crisis than other creatures. These often more 'pet' or what I call 'working pet' types of creatures tend to be doted over more and exposed to a greater amount of toxins in their feed and processed feeds, grooming products, external and internal parasite protection, travel and/or urban environment exposure than the more 'farm stock' oriented creatures. Their living conditions are often with less exercise, fresh air, and fresh live raw food than would be desirable. All of that 'doting' today seems to push them more often into dis-ease that used to be experienced mainly by humans. Horses and dogs with blood sugar problems? You almost never heard of that issue 25 years ago! Cancer? On the increase. You should know from my Husbandry chapter that I'm not saying they shouldn't have excellent care and be loved on, but that it is how we define and provide that care to give us a greater likelihood of having a thriving, long lived animal.

All of this is to say that if your creature falls into one or more of the above categories; you may want to either start cleansing slower or work under the supervision of a Master Herbalist as you start.

Also some creatures may fall into one or more of the below categories. For example, you may have rescued a senior horse that is failing to thrive. If that's the case then this whole chapter may seem like a few repeats, but absorb the information and use what you are led to use.

Failure to Thrive

You have just come back from the vet, perplexed. You have an animal that is not its same old self and maybe not maintaining weight, but the veterinarian cannot find any reason to explain this condition. Don't fault them, as there are problems where medical tools and labs don't yet have the equipment or knowledge to diagnose everything. Real sensitive animals can also be subclinical, which means their problem will still be undetectable, yet due to their sensitive nature their body will still be still off. This is where Iridology comes in very handy. If there has been a negative change in a body tissue for at least a few months, it can be detectable by reading the irises, often times years before a problem in that organ or tissue can actually be diagnosed. Then that system or organ weakness can be addressed with herbal and nutritional support so that the creature never has to face additional degeneration to that area. How neat is that? Even blockages in progress in a horse's intestinal tract can often be viewed long before they build up enough of a blockage to colic. That is why I LOVE iridology.

When I am faced with a failure to thrive creature, I run them through the cleanses and I increase their herbal nutrition to work on improving their metabolism. As a reminder, metabolism is the rate of exchange in a cell of nutrients and energy coming in and waste going out.   Going back to the Husbandry chapter to remind yourself of some basics, like exercise, fresh air, etcetera would be a good thing to do. Those basics ARE the foundation.

Your vet will also have ascertained (I hope) that you are not dealing with a parasite problem of some type. Not all parasites can be read with a simple fecal; some tests have to be specifically asked for of the lab. Please see the Parasites chapter if you feel you need to address this situation and choose an appropriate herb plan for the types of parasite possibilities that are in your area or situation. Just because a creature has been on a chemical or herbal deworming program does not mean they may be parasite free.   If the dosages weren't appropriate, or the correct parasites weren't addressed, or the herbs were incorrect you may still have a problem.

Nourishing herbs to consider adding to your creature's diet, of which some will be a *déjà vu* as several of these will have been listed in the Supplements chapter. Stinging nettle, comfrey, dandelion, chia seed, black strap molasses, red raspberry leaf, alfalfa, spirulina, carrots, apple, moringa, garlic, burdock root, plantain, cayenne, rose hips, rosemary, ginger, nutritional yeast, raw apple cider vinegar, organic apples, real raw honey, wheat grass, and kelp are some of those that come right to my mind without hesitation as some good 'farmer's friends'.   By starting slow and adding these to the diet, you should see some changes over time. Without the cleanses the changes will be much slower.   Fir Meadow makes a nice product, called Better Daze, and also a God's Greens, for these types of situations. Dr. Christopher has a very nice Vitalerbs and Jurassic Greens product.

Don't forget issues caused by stress.   Did this animal just move or move this year? Did one of its best buddies (or owner) get sold or pass away? Did you do several exhibitions in a row, or even just one if your animal isn't used to being out? Then besides some of the nourishing herbs, you might consider also using eleuthero herb, lavender, hops strobiles/flowers (do not use these by themselves with canines), chamomile, scullcap, or some of the other nervous system herbs listed in that chapter as well as extra attention and some appropriate spoiling. Find their scratchy spots.   Besides scratching you will be hitting reflex points if you get under skin depth and will relax them some more.   For the smaller animals including baby livestock, that may mean pulling it into your lap for some hug and/or nap time. It never ceases to amaze me how much better a baby goat can look after some appropriate herbs, a prayer and a nice nap in my lap.

Be sure to consider subclinical infections. Those are low grade infections that are not symptomatic (showing symptoms). Herbs are a safe way to go to help the body root those out. If the animal didn't need it they are just nourishing, but if your animal did you will be so thankful you did something! Herbs to consider would be antiseptic herbs such as: cayenne, garlic, myrrh, echinacea, thyme, goldenseal, Oregon grape root, oregano, and rosemary. Remember some of the nourishing herbs mentioned above too. You might start your herb plan as acute for day one to give them a 'jump start'; then move onto chronic from day two onward.

Failure to thrive canines and felines also can have some raw goats milk added to their diet. Start with small amounts at first with this nutrient dense food. Their herbs and other foods can be mixed in with the milk, making them more palatable. You can also add the milk to their senior and rescue diets. Fresh milk is preferred, but frozen milk can keep for up to 18 months if needed. If you are an operation that deals with these issues on a routine basis, then you will want to keep some backup milk in the freezer for times of the year, like winter and early spring, when fresh goat's milk would be harder to come by.

Rescues

With rescues you will work with them just as you would for the failure to thrive types, with this exception. If they are grossly malnourished and/or underweight you will start SLOWER (except for life threatening acute conditions)! You have the animal, it is still alive. If you put nutrition down it too fast at first, you may have a fatal enterotoxemia or Herxheimer reaction event as the animal's stamina and intestinal flora is not going to handle a fast change like that. Pretend they are concentration camp victims and go slow. I would start at 1/3 of the chronic dosage level, all the clean water they can take available all of the time, and clean, but not the highest quality of hay or feed. Lower protein grass hay and feeds is a good starting choice for animals in this situation, slowly working in alfalfa, SLOWLY, after a week. Just a large handful for a horse size is where you would start when you start adding something nutrient dense like alfalfa, but keep the rest clean grass hay. Every three or four days or so you can add a bit more until you have them up to full feed, then gradually increase so they are eating about a full feed and a half until they are stabilized to the weight where you want them.

Cleansing will be important, but please start at a slower rate.

Herbal deworming is the safest form of parasite control and should be started the first week, at normal single dose, then leave them on that twice per day for at least ten days. Plan to repeat that again in two weeks and which point you can often double or triple dose if the product or herbs you use gives you that option and the animal's well being is improving. Remember, their system will likely have little to no immunity to reinfestation at first, so keep monitoring their fecals and keep doing deworming cycles as you deem is needed.

Some fat choices to add SLOWLY to their feed would be mullein leaf powder, olive oil, chia seed, carrots, corn if non gmo, calendula seeds and raw sunflower seeds. If they are a hay eater, finding grass hay with the ripe, but not overripe, grass seed heads in it will also add fat to their diet. Start very slow on the olive oil, as it is very calorie dense. Slow would be a twice per day serving of 1/4 teaspoon for a small pet such as a toy dog or cat or rabbit adjusting up to a tablespoon for a 1000 pound horse. Every three to seven days you can increase that amount slowly upward to a 1/2 tablespoon for the small creature to ¼ cup for the goat/sheep sizes and 1 cup for the equine and cattle sizes. You can also rub olive oil into the skin and the body will take it in and use it that way.

Shelter is extremely important for them. Blanket them at night if needed, even in the summer as I write this where our days are 100 degrees (38 Celsius) and our nights are only in the 50's. That is too much of a temperature swing for a severely undernourished animal. Have them in shade during the day, building up to a 15 minute time period in the sun twice per day to encourage Vitamin D3 production to enable them to utilize the calcium needed to rebuild tissue. Then blanket them once you hit around 70 degrees, unless you see your creature needs it on before then. Keep them out of the wind, as wind will whisk precious body heat and moisture out of them. Also provide deep soft bedding for them to help them cushion their joints and bones to help prevent bedsores and improve circulation to those areas.

Seniors

Senior is a relative term here.   If you do some research, you will find, on average in many domesticated species in the United States, that prior to the 1950's, many of them used to have average longer life spans with fewer conditions than they do now. For example, I recently heard a statistic that old for a Golden Retriever used to be thirteen years old. Now eight years is considered old. What happened?!? Diabetes, glaucoma, and other conditions more common in humans were hardly heard of in stock. Cancer? What about cancers? Our war with cancer now includes our pets. Before the 1950's our stock and pets were subjected to far fewer vaccinations, processed foods, herbicides and pesticides on foods, fly sprays, grooming products, etcetera on the average farm.   We are now many creature generations past that time period and I believe, may be reaping what was sown, as weaker constitutions pass on more of the same to the following generation.   However, the sooner we get to work on cleaning and nourishing our favorite creature, the more likely we get a good response in the direction we want them to go.

Teeth are of special consideration in senior animals.   Animals that have periodontal issues such as weakening gums or infections can use antiseptic herbs along with gum tighteners such as white oak bark or comfrey along the gums to aid the body in correcting itself. Wounderful! or ReBuilld salves or Dr. Christopher's Complete Bone and Tissue Formula can also be a good nutritional support.   Older animals also need to have their teeth checked periodically to make sure that there are no sharps (sharp edges often on the outside molar edges that have developed over the years from chewing patterns). These can cause abscesses and other tissue damage inside of the cheek, which are or can get infected.   These also can cause problems with animals being able to consume enough quantity of feed to stay healthy due to the pain in the area. A painful mouth or teeth may also cause your animal to become dehydrated if the water is cold and causes additional pain to their teeth as they try to drink. In that case, they won't drink enough to thrive. If you see an animal dribbling food out of their mouth while eating, carefully check the teeth, or have your veterinarian do so. Checking the teeth of a goat by me sliding my hand inside of the cheek for a feel is quite a bit less risky (especially if I devise and use a speculum of some type) than if I slip while checking a horse the same way! If you are not comfortable with the procedure let your veterinarian do it. I have gladly paid my veterinarians to check my horses' teeth. They likely have a lot more practice in doing this without getting fingers severely crunched by powerful molars.

Older animals benefit from being offered warm waters or teas to drink to which unsulphured black strap molasses can be added for additional B Vitamins and easily absorbable minerals for them. Raw honey, if you can afford it, is another great water additive. Any alfalfa pellets, grain or grains fed can be presoaked for 12 hours at climate controlled room temperature to allow them to be consumed easier and broken down better. Even your poultry will benefit from this program. However, if you do this, you must absolutely check for mold. Raw Apple Cider Vinegar added to the mix can help prevent this from happening. If you have any doubt of your mix staying mold free, then don't presoak it. Or only presoak it during the winter months or for less time in a climate controlled area such as your kitchen counter.

For seniors, again, a good cleansing program cannot be overstressed, along with supportive feeds as mentioned earlier in this chapter and in the Supplements chapter. For specific body issues such as mental or physical ability, organs functioning properly, etcetera, please consult the related body structure chapter in Part ll.

Your seniors can stay functional to the end with appropriate cleansing and nutrition during their life. What a gift to give to them in exchange for their hard work and companionship for you.

How does Kat keep up her energy and health at these types of events? Ok, tell me, how?!?   You already know enough from this book, and probably some personal experience to start drawing a few conclusions, but I'll add a few more thoughts as well. First off, I will tell you, that when I don't take care of myself at these events, I pay for it! I suspect you may too. As mentioned earlier in the book; when that happens your creatures don't get as good of care as they otherwise would when you have to divert extra attention and resources to yourself to get better.   Here are some things to consider.

First, Kat tries to make sure that she is UTD (up to date) on her cleansings! You knew I was going to say that, didn't you? If you did, that's because you are a good student and are taking the steps to be a good Vitalist. Congratulations! Clean cells run so much better and can handle stress so much better.   Yes, fairs add stress.   I call them working vacations. I get to see my friends but it is much more work taking care of stock at an event then at home, with extra cleaning, adjusting heavy pens, moving extra and often heavy equipment around, water buckets to be hauling and dumping, dealing with extra hot barns (or cold ones), dust and other airborne particulate to breathe 24/7, keeping an eye out for what the public may be trying to do or feed to your animals, and *ad nausea*. Remind me again why I do this? Smile.

Kat makes up one or two quarts of carrot juice, which she spikes with cayenne the morning that she plans to haul out. Often she'll put an extra greens product in it as well.   She takes extra fruit, vegetables, plenty of raw nuts mixed with organic raisins, and salad with her.   A few gallons of distilled water, and a few quarts (or however many needed for the duration of the trip) of a good quality grape juice will be with her, that she adds a greens product to daily.   Hummus turns out to be a great travel food as it will keep for awhile at room temperature due to the olive oil and lemon in it (and cayenne when I make it from scratch).   Olive oil and raw apple cider vinegar mixed, with a few favorite herbs like a classic *Herbs de Provence* make a great salad dressing. She may even crush some garlic into it, and who can forget cayenne, the endurance herb?   She also takes herb capsules with her, usually cayenne (do you have this herb memorized yet?), herbal immune mixes, and Vitalerbs by Dr. Christopher with her. Since she is asking her body to perform more work for more hours at these events, she usually double or triple doses her herbs. Since her body is used to them, she is not going to get a "run to the bathroom" event. If your body is not used to all of this, start slow. You don't want to be standing or riding in a show ring needing to visit the restroom! That could cause you to blow your equitation seat in more ways than one. Okay, bad pun, but I'm leaving it in because you need the laugh. Grin. Usually for one or two afternoons at a longer fair she'll try to find a no MSG Asian food stand that uses brown rice instead of the worthless white stuff. So far they always have let her add extra vegetables to her dish. Believe it or not at some fairs you can find these! Yum. If she thinks she is going to end up eating some food that will plug her up, then she keeps a bowels product with her to keep functioning well. Also if she has done a long drive her bowels tend to want to stagnate, and this allows her system to not miss a step.

She does a lot of juice fasting at these, along with increased intake of distilled water. She is often drinking about one gallon of water per day if it is in 'sweating hot' weather; plus one to two quarts of juice per day, along with her fruits and vegetables. The olive oil, and sometimes avocados help provide fat. At Oregon State Fair there is a blessed couple that makes fresh squeezed organic orange juice at the fair. To me it has been worth every penny to buy a large cup for breakfast every day. Bless their hearts, they even bring it right to my milk area, as well as a friend's milk area! I pay them at the beginning of the week and enjoy the investment in my health every morning. Nearly nothing tastes as good or is as cellular stimulating as fresh OJ! See if you have an option like that available. They squeeze it right when it's ordered. Did you know that 60 or more percent of the Vitamin C is lost in orange juice in just 15 minutes? So fresh counts. When I read 'fresh squeezed' on a juice label, I just have to laugh. Adding back a chemical isolate like ascorbic acid doesn't cut it for your body.

You'll notice what Kat does NOT eat or drink. Things like sugared products, refined flour products, very little meat if at all, pastries, coffee or pop. These all serve to burn out your body, make it mineral deficient which negatively impacts every cell of the body, damage immune system performance, damage tender kidney and nervous system tissue, and dehydrate the body. Doesn't sound like a good recipe for stamina or well being to me. That kind of sounds like most fair food, doesn't it?

Biosecurity

Biosecurity is always a consideration when exhibiting stock or pets, to try to decrease the likelihood of bringing home microbes, viruses, or bacteria from other animals or even the facilities themselves at the show. We try to pen in an area where we are either by ourselves, or next to other breeders that have the same health standards as we do for our herd. Often I will purchase extra pens so that I can have equipment pens in between my animals and other herds. Sometimes we will put up plywood type of sheeting if I need a barrier between my animals and other animals. It can be sanitized, allowed to dry, and then painted over if one wants to reuse the wood later for a building project. We try to keep hay tarped to lessen the public's chances of touching other animals in the barn, then coming over and grabbing hay and trying to feed ours- passing along microbes as they do. For children intent on picking up hay or straw from the ground and then trying to feed it, I just casually ask them, "Why do you want to touch and feed the goats their dirty toilet paper?" They usually drop it pretty quick and stop the germ spreading!

DisNfect or other essential oil blends can be used, mixed with water & put in a handheld sprayer such as are used to spray fruit trees, to spray down pen or stall fencing, walls and floors before putting your animals in there. Buckets and equipment that you bring should also be sanitized, and sanitized again when you break down or once you arrive at home, and again at the show season end when you are ready to store your equipment. If you haven't sanitized your trailer or hauling rig, then you may want to consider that as well to prevent any microbial things from wintering over in your creature transport accommodations.

I like putting a small smear- not a whole drop, of Eucalyptus globulus essential oil onto the nostrils of my goats every day when I have them away from home. Besides expanding their bronchials it also serves to be a nice cooling antiseptic for the lungs, cutting down on the microbes that are trying to hang out down there, and encouraging expectoration of any material that has been inhaled. As we know, many barns and fairs are quite dusty, so any additional support we can give the lungs at this time is a good thing. I also like to dab them again before I load them up to take them home. Of course I'll dab a touch on my shirt collar to breathe in at the same time. After all, I'm breathing the same air.

Should you find out there was a contagious condition at a show, you can always proactively put your animals on the herb plans mentioned in this book to decrease the chances that they actually succumb to the problem. The best part is if they didn't need the support, it will just nourish them and not harm them. If it is a serious condition, then you can even act as if the first day you put them on herbs is acute, to get a real good jump start on heading off a potential upcoming problem. Then continue at a chronic level until the incubation period is over with (often around ten to fourteen days). Besides herbs for the condition, consider immune system herbs and yes, cleansing, as well. But cleanse at a slower rate so that any potential cleansing crisis doesn't happen which would lesson the system's ability to fight an incoming microbe. Raspberry, nettle, dandelion, burdock leaf, and alfalfa teas or herbs are nice gentle cleansers in this case, or ½ the normal dose of other herb products, such as Fresh Start.

I also put extra snaps and short leads onto pen or stall gates at events for backup latches, which makes it less likely my stock can accidentally get out and wander to other animals that I would rather not have them sharing microbes with, or into other tack areas that could allow them to overfeed on someone's grain. This protects my stock better, and the stock of others in the barn. Each farm has its own microbes that could be shared with animals that aren't used to them.

Chilled Animals

Either extreme (heat or cold) can easily happen at an event. With the distraction of all you have to take care of, it can be easy to overlook. Don't overlook these! Your animal, under more stress from hauling and stalling or kenneling, will be more susceptible to problems.

In a chilled animal I look for hair fluffing out, possible arched at the loin and/or wanting to lie down in a warmer corner, if there is a warmer spot. Take their temperature to be sure it is normal. If I think it is only chilled, I will put a blanket on it, give it some oral cayenne mixed with water to dilute the heat in the mouth and possibly offer some warm black strap molasses water (1 tablespoon of molasses per 100 to 200 pound sized animal). You can give some as often as every 15 minutes as needed. Besides providing those stress reducing B vitamins in the molasses and cayenne, the cayenne will also will help warm the body core, alleviate any possible shock, and encourage full body circulation even to the capillary level. Make sure your creature does have good dry clean bedding and plenty of it. Then I observe it to be sure I don't have anything else going on, like toxicity from something ingested or a pneumonia coming on. If I suspect those, I can start giving herbs for those situations without negatively impacting my animal, unlike drugs. See those chapters if needed.

Some of the nervous system herbs can help allay some stress as well as help the animal's musculature and nervous system to relax. A cold constricted muscle will not allow as much nervous system, lymph, or blood circulation, which will compromise oxygen and nutrition flow and warmth giving blood to every cell of the animal. If they are cold body wide, they are constricted and restricted body wide. Get them warm. If they are real chilled, you can fill some plastic jugs-gallon size will work great with hot water, put a wool or other blanket over the animal and the jugs. If you are at an exhibition sometimes you can bring your jugs with a bit of cold water in them (so they don't deteriorate from just very hot water hitting the plastic container edges) and buy hot water from hot drink vendors if you don't have a hot pot or other way to get or make hot water. Some barn or event bathrooms or shower rooms have hot water, some don't. Don't let the hot jugs touch the animal and burn it, but get them under the same blanket tent. I used this one day when we lived in the North Cascade Mountains in Washington in about 17 degree Fahrenheit temperatures, and it worked like a charm.

Hot Animals

If your animal gets overheated, it is an emergency to deal with right now. An animal that stops sweating, looses coordination, or is mouth breathing can be in great danger. Sometimes your animal will have labored breathing and be standing right over their water with their head hung low and maybe their mouth open. The first thing I like to do is to get cayenne in them- really. Cayenne will encourage more sweating and will expand the vascular system so that the blood pressure is normalized, helping to support the animal out of any early stages of shock. Then I will get them to where I can start hosing them off, starting at their feet, with cool to cold water. Have a thermometer with you, and monitor their body temperature about every 5 minutes if needed. Sometimes before I get them to the hose, if it's a walk for them, the first water they get is their water bucket dumped on them. It will be warm since it's been in the barn, but it helps with some rehydration and is still cooler than air temperature, because when it is hot like that you will find me refilling waters often. As soon as you start walking them their muscle movement is going to generate more heat, so this quick water bath from their bucket helps counter that some. Eucalyptus, Rosemary and/or peppermint essential oils can be added to apple cider vinegar, shaken well, and sprayed onto the skin at the rate of 80 drops of essential oil to one quart of water. This will provide additional cooling. Peppermint tea, made hot and then chilled with ice cubes, can be drenched. Any of the nourishing herbs or teas can be made and cooled with ice and given for support such as olive leaf tea, stinging nettle, comfrey, raspberry and yarrow. Monitor them, as they will be more susceptible to heat problems after that. Keeping them on a nourishing diet year round will allow their system to tolerate temperature extremes better than they otherwise would.

I have exhibited at fairs that have been as hot as 114 Fahrenheit and many where the barns were over 100 degrees. When that happens I take every animal out of their stall or pen, whether showing problems or not, and hose them down- and myself as well. Senior animals I have hosed down three to five times in a day. I also like to run one fan per stall making sure the electrical cords are nowhere where busy goat faces can touch them and we place equipment over the cords so the public and others don't trip on the cords. Be sure as you are doing this that you also hose yourself down and are drinking ample amounts of pure (distilled is the only pure) water. I can go through two gallons over the course of a day as hot as this when showing and it will not increase my need for bathroom trips, as it's all lost in sweat. Then I also give some grapefruit juice, fresh is best of course, for electrolyte replacement due to all the sweat loss. Drink some yourself throughout the day to make sure your electrolytes stay balanced. If you are on heart medications you will not be able to use the grapefruit juice, as it may make your heart medication less effective. You will have to use commercial electrolyte products in that case. If you are on heart medication, you will need to have a backup plan for help in case the weather or work conditions cause excess strain on your heart. That type of stress on an already overstressed heart can very easily be too much for the body to take. Animals with active heart conditions that are medicated should not have grapefruit juice either, but they also, for their well being, shouldn't be exhibited with those types of threatening conditions. Please leave animals with these types of conditions at home with good care until their bodies have healed through them.

Ice can also be added to drinking water to keep it colder, helping your creature to keep their core temperature down better. Plastic water bottles can be frozen and floated in their water buckets as well. If your animal starts loosing coordination or looses consciousness you will want to be soaking them in cold water, with some ice added to the water if possible to get their core temperature down better. You can also rub some cayenne tincture along the spine, along with Lobelia inflata tincture for the stress. Another favorite stress herb is eleuthero, but I would use the cayenne and lobelia first, then the eleuthero next for additional system support. Once you get the animal to come to, some additional heart support is also in order such as hawthorn berries, flowers, or leaves tincture or Heart-E tincture. Basic nutritional herbs or cooled teas can also be supplied such as yarrow, nettle, mullein, olive leaf, dandelion, and red raspberry leaf. Make sure the animal can safely swallow before you drench these, otherwise continue to soak their body in them and give them cool nourishing tea enemas.

Eating Foreign Objects including UFF

(Unidentifiable Foreign Foods)

So you are at an event, and your creature has eaten something strange- it could be a deflated balloon (heaven forbid!), some wiring (yes, I've had that one happen), or that nice healthful fair food that your creature just stole from an innocent and now sobbing child that was walking by. Of course there are other things they may get into, but we'll go with these.

If they have ingested something that can cause a mechanical blockage in the intestine, consult a veterinarian to find out which direction they would want the item to try to go (vomit, or let it try to run through the intestinal tract). Some animals, can be encouraged to vomit it back up, especially if you can catch them within the first twenty minutes or so. If your animal is cleared for vomiting, then Lobelia inflata tincture can be given every 3 minutes until vomiting is induced. After you get the first dose in orally, while you are waiting, take 5 drops of peppermint essential oil, mix with a teaspoon of olive oil, and rub some of that on the both sides of the body just beyond the rib areas, except in young animals, over the digestive tract. Drench young animals with peppermint tea instead of using the essential oil. This will help relieve and minimize soreness to the muscles after the vomiting is complete. If they are not cleared for vomiting, then it is time to start putting olive oil, mixed with cayenne down them. The olive oil will help lubricate the intestinal tract, helping the item to pass sooner. The cayenne will increase peristaltic action of the gut also helping to move it through the intestines quicker, and will relieve any bleeding that could take place from structural damage from having the foreign item in there. For a 100 to 200 pound creature I would start with 60 cc of olive oil and a teaspoon of cayenne, mixed together. Give every hour or two as needed for the first half day. Remember to not overdo the olive oil, due to the dense nutrition. Prune or Fig juice can also be given to speed things along, as well as prunes or figs if the juice isn't available. Chickweed, slippery elm, comfrey root, drinkable aloe, and marshmallow root teas also could be given, ideally with some of the powdered herb still in them. These are all soothing to any tissue they come in contact with, and should aid in tract lubrication. I don't recommend using cathartic herbs, like senna, in these cases. If the item could cause damage to the tract, the more forceful work of an herb like senna could create additional damage to the intestinal walls. If you have to use something like that, then start at ½ the normal dose, and work up from there every 30 minutes until you get the action you need. I still prefer cayenne. Every first aid kit, glove box, purse, tool box, tackle box, backpack, saddle bag, trailer and tack trunk should have a lot of cayenne in it anyhow. This blessing is of no help if you don't have easy access to it. You will want to immediately contact your veterinarian about some items, such as nails, hardware, hard wire or similar items. Some of those may need to be surgically removed.

If they have ingested something that might be considered food but is not normal to their diet, and it was more than a couple of little bites, then you might chase it with any of the above listed demulcent or lubricating herbs, along with some ginger or peppermint for potential nausea, and some nettle or dandelion tea to help cleanse the system of the insult. See the GI tract section for information on diarrhea should that result, but ideally you are catching it fairly quick. Remember that animal systems under stress will react greater to things then they would in their home environment. As you can see, I spend most of my time near my animals when at these events to keep an eye on things, especially if the general public is attending!

If they have ingested something potentially toxic, go to the Poisoning chapter for support ideas.

Feed

Where possible, try to bring all of the feed that your animals are currently used to. Making feed changes at an event, where your creatures are already experiencing some stress, is not the best of plans. Now that I have said that, I have had to purchase hay while at fairs or shows. Find out ahead of time if there is a company servicing the event, or if you will have to drive out for additional feed or supplies. If you'll have to drive out, do your internet and/or phone research before you get there so that you have directions, prices, hours of operation, know what is available and an idea of the quality. I have sometimes hauled alfalfa pellets, which I don't normally feed, when I've thought finding additional good hay would be a problem. When storing your feed at events, bring tarps to stack it on to keep it from touching the facilities floor and then to cover it to keep it cleaner.   Also watch your grain. If weather conditions are different then your home conditions or the manner in which you store it at home, you may find that moisture or mold may become a problem. I usually just keep one or two day's worth of grain in my tack area at a time, and keep it in weather proof bins with a lid that the goats cannot open.   I like gamma seals for this, which can be rubber malleted onto regular five gallon buckets. Just in case my (or someone else's) goats get out overnight, I do not want to have an overeating accident.

Flies and Mosquitoes and Spiders, Oh My!

So you thought you left them all at home!   I find if I'm at an event that is more than a day or two long that eventually these masters of harassment will show up. Try to keep the things that lure them picked up and blotted up.   Your lunch, manure and spilled milk are all strong attractants.   Sanitizing your pen, stall, or kennel will help, as well misting lavender, eucalyptus, citronella, and/or peppermint around will help (not around felines!).   Sixty to eighty drops of essential oil choices in a one quart spray bottle filled with water and/or raw apple cider vinegar will help. Two or three tablespoons of vegetable glycerin or natural dish soap will help the oils to hang around longer.   Mosquitoes repel very easily with the citronella.   You can also spray down a sponge or rag to wipe down faces or the animal as a whole.   Remember to not use these on cats, but to instead use hydrosols or strong herb teas instead, both being water soluble nutrients that are safe with cats. If you live in a part of the country where you have spiders that are not fun to deal with,   consider using the peppermint. You can even spray your tack area if needed.   Before you get spray happy, however;   do check around with people penning near you to be sure they won't mind you spraying.   Once I have run into a person allergic to lavender.   You just never know. Ask and then with their well wishes, spray away. I wish the people that are spray happy with their chemicals would ask me before they spray those toxic things around me for my lungs and bloodstream to absorb. I also like to put a couple of drops of the pure essential oil on the top edge of my fans. As the oils drip downward they are disbursed by the fan.   Your oil or oils of choice can also be mixed in baking soda, at the rate of 12 to 15 drops per cup, mixed well, then put onto the stall, pen, or kennel floor before placing new bedding over it.

Insects Bites and Stings

These will be covered in the Poisoning chapter. We have experienced this problem from toxic bugs at shows. It's good to be prepared!

Lungs

I have already alluded to these a few times.   Remember to watch lung health at events and for a couple of weeks after you get your creatures back home. Vehicle exhaust, penning, exposure to new microbes, dirty barn air and inadequate ventilation all create special stress on the lungs.   Have you ever, at a show barn, looked at a sunbeam and seen all of the visible particulate?   That is why I really like my bottle of Eucalyptus globulus essential oil with me at events and why my animals get a dab smeared onto their nostrils every feeding time. Being proactive takes much less time than having to manage a condition. Other lung support will be discussed in the Respiratory chapter. Don't forget yourself as well!

Milk Encouragement for Milking Stock Shown Uddered Up

The stress of hauling and a show can sometimes cause a milker not want to udder up to look her best for the show.   Besides feeding kelp to encourage water consumption, here are some herbs you can try. Alfalfa, comfrey, carrots, goat's rue, fennel, fenugreek, red raspberry leaf, kelp, blessed thistle, nettle and dandelion are all herbs you can use at the Chronic dosing rate. Fir Meadow also makes a MilkMaid herb blend for this issue.   I used to milk my goats three times per day after returning home from a show for about three days in a row, to be sure they were milking at their preshow levels.   Now I just feed them MilkMaid every milking for three days. I mix it right in their kelp that I serve with their grain. That adjustment sure made my after show schedule more efficient!

Strange Water

I once had a very smart dairy goat named Melody. She was so smart that for two years she would not touch the city water that we would invariably run into at fairs. I always had to pack home water for her and if I ran out I had to go to the grocery store to look for distilled or bottled water just for the princess. I think it's safe to say that many of us know the events we attend where the water is extra bad and where it's acceptable. One fair I exhibit at has so much chlorine in the water that you can smell the fumes come off of it as you fill your buckets! Ekes. So what's a person to do? Here are some ideas…

Pack your own water from home or purchase distilled water. For some of you that will be totally feasible, for people like me, showing 5 to 35 goats depending on the year and event, it's not feasible. I wish it were!

As much as I don't prefer baking soda, I will use it if needed to neutralize the chlorine in event waters. It works quite well for that. Then I make sure I double to triple their normal serving of kelp with added herbs each feeding or milking, to help compensate for the tissue mineral loss that the soda will cause. I continue the additional kelp for one day for every day gone from home beyond events to be sure their minerals are topped off. So, for example, if we are gone for 5 days then I will give them extra kelp for five days once we've reached home.

If the problem is water flavor more than chlorine, then you can add some black strap unsulphured molasses to some hot water, mix well, then add that to the buckets. That will give them some extra B vitamins for stress support, as well as more minerals. One can also make strong herb teas, like raspberry, and add those to water. Try to have your animals used to your herb of choice at home before you want them to drink it away from home.

Feeding additional kelp will help encourage more water consumption. Many animals, especially those not used to traveling need the additional encouragement to drink well away from home.

Remember your skin pinch test homework I gave you to learn from your vet or an experienced breeder. Events are a good time to do a once or twice daily pinch test to be sure your special animal is staying well hydrated.

Stress

For most animals traveling, stress will be a factor. If you have an animal that is very used to traveling, they are still breathing freeway fumes, subjected often to temperature swings, different scenery, different schedule, different neighbors, different scents and noises, often long days, different lighting at night, etcetera. A level headed animal may not show outward signs of stress, but I expect that inwardly and immune system wise, stress will still be there at some level.

Cayenne, catnip, nutritional yeast, and molasses are all great sources of B complex vitamins, which support the nervous system. Under stress, and under toxic stress, these vitamins are consumed in much greater amounts than normal. Support in this area will be greatly appreciated by your creature. Eleuthero (Siberian ginseng), is another nice system support herb when under stress. Remember cleansing herbs to back out the toxic fuel exposure from being on the road or in the airport.

There are several nice choices for helping an animal to relax. Keeping them warm by blanketing them if it is cool out helps; as does giving them a drink of warm water with added black strap molasses. Massages and scratching itchy spots, and feeding favorite treats can help relax them. If they are used to a certain essential oil smell at home, especially lavender, rose geranium, or clary sage, then taking that with you and spraying it on them, diluted of course, assists them. Bach's Rescue Remedy, lavender tea or diluted essential oil, scullcap, valerian, ladies slipper, hops strobiles (not for canines), and lobelia are all nice. Fir Meadow's Mel-O, as well as Dr. Christopher's Mind Trac are products one can consider if wanted. You can also take hot ginger tea, soak a towel in it, and lie that over the loins of your creature to help the back muscles to relax which in turn may help the whole animal to relax. Lavender and the other herbs can be used the same way as well. Ginger or peppermint tea will help a stressed stomach relax.

Remember that the day or days that your animal is under additional stress, besides their B vitamin support, they will also need additional mineral support. Stress, including stress from hard performance, or heavy milking, burns minerals at a much faster rate, so mineral supplementation is extremely important. Don't forget about yourself in this suggestion.

Upset Digestive Tract

Stress, feed they aren't used to, and consuming things they shouldn't, all can lead to an upset stomach or intestinal tract. Sometimes just licking a stall wall or fencing can introduce some microbes to wreak havoc with your creature.

Diarrhea can have microbial, parasite, chemical, and stress causes. Parasites will be covered in a following chapter, just remember that the stress of hauling and eventing or showing can allow them to more easily take advantage of your animal. For non parasite caused diarrhea I've had great success with GI Soother herb mix by Fir Meadow. This mix also is welcomed support in coccidia conditions, which can flair up with show stress. Cayenne, ginger, cinnamon, slippery elm, blackberry leaves or root, strawberry leaves, or raspberry leaves can all be of assistance, depending on the cause. Feed hourly at your event until the condition improves. The first one to three doses can be double or triple the normal dose. If the condition doesn't start improving within two hours consider adding more herbal variety, as well as trying to ascertain the cause of the diarrhea. If you are foraging for herbs on the grounds, remember to pick those away from roads, away from railroad tracks and chemical fertilization, or you might compound your problems.

If you believe stress to be the cause, then address it as per the stress section in this chapter, along with the GI tract herbs.

If you believe something toxic is involved including a possible problem with feed you just purchased, then the Poisonings chapter will have more information for you.

For microbial challenges such as in clostridium problems picked up from the soil, or other common airborne barn bacteria, the GI tract herbs along with antiseptic

The Accessible Pet, Equine and Livestock Herbal

herbs such as goldenseal, echinacea, garlic, cayenne, myrrh, and Oregon grape root are helpful. Usnea (pronounced oos-nee-uh') tincture can also be used. Usnea is a moss/lichen that grows in temperate parts of the world. I love seeing Usnea growing because it can only grow in fairly clean air situations, so it is a good barometer for air health in the location. Fir Meadow has a ClostridEaze product that is nice support in these issues, combining GI tract, antiseptic, and organ support herbs. Or HerBiotic can be used with GI Soother.

Impactions in the intestines caused by eating too much dry matter such as hay or bedding, without consuming enough water needs to be addressed fast.   Walking your animal along with the oral olive oil and cayenne mixes will give support to try to get the matter moving again. Fir Meadow's Better Bowels or the Dr. Christopher Lower Bowel formula can be given to help stimulate the bowels to move. I would start at triple dose calibrated to your creature's weight. Enemas given of lubricating teas like slippery elm, some olive oil, marshmallow, chia seed tea, fresh ground flax tea, or hollyhock root can be given to try and encourage movement and moisturizing from the 'south' end.   See the Eating Foreign Objects section earlier in this chapter for more ideas.   In this case I would consider increasing the amount of cayenne by double.   Also doing the peppermint essential oil diluted with olive oil externally on the intestinal region to help the body ease some pain would be desirable.

259

Chapter 12- Poisonings

Animal Poison Control, $65 for the call in 2010, 1-888-436-4435

Pet Poison Control, $35 for the call in 2011, 1-800-213-6680

Poisonings can come in many forms.   Coming into contact with chemical fertilizer, herbicides, or pesticides is somewhat common.   Ingesting paint chips off of barn or building walls may present a lead danger.   Poisonous plants, bugs, and snakes are yet another problem. Mold from moldy feed, sunflower seeds, or hay will cause trouble with the liver.   Ingestion of processed feeds that we accidentally contaminated by another chemical or fertilizer in a feed mill can also take out a liver and/or kidneys quickly.   Over exposure to medications including chemical dewormers also can cause liver, kidney, GI and other damage.

When assessing your creature you might look for several things.   If it is plant or chemical related, you may have a reduction in body temperature.   If venomous creature related, you may have a rise in temperature.   In any situation the animal may be listless or withdrawn.   There may be vomiting or vomit or foam at the lips.   Once the toxin has been in the animal for usually at least two hours,   diarrhea may occur, and the diarrhea may be very liquid.   Labored breathing may show up if prunus species wilting leaves are ingested.   If it is a mold, and it has been gradually accumulating, then there may a slow progression through symptoms.   If are being attacked, the animal may be caving in at the loin area due to pain or show blood in their urine.   They may or may not give you a distress cry. These problems can affect an entire herd, just a few animals, or just one depending on rate or route of exposure, previous toxic load of the animal, and individual constitutional strength.

Look for anything in the way of potential evidence to try and determine the cause of the poisoning.   Has a neighbor sprayed along a fence line?   Did the county come by and spray along the road? Are there new plants you haven't identified in your pasture?   Did someone feed the herd lawn clippings containing poisonous plant material or mushrooms or mold if it sat around?   Check your hay and grain.   Are some of your animals picking through it, sending you a red flag to inspect it

The Accessible Pet, Equine and Livestock Herbal

carefully to see if there is a problem?   Did the wind blow leaves or foliage into the pasture, either in small or large amounts? Did someone feed your animals tree and bush prunings, of which some could have been toxic? Included, but not limited to leaves of prunus species (fruit with pits in them such as cherry and peach tree leaves), rhododendron, azalea, oleander, laurel, or yew?   This can be a real problem for goat owners due to the fallacy that people think that goats can eat anything.   For cow owners, have you been feeding moldy 'feeder hay'?   This is a very common use of waste hay.   That cow may be large, so they can tolerate it unseen by you for awhile, but at some point the toxic accumulation to the liver will become too great.   Use wisdom.   Is it a bad year for spiders, bees, snakes? Look for swellings, bites, or sting marks or 'cores'.   Arriving to some conclusion will help you determine better what to do next. Pray.   I've had God guide me right to the problem when I've asked Him for help.   He loves your creature even more then you do, He'll help if you ask Him.

Chemicals

For chemical ingestion, whether it's a grooming product, herbicide, stall lime, pesticide, paint, or other, it is good to contact your veterinarian and/or poison control to find out if this is a toxin that you want to try to have vomited out.   They also may recommend diluting with milk (raw goat milk from healthy goats if possible), or water, or some olive oil.   Do NOT attempt to dilute any poison without professional advice, as using the wrong dilutant can cause another chemical reaction and this is not the time for a chemistry experiment.   Also, per your veterinarian, some animals are better to work with to try to get them to vomit than others.   Usually the vomit rule is only if you catch them within 20 minutes of ingesting whatever.   After that it is often beyond the stomach, unless it is a ruminant.   Again, get some professional veterinarian advice.   I listed two numbers at the top of this page that are 24 hour emergency numbers.   Have your credit card ready and they can help you immediately with the correct information.

Of course there are alternative things you can do to support your animal AFTER you get advice from poison control.   You can use activated charcoal and calibrate the amount to your animal size.   I would increase the dose stated on the bottle fivefold for the first oral dose. Note that adult humans, if using a human product, average about 150 pounds for the sake of labeling dosage. The charcoal will help absorb the toxins. Watch your clock and then twenty minutes after that, or right away if you don't have charcoal, you can follow with herbs. Don't give the herbs with the charcoal or it will absorb the nutrients in them that you want the GI tract to have. I would be using demulcent herbs to soothe the digestive tract, such as drinkable aloe, marshmallow root, chia, chickweed, psyllium, just ground flax seeds, olive oil, mallow leaves or root, hollyhock leaves or root or slippery elm bark. Any of the facial clays, such as bentonite or green can be used also to help encourage the absorption of the toxins, but mix the clay with some herbs half and half to keep it moving through the alimentary canal (digestive tract from mouth to anus).

Cayenne can be given after the herbs, along with other peristaltic action herbs such as cloves, cascara sagrada (use smaller amounts or mix it half and half with ginger root powder), prickly ash, or turkey rhubarb. Senna can be used as well, but I try to avoid this herb as it is habit forming and too much can cause some severe cramping. Your animal is going to be going through enough without that added stress. Especially avoid it with pregnant stock. With these your hope is to move the toxins out faster to elimination. Better Bowels by Fir Meadow also can be used if you have this on hand. Dr. Christopher's Lower Bowel Formula can be used also. Liver, kidney, and blood cleaning herbs should also be given afterwards. Start at ½ doses for a pregnant animal and work slower, if they are not pregnant then double or triple dose. Some favorites include wormwood, dandelion, and milk thistle for the liver and dandelion, uva ursi, citrus, grapes (not for dogs), and stinging nettle for the kidneys. Some nice blood cleaners include burdock root, raspberry, stinging nettle, red clover, yarrow and chaparral. Make sure your creature stays hydrated. At any time they become shocky, administer oral cayenne. Try to keep them at room temperature, quiet and in a shaded or darker area to reduce stress on their nervous system and keep them blanketed if they look distressed. Also give B vitamin support via black strap molasses, cayenne, nutritional yeast, or catnip. Give needed herbs hourly. Products that can be given are Fir Meadow's Fresh Start and Blood and Cells formula or ClostridEaze or DTox. Dr. Christopher's Blood Stream formula, Liver, and Kidney formulas can also come in handy.

The Accessible Pet, Equine and Livestock Herbal

Here is how I worked myself through a recent MSG poisoning for a chemical poisoning story. I was eating at an event that evidently used MSG liberally. My system, being fairly clean, absorbs much more of any chemical than the standard American with a gunked in digestive tract. The symptoms I get from this excitotoxin are listed below. I share this so you have an idea of some of the things your animal might feel when experiencing a chemical overdose (or chemical dewormer for that fact). I had a queasy stomach, racing heart (which only happens if I get into MSG), hyper and fragmented thinking, rising body temperature, and a feeling of being quite high. It also significantly slowed down my peristalsis. In an animal I will add fear to that list. I knew what was going on so I wasn't fearful. They won't know what's going on.

First I fished out my cayenne tincture and took a double dose (2 droppers full) of that to allow my body to stabilize my heart action. It worked within a minute. I continued that every 10 to 15 minutes the first hour as needed, then every 30 to 60 minutes after that for the remainder of the evening. Thankfully I had some herbs with me for liver and kidney cleansing, and I took a quadruple dose of those. I also took a double dose of bowel products. Then I went to the kitchen where I was able to get two fresh lemons. I squeezed the first one into a cup with some water and drank it to attempt to break down the toxin faster. I followed that by a second lemon in water an hour later. After that I slowly drank some nice herbal teas. Raspberry would have been a good choice, but I didn't have access to it. Dandelion, nettle and burdock would have been nice. Since I didn't have those a few hours later I took an additional double dose of the liver/kidney product, followed by a double dose the following morning, and then back to 3 times per day at normal dose. I was feeling fairly normal in about 1 ½ hours after first symptoms. I normally have symptoms for several hours before they begin to recede, with me being wiped out the following day. My eyes were still a little dilated the second day, and I was not at full energy level, but quite good for what I went through. The first day my liver reflex on my hand was quite puffy over a large area, so I worked that for about two minutes to also encourage toxin dumping. The second day my liver reflex was back to normal. Needless to say, this gives you a working model and some insight as to what our animals may be feeling when they get exposed to chemicals in quantity that would be uppers or excitotoxins. I did not have access to ginger, which I would have gladly taken to help my body reduce nausea.

I very recently ended up in MSG again from consuming some food at a church potluck. Let me tell you, if someone uses a spice packet in their concoction or a store bought regular brand dressing and mixes in their food I can be caught off guard at times. It may be home made but it's definitely not 'from scratch'. I did not have my herb first aid kit with me so I looked in the refrigerator for anything that might aid me. There was some moderate heat from peppers Mexican sauce. No lemons or limes or related juices. I put about ½ cup of that sauce in a cup of water and drank it. I was amazed. Even with that diluted store bought product containing 'red peppers' with some heat, I started getting results pretty quickly as my heart and mind starting coming back in line and my nausea & pain slowly started to dissipate. I'm thinking that any hot herb may give me a similar result in a pinch. Let me know if you have to try something different and find results. Obviously it's better to be prepared. From now on I'll be a 'Limey" and keep some limes and my cayenne tincture in my purse.

Vaccination/medication overdoses can be handled like my MSG overdose. In place of lemon juice, raw apple cider vinegar at 60 cc's for the first dose for a 100 to 200 pound animal followed by 30 cc doses afterwards can be used in place of the lemon juice. Remember to cut the vinegar with another liquid so that they don't choke or gag on it. Raw healthy goat milk, carrot juice, real fruit juices or water would all work. I would also add eleuthero root or ginger root to help compensate for the stress.

Contaminated Hay

If the hay is contaminated with mold or chemicals, please see those sections in this chapter.

Blister beetles are a narrow elongated dark to black beetle that can be found at times in alfalfa hay. Be very cautious of these; even just a few eaten can be lethal. Do NOT handle the beetles without protection, as toxins can be absorbed through skin as well. If you suspect a beetle poisoning, they will cause excruciating blisters inside of the entire digestive tract.   My focus in these events would be to administer activated charcoal or clays as mentioned in the chemical poisoning, followed by the demulcent herbs listed afterwards to try and soothe the damaged and inflamed areas. Ginger can be added to the demulcent herbs to help counter any possible nausea.   Then of course organ support herbs to start cleaning the toxins out of them. Fir Meadow's GI Soother and Fresh Start can also be used.

Watch your animal for shock, administer 40,000 heat unit cayenne if needed- which will not damage the blistered tissue, but be sure you dilute it with water to minimize the heat.   Manage pain with a combination of the soothing demulcent herbs along with mullein leaf or flowers.   The cayenne will also help with the pain.   Lemon and/or lime will help the body break down toxins. Remember to carefully inspect the remainder of your hay and remove any hay that is infested. Check hay that is still in feeders and remove it if any beetles are found. Look on the ground, in feeders, and under feeders for beetles or remains and remove from stock areas. You don't want your stock to even be able to lie on them. Keep a few in case a lab test is requested.   Inform your hay farmer or dealer so that they know there is a problem.   A good dealer or farmer will replace the hay and pay for lab work on the beetles to ascertain the species.   Your veterinarian will know where to have lab work done.

If you believe that the hay was sprayed and it is causing a problem, use the herb plan above for chemicals.   Notify your hay dealer and keep some hay for a lab sample if needed.   Make sure you always retain some of the sample in case something happens to the first sample.

Enterotoxemia

Enterotoxemia or "overeaters' as it is sometimes called,   can be caused by Clostridium bacteria, picked up from the soil, or from eating too much of a feed, causing a toxic response as the beneficial flora die off en mass in the intestines. The clostridiums can turn the kidneys into a pulpy mass, and soil borne clostridiums can hemorrhage the intestines.

If you know that an animal has gotten into too much of something, whether your herd had a barn party in the feed area, or you saw a tree drop a lot of leaves in the pasture, I wouldn't wait to see if it progresses into the diarrhea and listlessness. I'd start them on herbs immediately! For either of these problems, both of which we have experienced in our herd, herbs such as cayenne, slippery elm, and ginger along with kidney support herbs like dandelion, uva ursi, and nettle, and cleansing herbs to remove toxins like chaparral, yarrow, raspberry, and red clover are good body support. I like using kelp and Better Daze in this situation for additional supplemental support. Fir Meadow's GI Soother and Fresh Start or even KetoMix can be used or ClostridEaze. Dworm BWW has been used at higher doses in a pinch.

Inducing Vomiting

If your veterinarian or poison control has given you the clearance to start vomiting, Lobelia inflata can be used. The tincture is better than a tea here, as the tincture is more concentrated. If you were able to get clay or activated charcoal into your animal beforehand; that may help absorb some of the toxins before they travel further into digestive tract. I would give a full dose (a regular herb full dose, which will usually be double the Lobelia dosage) orally to your creature every five minutes until vomiting commences. Once you have the first dose in them, as mentioned earlier in this book, you will want to take your peppermint essential oil (not for young stock), take 5 drops per teaspoon of olive oil, and rub that onto the intestinal areas and rib areas to help alleviate any potential for soreness from heaving. It too, will help some with nausea. For young stock drench peppermint tea instead. Cayenne also can be used in large doses, again every 5 minutes, to encourage vomiting. Do NOT use poke root as an emetic (vomit inducer). Its action can be counted on, but it is far too slow. It can take hours to see what the final effect is of the amount of poke you have used, so there is no way to gauge a correct amount. Also, we need herbs that will work quickly in this situation. Once done, be ready to carefully hydrate your animal with some warm black strap molasses water and maybe some electrolytes too such as fresh grapefruit juice, diluted in this case as the GI tract will be tender. You can put some in your molasses water if you like. A weak ginger tea can be given to help settle any nausea and you can give slippery elm tea or gruel to settle the stomach and soothe. Offering warm raw honey and or warm oat water is a gentle nourishing support. GI Soother can also be used. You can give some cool (not cold) nourishing tea enemas, such as yarrow, nettle, raspberry, or dandelion to help them hydrate faster. Know that the first enemas will probably be flushed back out. If they are cool, the anal area is more likely to contract and hold it in. You can also have their rear end elevated higher than their withers/shoulders by having them stand their rear legs on something or placing something under if them if they are lying down, such as flakes of straw with a blanket over them. On oral use, it is better to give a little bit of fluid, or fluid and herb mix, every few minutes then it is to give a large amount just to have them regurgitate it. If they had diarrhea, don't forget to pinch test their skin to check their hydration level, along with supplying electrolytes like fresh juiced grapefruit. If they are having trouble holding anything down afterwards, resort to small doses such as just one teaspoon (for a goat) every 5 minutes of warm slippery elm, chia, or fresh ground flax seed, or oat teas and slowly increase the amount as you make progress on their not vomiting things back up. A small amount of soothing olive oil can also be drenched with a small amount of one of the above soothing herbs mixed in if wanted.

Insect Bites and Stings and Snake Bites

Whether it is bees, spiders, snakes, scorpions or some other venomous creature, we will handle all of these in the same manner. First, be sure your animal is not shocky, if it is, you know by now that cayenne is your herb of choice. However, along with that cayenne you are going to add echinacea. If you have a tincture you will give 60 cc's or two ounces right away to your 100 to 200 pound sized creature. I would continue to use the tincture at the rate of 30 cc or one ounce every hour afterwards for several hours, then 3 to 4 times per day after that for a few days as needed. If you don't have a tincture, I would very quickly tea 1 tablespoon of powered herb root in 30 cc's of hot water for that 100 to 200 pound animal, and then drench as soon as it cools some. Echinacea will actually help maintain the integrity of the cells in your creature, decreasing the toxin's abilities to break those cells down. Its ability to support a creature during exposure to creature toxins can verge on the miraculous. Liver, kidney, and blood cleaning herbs should all be considered and started a few minutes after the cayenne and echinacea are in.   Fir Meadow makes a product called DVenom. I have successfully used that product now on three black widow bites to dairy goats. Two of those bites were sustained about 18 hours apart at a show to the same goat! A salve or poultice containing plantain should be applied to the bite or sting area; immediately after the first oral herbs have been given.   These will help draw the toxins out via the damaged area.   Dr. Christopher's Sting and Bites salve or Fir Meadow's DBug salve are nice choices. They also will help with swelling and itching if used right away. Put it on thickly, and reapply until the tissue appears normal color and size. If there are any muscle spasms, seizures, or tight muscles such as abdominal, administer Lobelia inflata tincture orally. You can also spread some tincture along the area of cramping and gently smooth it onto the skin. If the animal is having seizures, remember to approach it from the backside and not the legs or mouth/head/neck areas to prevent accidentally getting struck.   Once seizures stop you might put a few drops of lobelia tincture into the ears of the animal, and onto the brain stem area. Remember to stay behind the animal, away from any potential swinging legs or a head.

If possible, try to find out what it was that caused the problem.   If it was a snake, you may have to go on a snake hunt. You ought to find two fang marks at the area of greatest swelling if it was a snake. If it was a spider or bee, see if there is a nest or area that is accumulating them, including under feeders. For bees you will find a single core mark per sting and for spiders you will find two tiny fang marks side by side, if you can find them. Two of our black widow problems were caused by udder bites, so I think in those cases the does laid right on them as the spiders were in or walking across the bedding. Just so you know, udder bites can be fatal due to the amount of blood being moved through the mammary gland, so they are nothing to ignore. In the black widow cases I have noticed these following conditions. The animal might be sweaty.   It may be arched at the loin from abdominal cramping. It will be off of feed if it's been a few hours.   There may be swelling at the bite site and it may be hot.   If it's an udder than has been bitten, the swelling will spread to the other half or quarter if it is near enough the other side. It won't stay just to one section as it would in the case of a mastitis problem.   You may have to shave udder hair to find a fresh bite site. Look for a bit of redness. A doe we had, that was bitten several years ago, started milking blood and serum in just hours from the half that was bitten, and I spent a week working with her to get her over the trauma, with us nearly losing her at one point. This was before I knew what I know now about herbs. My last two that have been bitten were back to visible normal in three hours, other than the point of swelling which in both cases took three days, even in the doe that was bitten twice not quite a day apart. In fact that doe was shown just two days later, getting a 12th place at the national show with an even udder! Feeling well enough to look her best after two bites I do not believe would have been possible without the herbs. It would have been more likely that I would have been burying her. Neither of these two does started milking blood and serum. Their milk stayed normal and the udder looked and felt normal after the three days. This was even though they were obviously very sick and fevered goats when I found them. If an udder bite is sustained, you can look at the mastitis section and use some of those herbal methods to head off any potential mastitis problems from the actual bite wound allowing bacteria to enter the udder. Always keep some of these herbs on hand in your first aid kit at home and on the road, as you want to be able to respond to these issues quickly if they happen. Don't forget that liver and kidney and blood cleansing are a must after an incident like this so that there is no toxic buildup in the system. Any toxic buildup could allow for a larger reaction should the animal be stung or bitten again in the future. That is the same reason why some people become allergic to bees later in life as they accumulate bee venom. I used to be one of those. Used to bee…

See the peppermint section below to reduce some pests. Also keeping white walls in your barn, kennel, and stall areas reduces bug and possibly snake populations. They generally like to hide in natural and wood colors and will avoid white, as it exposes them to their predators. Now you know why farm buildings often were whitewashed.

Moldy Feed

I have mentioned a bit about this before, in the Supplements chapter. Remember that even that 'dust' will often be a mold, not dust. Greying or blackish colors often are a mold problem as well. Again, see the Hay and Grain sections of the

Supplements chapter for how to look for mold. Mold is a direct enemy to the liver, so liver support is of utmost importance. When I have seen the problem here; I will usually have an animal that picks at feed, goes off feed, and starts to have diarrhea. Milk thistle, dandelion, and wormwood are some of my favorite liver support herbs. I personally use Fresh Start by Fir Meadow when I run into this problem. Thankfully I seldom see it here. I have had people use DWorm W or BWW when they've had this problem, but had no Fresh Start on hand. It takes higher doses, but has helped the body clear out the problem.

Listeria bacteria harbor in the soil and can be a byproduct of mold formation in hay or silage that was not properly put up or stored. Dairy inspectors will find it nearly every single time on the boots used to walk around on the dairy or in the product handling rooms if they take a sample on the boots. I mention it here just so you realize how common listeriosis is in the soil. Therefore; don't be puzzled if you show up with a problem at some point. We'll discuss this problem more in the Nervous system and Brain chapters.

Mold can quickly use up vitamins in the digestive tract, especially B1 (thiamine). By now possibly you can name your Vitamin B support herb friends yourself, but to remind you that I like cayenne, catnip, nutritional yeast, peppermint and black strap molasses. You will want to give these every 15 to 30 minutes for the first hour or two and then hourly the first day if you have symptoms. This problem can result in a condition called 'polioencephalmalacea' or 'polio' for short which is not the same condition as polio in humans. An animal not corrected from this problem will go down, at some point lose their vision, have convulsions, and die. If it is polio, and you are getting enough herbs down them, they will turn around fast. Don't let that fool you. Keep dosing them for a full day after they improve to stay ahead of it in case some of the toxins that caused the problem are still breaking down in the rumen and burning up more thiamine. All of this is to say to not ignore their needs for thiamine if they have been around mold! It is possible for them to have listeriosis and polio simultaneously. Better to give the herbs ahead if you find they have been into mold then to wait for a problem as both of these are fatal if unattended to.

The Accessible Pet, Equine and Livestock Herbal

Over Medicated

There are several ways your creature can become overmedicated. They can be slowly overmedicated over time, have too many medications at a time, too much of one medication and inherited medication at conception and during development in the womb. Even overzealous use of your non chemical essential oils can overwhelm the liver. I once had a friend called that had accidentally given two bo-se vaccinations to the same animal while doing a group of them, which can be lethal with that amount of overdose. Remember that as the FDA approves a drug for use there are no tests done nor statistics collected for how it will interact with other drugs or chemicals, such as grooming products in the system, yet many times drugs and chemical products will be used in combination. For example, one might chemically deworm their animal while it's wearing its flea collar right after a bath with a medicated shampoo. Now let's add that this same pet may be on a prescription. I think you get the idea.

Your cleanses are your best friends here, along with digestive tract soothers. See the Liver, Kidney, Blood and Digestive tract chapters, as all need to be considered. As long as the animal is still alive you can see if you have enough time to bring them through it. Don't give up. Start with the more gentle herbs first, then move into larger doses and stronger herbs as your creature gains strength. Remember to keep them warm and to give some loving attention if they will tolerate it. Ginger or other soothing demulcent herbs in case the GI tract is nauseated will help them relax.

If this is an acute poisoning such as in an overdose or your animal suddenly falls quiet ill after being subjected to several chemicals such as the example situation above, call one of the poison control numbers at the beginning of this chapter immediately. Find out if you can use lemon (make sure it isn't contraindicated – against indication) in your situation and squeeze a fresh lemon or lime and get 1 tsp down a small pet immediately. You want stronger tasting lemons; the mild varieties will not do as well. If you have a milder variety, you will want to double the suggested doses. For 20 to 35 pound creatures use ½ tablespoon; for 35 to 100 pounders 1 tablespoon, for 100 to 200 pounds 2 to 4 tablespoons, etcetera. A 1000 pound horse may require a full cup which may be about 4 lemons. Then follow up at ½ dose every 15 minutes the first hour, and then ¼ to ½ dose per hour that day based on what you are seeing in your animals attitude and ability. The lemon will help break down most toxins, but will not help as much on assisting the body in damage repair to the organs. Using a product like Fir Meadow's DTox herb mix will help the body do that. Or choose from several liver, kidney, and cell support herbs for a few weeks.

Peppermint- Mentha piperita

This seems like a strange place for me to slip in an herb even though this is an herbal, doesn't it? Have you ever wondered why old farmsteads often have peppermint planted around the barn, milking areas, farm houses, etcetera? I'll let you in on our forefathers' secret. Mice, ants and spiders hate peppermint. So much so that they will pack their bags and leave if ample peppermint is around. That reduces disease carrier and bite problems. It may work on other bugs around, but those are the only documented pests I have seen and used it with. Peppermint essential oil can also be dabbed straight onto real cotton balls and put around in places (where your stock doesn't have access to trying to eat them) to ask the vermin to leave. You can drop them into mouse holes and then refill the hole. Under counters and on windowsills are other good choices. Many bugs, including some flies, and moths, don't like lavender, so you can use that as well. Lavender also reduces mold problems, being antifungal, so dried lavender flower buds can be mixed in your grain if you are in a humid or wet winter area. You can leave them in and feed the lavender buds right along with the grain. Peppermint essential oil can be added to your stable baking soda blend if some of these pests are a problem before you rebed. However, the peppermint won't stay around very long it's quite volatile, which is why the tea smells so good as it wafts away quickly. This is why it is good to have peppermint plants growing around your farm. Stick with the medicinal plant, Mentha piperita, as once you get into the apple mints and other types you lose the strength you are looking for. Peppermint plants are also safe to have around your feline friends while the essential oil will not be.

Poisonous Plants

If at all possible try to identify the plant you are working with, as a wide range of symptoms and chemicals can come into play here. I will mention a few common ones to give you an idea of how to work with these varying types of problems. For all of them I would be giving organ cleanses, especially the liver; along with working the situation as if it was a chemical or medication poisoning, as mentioned above. I'll make a few notes below though to stimulate your thinking. In all of these, the faster you catch them the more likely you will have a favorable result. Keep herbs needed on hand if you know you have some of these plants around, or better yet, get rid of the plants if that is possible. When we moved to our current farm there were four rhododendrons here. I love rhododendrons and azaleas too, but I love the safety of my goats more. So we ripped them out. Call poison control and try to find out the action of the plant involved, and that will give you further direction. As always, contact your vet and see if it would be appropriate for you can encourage vomiting in that situation.

Toadstools or mushroom poisonings do happen with livestock and pets. The most common way they ingest these is for someone to give them lawn trimmings that have mushrooms mixed in them. Young animals may sample a strange new plant growing in their pasture or yard. Most mushrooms are very active right after a rain, so if problem ones are an issue where you live you might walk your pastures, if that is practical, and look for new ones to remove. Wormwood and milk thistle work very well in these situations. Fresh Start by Fir Meadow also works well. DVenom could be used, but DTox by Fir Meadow is targeted especially for support in toxic plant consumption. DWorm BWW and W have been used in larger dosages, but are not as ideal as the other blends.

Horsetail is not a poisonous plant; we use it all of the time for its silica content enabling better calcium absorption. Now having said that, horsetail eaten whole can cause serious life threatening mechanical damage to a horse's digestive tract and perhaps other simple stomached animals. If you have horses, this is a plant to keep out of the pasture. I did have a horse that would eat this when it was around. Due to the mechanical nature of the herb, the main focus will be demulcent herbs like marshmallow root, comfrey root, mullein leave, slippery elm, psyllium, drinkable aloe (NOT the gel sunburn products and not fresh from the leaf which contains a purgative), chickweed, flax oil, and olive oil. Cayenne can be added for support in the case of any hemorrhaging of tissue or shock. Fir Meadow's GI Soother can be used also for support.

Poison hemlock is kind of a parsley looking plant from the parsley family that prefers moist areas. I find it here abundantly in the springtime. Its main identifying feature is a green, hollow, smooth, vascular stem with purple streaking, or spotting on the lower stem, depending on your local variety. It has an obnoxious sort of mousy smell as well. White umbel flowers and finely cut delicate leaves. As pretty as it is, this is no plant to mess with, as all parts are extremely poisonous at any stage including dried. Socrates can vouch for that! This herb slowly reduces nervous system ability as it paralyzes its victim, shutting down all of the body organs and processes. I got into quite a patch of it last year; grubbing it out behind my barn. I had on long jeans, long sleeves, and leather gloves. Yet after awhile of pulling it out I started getting nervous system tics on my cheek and feeling woozy. As I was weeding it out I could smell ample amounts of its volatile oils (essential oils) rising in the air. Of course, what was I doing? Breathing it in where it had instant access to my bloodstream! So off to the house I went where I slammed a large dose of cayenne to punch my nervous system back up. Then I took large doses of the powdered herbs mixed with distilled water that would be in DTox while I was waiting on my DTox tea to steep. I did not return back to the patch that day, but continued with cleansing and resting as well as laundering the clothing that was also soaking in the volatile or essential oils. So, should I decide to tackle that patch again next year, it will have to be with a respirator and face mask on! Remember this with your stock-cayenne first, and then a mix of herbs mentioned for detoxifying such as wormwood, nettle, milk thistle, dandelion, chaparral, red clover, etc. Make sure you cover the liver, kidneys, and blood. DTox has been a good friend! I had a similar reaction to the very poisonous baneberry a couple of years ago, when some of the juice from the berries got on my hands from cleaning a friend's vehicle of a few crushed berries that I didn't want to risk children getting into. Cayenne tincture pulled me right out of it that time too. Then I was able to start cleansing later that day when I gained access to herbs. Do not forget about ample water as part of your cleansing program.

The Accessible Pet, Equine and Livestock Herbal

Yew will not usually give you an opportunity to use an herb plan. Horses have been found dead from yew poisoning after just a mouthful, with needles still in their mouths. It stops the heart. If there was any chance to save them, I would go just as I would with chemical poisonings WITHOUT ANY USE OF CAYENNE which would run the toxin involved straight to the heart. The reason I mention yew is that it is a popular ornamental fine needled shrub to tree that I have even seen displayed at fairgrounds as some of the pretty potted plants surrounding livestock show rings! Learn what this plant looks like and keep your stock and children away from it. If you have it growing at your farm, consider uprooting and disposing of it. It's just not worth it, as beautiful as it is.

Tansy tends to grow in waste areas, roadsides and pastures, and sometimes is used as a fly repellant. Bright yellow flowers make this a cheerful looking plant. Don't let it draw you in. The very, very high thujone content of this herb can take out a liver ever so quickly and is something that horses might ingest if it is around, especially those lower on the feed pecking order. This plant, though available as an essential oil, is just too dangerous to use. It blows my mind that it is even available in that form. I have counseled people through tansy poisoning in horses with very good results. Depending on the level of damage it can take a year for their lab work on their liver to return to normal. The good news though is that it CAN return to normal! Milk thistle has been very helpful, as is dandelion. As serious as this is, my clients have always used Fresh Start for this situation, sometimes supplemented with Better Daze for additional system support or pick some of your favorite supplements from that chapter. As long as your animal is still alive it is not too late to start! Go for it and see if you can get ahead of the damage. I had one mini donkey client this past year whose veterinarian had given it two days to live due to 'irreparable' liver damage. Three months after that while at an event I got some feedback that he was still with us and was doing well. That's why I do this.

Braken or brake fern accumulates toxins in the animal and with daily consumption can become symptomatic within a month. All parts of the plant are poisonous. This is a plant that you want to keep weeded out of your pastures. I had a horse that would seek this out; even on a trail ride he'd be trying to grab them! Evidently it is a habit forming plant, as the animals possibly get some kind of endorphin response to it. Hemorrhaging causing anemia, carcinogenic problems, and thiamine deficiency along with thiamine deficiency blindness are problems caused by this plant to the point of causing fatalities. Knowing those things, herbally, cayenne will be a good friend, as well as GI tract demulcents, and liver, kidney, and blood cleansing herbs. Sounds like I say the same thing a lot, doesn't it? If it does, then you are a good student with a good memory! Herbs work in patterns for systems. We'll address that in part two of this book. If you find your animals have been into bracken fern, don't wait for symptoms; start them on an herb plan today. I've heard sad stories about people that waited too long to help their barn buddies.

Prunus species trees and shrubs such as cherry, choke cherry, apricot, plum, prune, peach, and any wild versions of this list. Do you notice a pattern with these plants? These are all plants that contain a pit within the fruit. Can you think of another plant for the list? How about nectarines and the other cot types of fruits? They can also be ornamental trees, like a flowering plum we have at the beginning of our driveway. Please note that your apples and pears are safe as long as your creatures can't gorge on them. The problem from these plants comes when your animals come into contact with leaves in any stage of wilt before fully wilted. A branch may break and fall into the pen, someone may feed pruned branches from these plants, or the fall wind may blow a bunch of these leaves into your pens or pasture. When we moved to our existing farm, it was with great sadness that my husband and I removed a full grown productive plum and also a mature cherry tree from right next to our pasture. We simply did not want to experience any potential problems. The leaves, when wilting, release a free form cyanide that ties up the oxygen in the blood stream. Any labored breathing, mouth breathing, or anemia when looking inside the eyelid would tip me off to who is having the problems. The ideal support for this problem would be to get a hold of any oxygen tank from anyone that welds or has access to medical oxygen to get them onto oxygen. You can make an impromptu mask from hose tubing and a rubber glove or plastic container like a water bottle- whatever you can come up with for your size of animal. Some duct tape edging around the cut plastic water bottle end will make the edge safe. Put that on after you get some first oxygen into your creature. Don't waste time getting that all set up first. You need whatever you can use to focus the air to the mouth and nostrils without it collapsing at the nose and mouth which could suffocate them. Herbal support would be FRESH juiced wheat grass and also fresh juiced apple juice to help the body increase blood oxygen levels, given every 15 minutes at first. They should also have herbs to help relax them, as they are going to be fearful while they are not breathing well. Those could be lavender, Lobelia inflata tincture placed along their spinal column, valerian, ladies slipper, Bach's Rescue Remedy, Dr. Christophers Nerve or RelaxEaze formulas or Mel-O or NervEaze by Fir Meadow. Of course cayenne should be given to reduce the likelihood of shock and to support the heart under stress would be a good thing. In this situation the easiest way to administer the cayenne would be to place some tincture near the front of the mouth so that that mouth lining can absorb it. Don't place it near the rear where the oxygen could force it towards the lungs.

Rhododendron and azalea toxins are bad indeed. It doesn't take very much of either of these plants to send your animal to the Good Shepherd. The herbal support for these is cayenne to get their blood pressure back up and to counter any systematic slowing down of ability. As always liver and kidney and bloodstream herbs will be used to support the body in its cleanup work. Fresh Start is ideal for this support. DWorm BWW has also been used in larger doses as a backdoor approach to this problem. As in other problems, don't wait to see if your creature ate enough to get a reaction. Act as if they did indeed poison themselves and start with the cayenne and liver and kidney support herbs immediately.

Chapter 13- Parasites

As animal owners, a lot we have to do is made or broken on our parasite programs. Immune systems, body systems, growth, longevity, productivity and nourishment to every cell of the animal can be negatively impacted. Parasites also eliminate their own body waste, which is toxic to their host. Body, organ or intestinal tract structure damage can occur as they feast and tunnel through your beloved pets or stock. Young, weak, and senior animals are most susceptible, but even stress such as those caused by heat waves, third trimester pregnancy, moving to new homes, and exhibitions can make all animals more susceptible. Wet and humid areas that are temperate have the worst problems with them, but every area and every creature can, and likely does, have parasites. What we do oft times, especially with internal parasites, is merely control the numbers. Remember that animals, for the most part, are reinfecting themselves with parasites daily, all day long as they come in contact with larvae or eggs while they graze or come into contact with contaminated soil, feeders, fecal matter, and the like. Each of these daily exposures start a new batch of parasites that typically run a pattern of 10 to 28 days from host entrance to mature, egg laying adults. These cycles can take longer and occasionally run faster, dependent upon external factors such as weather and humidity, and internal factors such as the overall wellness of or stress impact in your creature. If a chemical approach were used to really try and break this cycle, chances are good that we would increase body and organ toxicity to the detriment or loss of the animal. In fact, I just recently counseled someone with a 6 year old dairy goat that has been diagnosed with failing liver and kidneys. This age places her as a senior goat, but not an old one. Just a few months ago this goat went through several large doses of chemical dewormers to go after some aggressive parasites.

Herbs make good friends when it comes to alternative deworming options. We can use them frequently and be nourishing to rather than toxifying our animals. Also, as designed by our Wonderful Creator, the parasites do not build immunity to them as they do the chemicals. Remember somewhere around the 1980's when everyone was saying that a dewormer was finally developed that parasites couldn't develop immunity to? That was Ivermectin™. And have we found that to be true now that we are in the 21st century?

I have an interesting story on chemical dewormers. In the 1990's I managed to pick up hookworm in Mexico. Oh fun. Once back in the States I had the strange red discoloration pattern near my wrist that had been itchy before the pattern emerged. I had it diagnosed by a dermatologist that recognized it for what it was; a hookworm entrance area. He put me on a bendazole chemical class prescription. Let me tell you how very nauseated and sick that synthetic dewormer made me as it was poisoning me along with my parasite. That gave me a whole new awareness to give my animals a couple days off after using chemicals on them. If I felt that bad, I couldn't imagine asking my horse to do anything after a chemical deworming. Of course, that was before I knew what I know now.

I have to laugh when I think of this one college professor speaker I was listening to one year at a convention out of state. Someone had asked him about herbs for deworming to which, in my paraphrase, he stated that they didn't work and that they caused diarrhea. Then he went on to teach, for a large part of his presentation, how meat goat producers were experimenting with different pasture types and getting some real neat results with lower fecal egg counts. Was this not herbs he was talking about? Hmmm. He did mention that these daily grazed upon pasture plants used in experimentation were higher tannin herbs. High tannin herbs can have a negative impact on milk production when used daily. His studies were done with meat goats where that would not be as large of a concern. But in this case the audience was dairy goat producers where milk and consistency of lactation as well as milk flavor mattered a great deal. Anyhow, I found his comments on herbal deworming interesting, but uninformed beyond his pasture planting data.

Dosaging

Oral dosaging for internal antiparasite programs is the same as for other herb uses, and it is different too! I have people start at a baseline, set in part by their geographic situations and dictated by chronic and acute stage issues. Then they are the ones, through fecal exams or other appropriate testing and observation that are going to have to adjust the program exactly for their pet or animal or herd's needs. I can't do that and neither can any other herbalist. Variables that come into play are geography, climate, individual pen situations, husbandry, individual farm and pasture conditions, toxic buildup within an animal, time of year, constitutional (inherited) strength of each individual, stress factors, personality factors, diet of the creatures and manner of feeding, immune system strength of each individual and on the list goes.

Animals normally are not fighting conditions like contracting pneumonia every day of their life, but as mentioned above, they are eating, licking up, or inhaling parasite ovum or larvae every day. So we address these a bit differently. Therefore, if an animal is reinfecting themselves every day, as you deworm them you are only getting the parasites that are accessible to the dewormer. Often that is the adults. So when you deworm, you may get the parasites that mature and just ready to mature. You may not get the earlier stages. Keeping that in mind you will want to herbally deworm AT LEAST weekly to clean out any parasites that have matured since the past herbal deworming. Twice a week is even better. If I had a large parasite problem in my herd or very infected facilities I would consider starting my herbal deworm program for 10 days once or twice a day at double or triple doses as long as you know you can do that with the herbs or products you are using. Then you may want to follow that up after a one to two week break with a second 10 day session at double dose if the facilities are really infected. After that you may be able to settle to twice a week for these animals and then perhaps weekly. Areas that have humid summers, don't have a good winter kill from several good freezes to help clean the pasture, areas that have flooded, or areas that have had severe parasite problems will probably have to continue on a twice a week program. Then remember that the animal's immune system, GI tract (or related attacked body organ) will want some additional herbal support until the animal has greatly improved in its wellness.

For herds or flocks that have a good working program in place, but finds they have one or two animals that need more support, you may do them more often. I often suggest double dosing two times per day for three to five days in a row for an animal like this to give them a good jump start and then leaving them at twice per week, single or double dosing depending on what you determine that creature's needs to be.

Herbal deworming does work well, as long as you understand some of these foundations.

Assessments

Assessments should be made on a regular, if not daily basis on your creatures in charge. Don't get anxious about it; just keep good tabs on your creatures so that things never get out of hand. We do morning and evening chores. During the times of year where evening means it is dark out already, I will add a late afternoon walk while it is still daylight to check on any feed needs, as well as do a quick check on the animals. I also do any chores that can be done that are easier to accomplish during daylight.

Taking random samples to run fecals with is a good habit to develop. My friend, Mike Korhonen, a well known and respected retired Toggenburg dairy goat breeder, taught me to keep plastic sandwich baggies in my pocket to collect manure samples at a whim. Just put it on like a glove, collect your sample-preferably fresh from the animal if possible, and turn it inside out and seal. If you keep a permanent marker in that pocket, then you can label your bag with whose samples those are if you know the animal they came from. Fecals are another one of those wonderful tools that most veterinarians are happy to teach their clients. A fecal is nothing more than a simply prepared manure sample in a way that mixes with a prepared solution such as a Fecalsol™ or a Fecalmed™ type of product and then placed on a slide with a slip cover. Then it is read through a decent quality (not cheap) microscope. The newest microscopes are digital and can hook up to your laptop computer where you can increase the image size many fold, as I do in iridology with my eye photos. Someday, God willing, I'll have one. For now I still have my faithful manual scope. I know there are home recipes for fecal floater types of solutions, but if you glitch your recipe at all or don't have a correct recipe, the gravity will be wrong and you won't get an accurate count. This is too important of a task to risk that. Invest in a good book on Parasitology. I will list one in the appendix for those that aren't sure what to look for in a text book. Do not rely on doing a onetime fecal to tell you if you have a worm problem. The fecal will only be accurate when adults are actually shedding eggs in the digestive tract, which might be every day if your animal is really infested, or may be only once or twice in three weeks if your situation is better. You can have younger non egg shedding stages present in your animal, and still have a fecal appear normal. Continue to do routine fecals every few days. Also be sure and test several animals, individually, each time if you have more than one. However, there are some parasites, such as those that do not shed eggs in the digestive tract that don't sample this way; so you may need to send a different type of sample to a university lab with your specific request to test for those. Those detailed instructions can be obtained from the lab. Sometimes veterinarian services will be needed to get those samples or supplies to collect the sample from them. Liver flukes may require a different floating solution and protocol. If those are a problem in your area see if your vet will teach you how to check for those.

Other things that may alert you to a parasite problem might be: hair coat roughness or bent/barbed hair tips, diarrhea or looser than normal manure, fluid filled swelling under the jaw also known as 'bottle jaw', listlessness, difficulty maintaining weight, vomiting- especially in pets, dullness to the eyes, eye discharges from weakened immunity, pale or paling mucous membranes such as eyelids and gum areas, a drop in milk production, a change for the worse in milk flavor, the appearance of worms or 'rice' (tapeworms) or moving threads (pinworms) at the anal opening and blood mixed with feces, among others.

For external parasites you may notice a change in skin health, itchiness, a protrusion of many different colors or sizes indicating a tick, damage, flaking, redness, or witnessing tiny creature movement or eggs at the hair shaft base may clue you into something hitching a free ride and free lunch on your animal. Please note that none of these observations other than witnessing the actual parasite or eggs in a fecal exam or other testing are fail safe, as other conditions may be occurring concurrently or separately. Ruling out parasites, though, often can be a good first step to take, as long as the life of your animal is not in immediate risk. If you do not know if your animal is in immediate risk, then employ the services of your veterinarian for a diagnosis until you become more experienced and have a higher comfort level with your assessments in your creature family. Should you witness blood in the manure, moderate to severe diarrhea, moderate to severe fatigue, swelling under the jaw, paleness or whiteness to the inner lower eyelid, or tissue damage, or see an actual parasite, you probably do not want to waste any time in working with your animal. Some causes of livestock and pet death are attributed to various parasites. If you find you get more than one death in close timing to a first one and you did not get that first one autopsied, contact your veterinarian to have a post mortem (autopsy) done as soon as possible to try to ascertain the cause of death. You do not want to wait until there are 3 or more deaths going on to do this. Some of the flukes such as liver types and parasites like barberpole worm or coccidia can pull down a lot of animals in rapid succession. You do not want that heartache if you can prevent it. Certainly any time you get a single death, you can hire your veterinarian or your state veterinary college if you live near one to do a post mort. You may still learn valuable information that you can use to head off a larger problem in your herd, kennel or flock. Some people do these themselves, like folks that have experience dressing out livestock or that hunt. Be SURE you exercise biosecurity for yourself, so that you don't contract something you don't want. Wear gloves and boots and clothing that can be properly sanitized afterward. If you cut or nick yourself in the process, stop the procedure and attend to your injury IMMEDIATELY with strong doses of antimicrobial herbs both internally and externally. I personally don't have the heart to do this beyond poultry. The poultry ability all started with a gorgeous silver laced Wyandotte rooster that stalked me for weeks before he managed to sink a spur through my clothing, through my skin, and into my knee... I still can't do ducks though. Their eyes and faces are just too cute. If you perform a post mort on your animal and if you still don't find anything, you may still want to hire your veterinarian to look at the remains. Their eyes are trained to look for all types of detail in various areas and they know what to send in for lab samples if needed for further data.

Biosecurity/Avoiding the Importation of Parasites to Your Farm

Deer and other creature contributions, including new animal purchases, are something one ought to consider. Animals that are a bit more similar to one another, such as cats and wild species of cats like bobcats, dogs and wolves or coyotes, poultry and wild birds, sheep and goats, the camelids, sometimes ruminants with other ruminants, etcetera often have several species of parasites and some diseases that can be passed back and forth. If possible, limit your creature exposure to other animals of their kind and related or similar kinds. This is another form of biosecurity to consider.

Our guardian dogs prevent white tailed deer from coming onto our pasture, thus eliminating our risk with our goats coming into contact with menengial or 'deer' worm which is fatal in some instances. When you purchase a new pet or animal for your flock, home, or herd, keeping them quarantined for a month does more than just allow you to watch for conditions of dis-ease. It allows you to test for parasites a few times and to make sure that you clean out parasites real well, before your new creature has the opportunity to infect your place with whatever parasites that hitchhiked in with it. Remember that their move to you will cause stress to their immune system, allowing their parasites a shot at taking hold and multiplying more rapidly. It's definitely worth some thought and effort to reduce these sources of cross contamination. I've heard from many people that have had to fight parasites new to their herd once purchasing and integrating a new animal into their herd. Exercise wisdom. You just may be very glad that you did. We ourselves have dealt with coccidia, stomach worms, and lungworm in quarantined new stock. You just never know.

Another biosecurity issue you might consider is your free run poultry, often chickens. Chickens are notorious for walking through animal pens and their manure, picking up coccidia and other parasites on their feet. Then they go to roost on, walk through, or nest in your hay or grain feeders or hay stack all the while applying your creature's parasite larvae and eggs onto their feed. If you are dealing with a parasite problem on your farm, consider keeping your poultry in an area away from your stock. Also consider not having people and children climb on or play on your hay stack. They will contribute to the same problem.

Bottle Jaw

I'm going to put bottle jaw here. Bottle jaw is a symptom of a severe internal parasite infestation and should not be ignored. The animal could very well die that day or the next with this problem.   Bottle jaw shows itself in ruminants as a swelling below the jaw of the animal, usually along a larger portion or the entire lower jaw starting somewhere behind the chin as you look towards the neck.   If you have never seen photographs and you have internet access, take a look so you know what to watch for. It is caused by serious changes in the bloodstream from the protein separating out.   In these situations I have people triple dose Fir Meadow's herbal Dworm BWW product every 2 to 3 hours that first day. I won't be able to comment on other products because this is the only one I've worked with in this situation. Besides serious herbal intervention, you will want to consider cleanses and rebuilding the blood stream and GI tract. Do not place extra stress on your animal while it is rebuilding. Watch your new purchases for this issue. I saw it once in a percentage boer goat I had purchased several years ago and brought home from a wet part of the state.   That herd took excellent care of its goats, but the internal stress of the move on the goat and me forgetting that she had come from a heavier parasite area caught me off guard. She recovered just fine, but that was a good lesson for me.

Herbal deworming is one of those areas that I can catch a lot of people's disbelief in whether herbs are or are not suitable for this issue.   If the herbs really didn't work in body support for deworming, then they sure wouldn't have the success stories they have garnered from dealing with bottle jaw where we are hitting a 'life and death' issue. Just remember the herbal foundations chapter and be sure you are using the correct herbs and quality herbs and the correct dosage and time for your situation. Most people get into problems by getting to relaxed in their herbal deworming program and not keeping up to date with it.

Pasture Considerations

Pasture height is something you'll want to consider.   Most parasites that are ingested with grass or other plants stay at or below the two inch level of pasture height.   Rotating or removing your pasture grazers once that pasture reaches three to four inches of height will reduce exposure and will give you a healthier pasture since the roots won't be overstressed from close to the ground eating.

Soil moisture, ponds, streams and the like can harbor some problems. Humid climates, irrigated pastures, and water features will increase the ability of parasites to survive in greater numbers on your property. In addition, snails are intermediate hosts for some types of flukes, worms, and parasites. So doing what you can to reduce your animal exposure to them is something you will want to take note of. These same conditions encourage mosquitoes which are the intermediary host for disease and some parasites in various species. Contemplate that thought when you wildcraft herbs or harvest vegetables and herbs from your garden. Inspect and wash plant material carefully to remove any chance of snail eggs. You don't want to be consuming them either!

Deworming with the Moon Cycles

Timing with the moon is an interesting topic. I don't have a lot of background in working with the cycles of the moon, which do affect the gravitational pull on the earth. I do know that tinctures measure out with a stronger level of phytochemicals when extracted at full moon. There are many that say that timing some deworming with the moon will catch more activity. It's something one can ponder, but since I herbally deworm on a once or twice a week basis, I'm going to be catching all phases of the moon. You certainly don't want to wait for full moon to work on an issue that needs to be addressed today! However, on the week that you have a full moon to work with, you might just take advantage of it and deworm on that day instead of your regular schedule. Just make sure that you don't get spread out too many days apart before you give them their next measure. I personally do not like to go more than 4 to 7 days depending on the animal and climate in between dewormings.

Deworming Herbs

I get asked about using tobacco from time to time because of historical use of tobacco for deworming. Here I'll review the "do no harm' clause espoused by Hippocrates. I do not use habit forming, toxic, or poisonous herbs and tobacco breaks all three rules. Who, in their right mind, wants to put cadmium, arsenic, and other heavy metals such as those found in tobacco in their creatures that they love? It just doesn't make sense. Also nicotine, a powerful alkaloid, has a detrimental effect to the nervous system, endocrine glands, and even the heart muscle as they are over stimulated. Tobacco used in any form by humans is also a proven carcinogen. I'm trying to avoid that problem, not encourage it.

There are many, many single herbs that are used in deworming. Some of these are: wormwood, cloves, ginger, plantain, pumpkin seeds, European male fern (do not overdose during first trimester), hyssop, wormseed, mullein, fennel, nettle, black walnut hulls (not for equine/camelids due to founder risks), quassia bark, garlic, and many herbal books will provide you with a plethora of more choices. My preference, however, is to work with blends so that I can boost plant efficacy through the synergy and additional nutrition of a balanced plant blend. I always also consider digestive tract support, some body organ nourishing, and parasite waste disposal, as well and choose herbs that will contribute to double duty. So unless I have no other options, you won't find me using single herbs or even just two herbs with parasite issues. Also, heavy dosing single herbs can get you into problems, especially with fragile or pregnant creatures. Be safe and work with blends unless you are confident in your herb choices.

I've heard many times from various veterinarians that up to 80 percent of the parasite reinfestation problems come from about 20 percent of the herd. You ought to be able to single out the worst offenders, and then work on them longer with additional cleansing and body support. You may even consider keeping them quarantined from the rest of your herd until after you turn them around and build them up. How will you catch them? With your fecals and in some types of blood feeding parasites perhaps your FAMACHA™ technique talked about in the next section under barberpole worms. Working on them for six months to a year is not an unrealistic expectation.

Remember, you as the pet or herd or flock owner is the one responsible for deciding how often and at what dosage each creature needs herbal support. Be diligent. You'll be rewarded with better feed conversions, healthier stock, healthier progeny and less stress on you and them. Herbal deworming is an investment with great dividends!

Parasite Profiles and Plans

Blackhead

Blackhead is also known as histomoniasis and is caused by a protozoa. There are several types of poultry that are carriers, however; it shows itself the most often in turkeys. Often once blackhead gets established in a flock, bird losses will be high as the parasite does terminal damage to the liver and ceca of the birds. It can be picked up through infected feces and also from other carrier poultry. Your focus will be using some of my favorite anthelmintic herbs including your choices of cloves, wormwood, black walnut hulls, garlic and ginger. I would also support the liver and GI Tract with appropriate herbs to which cayenne is added to assist the body in arresting any hemorrhaging that may come about. If you like Fir Meadow products my favorite for this situation would be using DWorm MLL tincture at double or triple dose at least 2x per day for 10 days in a row to really try and get on top of the problem. If a few birds in a pen are affected you might consider working with all of them as being affected, as likely they all are. As with any parasite problem (most are spread by feces), feed and work with your affected birds last and be sure you sanitize your boots as you leave that area, so that you are not tracking infected feces around to unaffected areas or birds. You will also need to remove and/or sanitize their coop and run.

Barberpole Worm or Haemoncus contortus

Barberpole worm, sometimes abbreviated as H.c., and also known as wire worm and red stomach worm, is a much feared nematode in sheep and goats. One female worm can lay 10,000 eggs, so it can become prevalent on a pasture quite quickly from just one goat or sheep! An over infestation of this parasite can take an animal down to death quickly. It is said to be able to survive well in any areas that can grow corn without summer irrigation. Remember, your irrigated field may count for that. It is most common a problem of the warm and humid Midwest and South, but of course can be found anywhere if the conditions are right.

The Accessible Pet, Equine and Livestock Herbal

FAMACHA™ observation techniques for goats and sheep are sometimes used for this. You can attend a class and learn to rate the color of the inner eyelid from a 1 to a 5 based on the pinkness or paleness of the inner eye. Remember, FAMACHA™ technique will not tell you what the problem is that causes the anemia, but if you are in a barberpole worm area or purchasing an animal from one, learning this technique will help you to better manage your herd. Your ovines and caprines ought to be checked a couple times per week if possible. You don't want to let H.c. get by you for very long. Garlic, cayenne, and ginger are all enemies to this parasite and I would use more than regular dose of a combination of these in an emergency, along with GI tract soothing herbs. In the worst situations, I would follow with the soothing herbs at least 20 minutes after the target herbs to allow more contact in the intestines. I would also give cayenne to help the body to stop any hemorrhaging that might be taking place. Then follow up with overall creature support including cleansing with herbs from the Supplemental chapter or a product like Better Daze. WATCH your fecals. Different animals will need different amounts and durations depending on their constitution and current inner level of health. Most areas with barberpole worms have to stay on top of them from spring through fall, and in moderate climates in winter as well. I have people use GI Soother for this in their herd, if they have a problem and sometimes at quite high doses in an emergency. The herbs in this blend also support the body to do intestinal repair work from the parasite damage. It can be fed on grain, mixed with a liquid and drenched, or mixed in a bottle or lamb or kid feeding bucket with their milk. If you live in an H.c. area, practicing Offensive Herbalism™ would be a wise thing to do along with at least weekly random fecals and eyelid checks.

Coccidia or Coccidiosis

Coccidia are one of those host specific parasites that can affect our mammals or our poultry, each with its own special variety. Cocci (kok-see) are a single celled parasite that does not respond to most of the common deworming herbs. It doesn't respond to the common stomach worm chemical anthelmintics either, so don't be surprised that this problem needs its own herbs. Cocci are also highly infective. Its eggs, or oocysts as they are more correctly called, are shed by the thousands and very, very few need to be ingested to get a big problem going. It favors damp climates and baby stock or small stock like poultry, but it is another that can take off after a major stressor (such as a heat wave); even dropping mature cattle. Animals that don't look quite thrifty, have hair coat health issues, and diarrhea may all be signs, but please don't wait that long. If you get blood tinged diarrhea the time to work on them was yesterday, as by this time there is a lot of internal damage done. However, get to work right now (yes, put this book down, grab your herbs, and go!) and you may still have a good result. I've also helped clients with stunted animals due to chronic coccidia bouts. While on several months of GI soother and Better Daze, these animals begin to grow again, regain their appetite, hair coat and eye health, and thrive. They often catch back up with herdmates within a year in height, weight, and condition. It's never too late while they are still here to work with them.

We feed GI Soother to our kids here every day that it rains, and 3x a week when it isn't if the ground is fairly dry. After putting an inch or two of milk in the lambar (kid nipple bucket), we place our measure of herb into the bucket and shake it around some, then fill the remainder of the way. Cayenne, ginger, cloves, and garlic are all herbs to consider when working with this problem. If you get to the point of seeing diarrhea, then double or triple dosing the first dose and then double dosing hourly after that until you see progress will help the body to turn it around. We are not controlling the diarrhea here as in controlling the symptom, but are giving the body what it needs to fight the problem and solve it. Once you have the dose of herbs in needed for your situation it will take about 2 hours to see the effects of that dose. Once you get marked improvement you can drop them down to regular dose, but consider keeping them at 3 or 4x a day for the next 3 or so days. Then keep up with them more frequently than you were before. For poultry or other animals it can be mixed with their feed or damp mash. This has worked wonderful for baby birds as well. If you are having a coccidia problem in your mammals, remember to keep your poultry away from them and their feed areas.

Fleas

Fleas are one of those things that come to visit from time to time. Thankfully it's extremely rare we see them come visit our farm. Watch your pet exposure to other pets, areas that other pets frequent such as rest areas on road sides, pet stores, pet clinics, and even those floor rugs you bring home from the store. Many a person has gotten fleas in their house, bringing them home that way. Any new rug that I brought home would get a hefty spraying of diluted lavender and peppermint essential oils mixed with apple cider vinegar (outside in my driveway). No way would I want fleas in my house. They can transmit tapeworms to you, your cat, or your dog.

Fleas are sending you a message. They have found a home suitable for them and have set up shop. Healthy skin from a creature with a clean internal system just will not taste good to them, so they tend to move on. They are into junk food rather than health food! That explains why some animals may become covered while another pet in the same home or farm won't have them or have very few. If you are seeing fleas, besides the herbal support externally, I'm going to suggest that you seriously consider cleaning the bowels, liver and kidneys of your creature as well as adjusting their diet to more raw foods as discussed in the feeding chapter so that their internal pH can become more alkaline and less toxic, the source of the true problem.

For external help, you can make oil of garlic. Take 4 to 6 cloves of fresh garlic and thinly slice, chop, or press into a small glass or canning jar. Cover that with olive oil, going one half inch over the top of the garlic, 1 inch if the garlic is pressed into teeny bits. Then put a cloth over the top and rubber band it on, so that any moisture in the garlic that wants to evaporate out can. Shake this daily and at three days it is at its prime, though you can use if after a half a day, or if you want to stir it for an hour straight you can start using it then. If it's NOT a cat, I like to add 5 drops per teaspoon of lavender, citronella, and/or Eucalyptus globulus essential oil to it, or 3 drops of each until I have 5 or 6 drops total to a teaspoon of the olive oil. Then smooth it onto the skin. Be sure and get the top of the head, the neck, and along the spine for starters, then anywhere else you see the creatures. If it's a cat, use a salve containing one or both of those herbs to put on the damaged skin after you apply some oil of garlic. It will soothe and encourage the body to heal that damaged skin faster.   Adding oral garlic to their diet, appropriate for your creature's size, will also discourage them. For a reminder, that would be 2 cloves of garlic for 150 pounds, 1 clove for 75 pounds, ½ clove for 38 pounds, ¼ clove for 19 pounds, and 1/8 clove for 9 pounds. Peppermint and rosemary may also be deterrents, but I haven't tried them. Let me know if you do. Wounderful! salve or some other nourishing salve can be placed on damaged skin to encourage the body to heal the damaged and/or hardened tissue. Keep applying it 2 to 3x per day until the skin and hair appear normal.

If you believe your yard is infested, this is one case where you might pull out the diatomaceous earth. Sprinkle it on and remember to wear a respirator, as it will go airborne.   Keep your pets and family out of the area; you don't want them breathing it either.   Then the following day water everything down real good which will render the DE infective and thus make your yard safe again for your pets and children. Remember that you will need to repeat this in 10 days to catch any fleas that hatched from eggs after the first application. Don't wait longer or those new fleas will grow old enough to lay new eggs, making a new cycle to have to deal with.   For your carpeting, you might mix baking soda with some of the above essential oils at a stronger rate, 30 drops per cup of baking soda. Sprinkle on your carpets, let it sit for an hour, and vacuum it back up.   Keep all cats away from the area. You will have to air out the room for a day before letting cats back into that area if you have indoor prince or princesses.

Gapeworms

Gapeworms are a red nematode small looking worm that hangs out in the trachea (windpipe) of poultry. They may suck blood and in larger numbers will obstruct the trachea causing difficulty in breathing or even suffocation of their host. Chickens, turkeys, pheasants or other birds may hang their mouths open as they gasp or 'gape' for air.   The weakened birds can become quite susceptible to pneumonia.   Poultry can pick up 'gapes' from wild birds, infected feces, earthworms, snails, slugs and cecal worms (another poultry parasite).

Should you find this problem in your flock you will need to sanitize the poultry yard, move the affected flock (treat all as affected) to a location that can be easily

The Accessible Pet, Equine and Livestock Herbal

sanitized later and put them on an aggressive herbal deworming program. If you suspect that you may get lung issues concurrently, then work with the lung issues also. You can always support their lungs before a problem were to develop to be on the offense.

Herbs I would consider are Black walnut hulls, male fern, garlic, cloves, and mullein in larger than normal doses. If I had this in my flock I would want them on a ten day program, putting fresh litter in their rehab area daily. Kiln dried cedar or pine shavings would be excellent as those woods are also tough on parasite larvae habitats. I would also supplement my birds with a product like Better Daze, Layer Support and/or kelp. If you use Fir Meadow products then Dworm MLL would be my choice in this situation. I would want to keep my flock on herbs at least twice per week after a problem like that.

Heartworm

Heartworm lives a portion of its lifecycle in mosquitoes, so reducing exposure to these pests at dusk will be of benefit. Dogs that are bitten by infected mosquitoes receive this problem into their bloodstream, which then seeks out the heart and begins to grow and multiply. Any balanced herb plan is going to discourage mosquitoes, support the body in its riddance of the parasite, and give the body what it needs to heal a damaged heart and clean out heartworm waste products. That means the lymph system should be supported as well.

Citronella and some of the other citrus essential oils discourage mosquitoes. You can put 5 drops per teaspoon of essential oil and rub that on your pet, especially on top of the head and along the spine down to the tail tip, staying away from the eyes. A little oil will go quite a ways. Remember that with citrus can come increased sensitivity to the sun, but that is not a large problem since mosquitoes are usually only an evening occurrence. As long as you are not using the oils 2 or 3 times per day you do not need to take a break from them. But if you are, then after 10 days of use take a 3 day break then start again. Keeping those citronella candles around really does help if you are spending time on the porch or patio. Get good quality soy or other alternative ones though or you may be breathing lead from the candles as they burn. Raw garlic in the diet will also discourage "Alaska's state bird" from pets when garlic is in the bloodstream. Therefore, you might want to give them garlic, appropriate for their size, rolled up in a pet goody, an hour before 'squito' time arrives. Running your pets through ample cleansing will make them less appetizing to the pests also. Like fleas, they are more attracted to 'dirty' blood. Have you ever noticed that some people or pets attract more mosquitoes than others?

Black walnut hulls, thyme, rosemary in larger doses, horsemint, and garlic, along with cayenne to run them to the heart, are all herbs that this worm pest will not appreciate. This needs to be done on at least a weekly basis during mosquito season, after top loading their system for a few days in a row, and for 3 to 4 weeks following mosquito season to be sure you get the last of the problem. Cayenne and hawthorn berry, leaf, or bark supports heart repair, as do other nurturing herbs such as comfrey, raspberry, nettle, dandelion, blueberry leaves and berries, and yarrow. The liver, kidney, and blood cleansing herbs should be considered as they help the body take out toxins that have built up in injured heart tissue, as well as any left behind by the worms. Mullein is a great herb for lymphatic support. So is exercise to help move the decaying worm bodies and waste out of the system. You certainly don't want that stagnating in the body to create something else!

Lice

Work with lice in the same way as for fleas and address the same causes. Also be sure and look for and remove any lice eggs that could be attached to hair follicles. Repeat anything you do ten days later to catch any newer hatched lice before they become mature enough to lay more eggs. Standard laundering of bedding in very hot water, or putting it in garbage bags sealed off for two weeks with several drops of thyme essential oil will disinfect the bedding. Dogs do benefit from dog pads filled with fresh cedar shavings. Besides benefitting the respiratory system, many external parasites hate cedar. You will have to refill or renew the bedding every so often with 5 to 10 drops of cedarwood essential oil. Try to find a dog bed that will unzip so that you can do this. Then shake or stir the shavings so that the oil is reabsorbed into the bulk of the shavings.

Liver flukes

Liver flukes are one of those problems that sometimes announces its presence with animals collapsing and dying rapidly, and with their owners scrambling to get a diagnosis fast enough to save other animals. If you have more than one animal die or have snails in your area, which are the intermediate host, you may want to have a veterinarian come out and inspect the liver and gallbladder, as well as other organs and tissues they look through during a normal post mortem procedure. Knowing you have this problem in your mammals is the biggest part of the battle in this one. One mammal can pass this problem onto other mammals. Cattle and donkeys get sited quite frequently as reservoirs for this problem, and I know of goat herds that have experienced losses from this nasty parasite, but it can occur in any mammal. Your mammals (or you) can be infected by ingesting uncleaned vegetation, including garden plants, and even from drinking up larvae from streams. This is one situation where I would prefer to offer my creatures water in stock tanks then from a slow stream, pond, or irrigation ditch.

Herbally it is better to have animals in areas prone to this problem on a regular program to help the body avoid these from ever taking hold. Liver flukes require a lot of herbs and work, especially if you have already lost animals to them. This is another one of those 3 x a day at triple or even quadruple dose of herb blends for ten days in a row to get a jump on this tenacious parasite. In this case if you have first trimester pregnant animals, you may have to still go with herb doses that will be higher than would be desirable with them, but that is better than losing the dam! High doses of garlic (quadruple dosing in an emergency) along with high doses of black walnut, wormwood, goldenseal (use with cayenne), cloves, European male fern, pumpkin seeds, and/or mullein. Pick at least three of these for your blend, then quadruple dose the blend, plus the garlic. Add 10 to 20 percent Lobelia inflata to it to help the body run the herbs right to the liver. Also consider liver support and cleansing herbs such as milk thistle, wormwood, and dandelion. Fir Meadow's Dworm MLL, Fresh Start, and GI Soother are products that can be used. GI Soother or alimentary canal soothing herbs should be considered afterwards, to help soothe the areas damaged by the eggs which are covered in sharp points. Essential oils can also be used. The advantage to adding essential oils for this problem is that they will run right through the liver, being fat soluble. You do need to consider however that the liver is damaged and won't be able to metabolize out the oils as fast, so use regular doses (5 drops per teaspoon of olive oil) for only two or three days in a row on the skin at 3 times per day. Then give the liver a break from them for an equal amount of days. You would rub this on the skin beneath the right side of the ribcage. Cloves, peppermint, thyme, and cinnamon can be considered. Do not use cinnamon in pregnant animals unless you know how to counter it in case of uterine contraction stimulation. NEVER EVER use wormwood in an essential oil. NEVER.

Lung worm

Lung worm is another of those that use a snail as an intermediary host. Are you beginning to see a trend here? You may notice your animal having a wet cough that is not responding to lung support or general deworming support. However, be sure that you are not mistaking pneumonia for this problem; you might cover both bases to be safe, as they can occur concurrently. Animals can carry the eggs for months before an immune system dip will allow them to take hold. If that is the case using an herb plan for lungworm is not a bad part of your plan, but always be sure and rule out all other lung issues. Work with your veterinarian if you are not confident in your assessment skills. Ask them if they will teach you what they are looking at and listening for and why they are doing those things when they are there and you are paying for their time. Most vets enjoy teaching from their vast collection of hard earned knowledge and will be encouraged by your genuine interest to become a better creature keeper. As far as lungworm herbs, go back to the liver fluke section and grab your list from there.

Additional lung herbs for support would be thyme and comfrey. I'll also reemphasize mullein. If you are dealing with moisture in the lungs and you know it's not pneumonia, then some astringent herbs like sage (not in lactating creatures), white oak leaves or bark powder, apple bark, apple peels (use organic), black berry leaves or roots, red raspberry, nettle, yarrow, pleurisy root, and cayenne can be used. Expectorant herbs will be desired to help move moisture and any pus leftover from damage out of the lungs. Those will be garlic, ginger, lavender, eucalyptus, Lobelia inflata, lungwort, coltsfoot, comfrey, hyssop (do not use the essential oil), parsley (not in lactating creatures), and yarrow.

The Accessible Pet, Equine and Livestock Herbal

You can also look at the Respiratory System chapter in Part ll and use an onion poultice to help the body break up gunk in the lungs and move it out. I LOVE these poultices! Also, your parasite collection is not going to appreciate the onion.

Remember the additional systems cleansing, as per the liver fluke section.

Menengial or Deer Worm

This really is a parasite of white tailed deer, but they can host and act improperly in goats (caprines), sheep (ovines), and alpacas, llamas, vicuñas, etcetera (camelids). If you have white tailed deer that have access to your pastures, be on the alert for this problem. In their wrongful creature hosts, they tend to wander to the spine and brain stem causing neurological conditions and sometimes pain. They can also cause fatalities. I use the same herbs and doses as in the liver fluke section, along with Lobelia inflata, to take the herbs to the locations needed, rosemary to nourish and improve circulation the brain stem. I like scullcap to nourish the spinal nerves. Hops and lavender can also be used. Pain can be assisted with mullein or topical arnica along the spine. Never use arnica internally, unless you are using the homeopathic (little white pills) remedy. In all of these parasite cases, Better Daze and kelp can be used for additional nutrient support during the organ repair process. Comfrey (as long as there isn't severe liver damage) and plants from the Supplements chapter can be used too.

Mites- Sarcoptic and Demodectic

Sometimes referred to as mange; any mammal, bird, human or reptile can show up with these annoying species all the way down to microscopic sizes. When you can see them you will find that they can come in several different colors, from black to red to cream colors. We even had a broody chicken get infested with them once when she was sitting on a nest, so be sure and watch your egg hatchers. You may notice specks of dust, irritated skin of several types, itching, hair or feather loss or poultry leg thickening or scaling. In the case of demodecs, you may get pustules or bumps under the skin. Press one out and you'll get a cigar shaped bunch of thick white pus that will be complete with the invisible mites and their eggs. They tend to become visible as far out as two or three years after an immune system lowering.   We had it show in up two goats that were from the same dam three years after we had moved the farm 700 miles. Interesting.

I'll refer you back to the fleas section for some tools for these.   I also like making an essential oil blend containing a strong oil of garlic for the base, then some cedarwood essential oil (do not use in pregnant animals), some thyme essential oil (do not use in pregnant animals), some lavender, some rosemary, some eucalyptus, and maybe a citrus type to help draw toxins at the skin level. Peppermint can be used too. All of these are for a total of five drops per teaspoon of olive oil base. So if you are doing five drops of four different essential oils totaling twenty drops of essential oil then there needs to be four teaspoons of the oil of garlic base. Remember sun sensitivity with citrus essential oils, both for you and them. Then rub your blend in to the bumpy areas, two times per day for up to ten days. If you might be pregnant, but your animal isn't, be sure you avoid contact with the essential oils that the pregnant animals shouldn't be around.   You don't want to be breathing or touching them.   Any tissue damage then can be addressed with demulcent, cell proliferant or emollient herbs mentioned in the Epidermis chapter plus some antiseptic ones mentioned in the Immune system chapter. Or you can use Wounderful!, ReBuilld, or Dr. Christopher's Complete Tissue and Bone salve.

Pinworms or Threadworms

Work with these just as for stomach worms listed later in this chapter. They seem to need higher doses of herbs than some of the other stomach worms. Besides the normal route of transmission, these parasite eggs can become airborne and be breathed in to cause a parasite invasion. Ick.   Be alerted if you see thread like worms around the anal area, tail or butt rubbing, or a raised tail. They tend to be more active around full moon time and at night, although a severe infestation can show itself at any time. Besides the oral herbs, you can make an infusion (tea) of the stomach worm herbs including ground fennel seed, double dosed, and then carefully enema them into colon.   Remember your first enema or two will probably get pushed right back out with manure, so you will want to get a third one in there. You'll find you can get more liquid in that third time, as it's able to get further into the colon. Remember your personal safety when working on the back end of an animal, as well as safe restraint for your subject. Be careful with the tender anal tissue. Reread the enema section in the Dosaging and Methods of Administration chapter for safely using an enema. Dworm BWW, W, or MLL can be used if wanted. Dr. Christopher's Parasite formula can be used in pets.

Protozoa- Cryptosporida, Toxoplasmosis, et al. Also Amoebas.

These single celled nuisances can be very easy to pick up from the environment. Some of them can survive long dry periods. Strong freezes or high cooking temperatures will remove many types from the envment (or your meat). Try to get your raw meats for canine and feline use from uninfected sources as we know once we cook the meat it will be very acidic for your pet's system. Some, like Toxoplasmosis can easily be ingested in the cyst form. Cats often carry some Toxoplasmosis in them so please consider keeping them on some type of management program if they are around anything or anyone pregnant to protect the unborn baby/ies. Single celled parasites can end up in any cell of the body, though many prefer the digestive tract as their home base. They can be involved in diarrheas, colitis, some autoimmune issues, some rheumatoid arthritis, some asthma, some cancers and dermatitis to list some situations they sometimes contribute to. If you have a creature that is just not getting well although you are confident that you are covering the perceived problem with a good program you might just consider herbally supporting your animal for these situations and see if that is what gets them over the hump.

Some herbs I like to consider for these rotten little creatures are black walnut, cloves, garlic, ginger and cayenne. I would also consider having the creature take antiseptic herbs concurrently as well as providing general overall nutritional support. Some products to consider might be GI Soother, HerBiotic, and Better Daze. Dr. Christopher's Parasite formula (liquid) and his Vitalerbs can also be considered.

Stomach Worms- Bots, Roundworms (Ascarids), Strongyles etc.

These are the parasites that most of the commonly available parasite formulas concern themselves with.   These are worms that lodge into the intestinal tract, often attaching to the intestinal walls causing damage as well as swiping nutrition from their host.   All of the other parasite herbs mentioned above will help the body with these. I personally like garlic, black walnut hulls, wormwood, thyme, white oak bark, aloe (be careful of purgative tendencies, not for pregnant animals), parsley (not during lactation), pau d' arco, plantain, mullein, pumpkin seeds, fennel, and also cloves for some selection. Cloves is interesting in that the essential oil (the oil in cloves is what gives it its heat or bite) has been noted to dissolve intestinal worm eggs. I always include powdered cloves in recipes because of this reason. Taste your cloves before you use them as they do need to be hot.   I don't recommend using the essential oil itself at this time as I don't know what amount we would need to be effective and it may be an amount that is too high to be safe. Remember, we have a lot of intestine to work with that may have eggs in it. Two drops of essential oil diluted are not likely going to be able to cover enough geography in the gut. Stick to the powdered herb because of this. Weaker animals may require additional dosing, as the parasites are able to take a greater hold on the weaker, more toxic host.   Remember to assist your creature in GI tract wellness as well as cleansing. Be sure to check your progress with fecals every few days to see if the herbs you chose were efficacious and the correct ones for the issue you were working on. If you are working with pets that eat a lot of processed or packaged feeds or only on animal protein foods, consider cleaning the bowels as well. Livestock on excessive amounts of processed grain with lower quality molasses (not black strap) and not enough long stem fiber may also be in need of a digestive tract tune up. Dworm BWW (not for equine/camelids) or DWorm is commonly used for these problems, as is the Dr. Christopher Herbal Parasite Syrup (not for equine/camelids).

Tapeworms

The Accessible Pet, Equine and Livestock Herbal

Tapeworms find their way into our creatures two ways. Those that ingest plants may pick them up off of the pasture. These hatch and become encysted into the muscle of their host. When that raw or undercooked infected animal's muscle (meat) is eaten by a human or pet, then the human or pet is infected with the intestinal form. As that form matures up to 20 feet long, the tail end segments break off, come out with the manure, fall to the ground and restart the whole process. Pets can have both cycles concurrently if they ingest infected vegetation and eat infected meat that has been underprocessed or raw. Fleas are also sometimes an intermediary host for tapeworms infecting dogs, cats and humans. They are voracious feeders when in the digestive tract. Animals that are having trouble holding or gaining weight even though on a good feeding and regular parasite program might be suspect for this problem. Now that you understand how they are picked up, you may understand how we are going to help the body to go after them.

Tapes, as they often called, are resistant to being pushed out of their comfortable creature homes. They require larger dosing for several days in a row. Use of garlic and onions in the diet in larger than normal quantities for a few days, then following them with herbs like mullein and European male fern and high doses of black walnut, cayenne, cloves and raw pumpkin seeds (fresh is best) will help discourage this pest. Keep the garlic going along with the other herbs. Be careful with using too much garlic with dogs and cats. I would use a three days on and three days off approach with my cats and dogs if I found this issue in them. If your creature is not pregnant or lactating, fasting them all day then giving them and the other herbs, will increase the likelihood that these nasty things let go. Carrot juice can also be used with ginger, some cayenne, and garlic bulbs juiced into it for additional support- parasites not liking any of these four ingredients. I also would add some peppermint and/or rosemary if not just for tapeworm harassment. If you can juice fast your animal on this and add some of the other herbs to it, even better. Remember that your small livestock will still have to have some of their regular hay and feed ration, as you will not want to cause an enterotoxemia event in them by too quick of a feed change. I also have developed DWorm MLL for this foe. For animals that may have the encysted form in their muscles, you will need to keep them on regular garlic feeding 5 or 6 days per week to try and get the body to fight them. When you are feeding raw meat to your pets, try and find out if your meat source has a tapeworm problem. If that is the case, then you will want to get your meat somewhere else. The humid, warm summer climates tend to have greater problems with them, though they can be transported to and live in just about any climate. Pomegranate skins are sometimes used for tapeworms, but I don't have experience working with them so don't know the dosage. If you want to use them, then do some research before you experiment with pomegranate skins as I believe the dosages will be lower than normally used for herbs and I wouldn't try these with your smaller pets until you were comfortable with using them. From what I've heard they can be quite strong.

Ticks

It is just oh so much fun to be hugging your dog and simultaneously getting a glimpse of something round and fat protruding from your dogs face inches from yours. I haven't done this, but my husband has! Ick!!! They come in many sizes from pin head to almost as big as the top joint on my pinky finger. Some carry the infamous Lyme disease; some don't but may carry other things we have yet to identify. They are flat bodied when ready to find their next meal, and ready to pop when engorged on your pet or livestock's blood. They have a unique carbon dioxide sensing system which is what your mammals exhale. When they sense the carbon dioxide, they let go of their branch or tree to land on their next meal. The anesthetic in their saliva often makes the host unaware of their presence. I simply find these amazingly engineered details in creation nothing less than fascinating! So how will you herbally work with these pests if you run into one of these on your pets, livestock, or even you? I'll bet you already have an idea or two from reading this section.

First we want to consider how we are going to try to get the tick to back out without releasing any more body fluids into your creature. I like to wear rubber gloves to protect myself from them clinging onto me and truth be known, because I'm a wimp around these! To save face let's just call it 'biosecurity' for me. One thing that can be done is to put petroleum jelly around the mouth of the tick to try to get them to back out to take in some air. I also discovered something quite by accident. For one tick removal I used an alcohol based tincture on its backside.

Then was able to gently pry it off of my dog.   Remember any pinching of the creature can release tick fluids and microbes into your animal's bloodstream, so use care.   After I got it out it was not longer moving, so I assumed it was dead and placed its motionless body on a napkin on a counter. About three hours later I walked by just in time to see the little legs just barely beginning to move.   I think I intoxicated it into pass out mode with the alcohol! That spurred some of my removal technique ideas. So you have one idea, using a food grade alcohol without additives like an Everclear or vodka type, or a tincture containing alcohol and saturating its bottom as well as the area around the mouth. You can do this before you put petrolatum around its mouth to try to suffocate it.   I also like to take some of the hot essential oils, like thyme, oregano, cinnamon, or cloves and put some of that on the tick as well. I put it on full strength with an eyedropper, or by dropping a drop of it onto a cotton swab then wiping the tick without getting any of the essential oil on my pet. Do not do this if you are within ½ inch of the eye, as you don't want to risk getting an essential oil in their eye. My goal here is to 'tick off' the tick so it will back off. Once I'm able to get the monster I smash it if it is smashable, or cremate (burn) it if it is not and dispose of it.   Then I take a tincture of antiseptic herbs and flush the bite area well on my creature as well as giving them a double or triple dose orally.   Then I continue on three times per day for a few days giving topically and orally until the bite site is well healed.   I use HerBiotic glycerite by Fir Meadow. You can also use Dr. Christopher's Infection formula and garlic is always suitable. Just make sure you calibrate your dose to your creature, especially the smaller ones.   This alleviates me from worrying about what the tick may have had in it to share with my creature, as well as any chance of secondary infection. We have never had a problem afterwards doing this, even though Lyme's is present in our area. Populations of these pests can be reduced by running guinea hens on your property. Also avoid having your pets and stock come into contact with brush, oak trees, and deer areas if at all possible or at least keep those things away from your barns and where your animals congregate.

Warbles and Bots

Both of these flies lay eggs on their host, usually on the front legs and withers and sometimes on the flank area. These are areas where the host will reach with their mouth to lick or itch with their teeth. As their saliva touches the eggs the tops come off and the larva enter the mouth to begin their journey down to the digestive tract. In horses the bots stay there, adhering to the stomach lining. In cattle, deer, an occasional horse, and other animals, warbles continue their journey usually along the spinal column area. They can damage muscle and do damage skin as they punch through it as a mature fly. Then they begin the process over again.

If feasible, clip or pull off the eggs as they are laid, doing this in an area that your horse or other animal does not graze or feed. Keeping essential oils of eucalyptus, lavender, rosemary, or peppermint mixed with olive oil smoothed onto the areas where the flies like to lay their eggs will confuse them and likely have them go somewhere else. You can use other oils, but I choose these because of their obtainability and reasonable safety levels in case you have pregnant creatures. For horses internally, I would put them on the stomach worm program, with additional garlic. For warble fly larvae that have created their lump under the skin along the spine, I would keep it saturated with a strong oil of garlic mixed with some of the above essential oil choices or as in a demodectic mite problem. This will be used by the body to discourage any potential for a secondary infection. It that kills the worm then the body will eventually break the body down and move it out via it's lymph system. Wounderful! or GlandAide salves can be applied to the area until the body returns it to normal.

Wound worms

Wound worms are parasites like screw and blow worms which are considered eradicated from the United States. However, they can still make an appearance from time to time, especially in the warm southern parts of the USA. Growing up all the way north in Washington State, we would see these once in awhile if a cow was injured. Live worms or maggots would be hanging onto the wound, consuming the flesh. If you run into a situation like this, flush the area with water to remove any debris possible, then apply oil of garlic to the area or apply an antiseptic herb salve such as HerBiotic. You can add a few drops of lavender or eucalyptus essential oils to your oil of garlic blend to discourage more flies from the area. Powdered herbs can also be applied such as: cayenne, goldenseal, myrrh, black walnut, or slippery elm into the wound. Do not use black walnut on equine or camelid species. Mixing some comfrey leaf or root powder with it will speed up healing by the body. If you use the powdered herbs, you'll probably have to bandage or add a veterinarian type of wrap to hold the herbs in. If you use a salve you won't have to bandage it as the salve will stick to the wound. Complete Tissue and Bone ointment, Wounderful! or ReBuilld salves can be used to encourage the body to heal itself faster.

Deworming Effects to Expect

If you build your herb program properly for your situation, besides drastically reducing or eliminating the parasite pests you don't want to deal with and cleansing and nourishing your creatures in a way that enables their cells to get cleaner and stronger; there are a few other things to watch for.

In most situations, you won't notice anything other than improvements in coat, health, and energy over time. You may also notice that your animals become more efficient in feed conversion. This is because they are feeding fewer parasites and have a healthier digestive tract, so it requires less feed to maintain them at proper weights. Sometimes, however; a creature will get diarrhea. These situations are usually in animals that have high parasite loads and sometimes those that have been let go a long time, are what we call failure to thrive, or may have a reaction to one of the herbs (though that is rare). When there is a large parasite die off that happens quickly, many toxins are released as they die giving the system an overload to deal with. So deal with it the body does, by flushing the dead bodies out quicker to protect itself from absorbing the toxic matter. Should this occur, focus on some liver support herbs and maybe some gentle blood cleaning herbs until the animal is stabilized. You can also do some digestive tract herbs for diarrhea, but I try to focus on working with the cleansing organs and use the diarrhea to monitor their progress, allowing me to know when they are over the hump by its improvement without me trying to control it. If I just do the digestive tract diarrhea herbs then I'm controlling more that cleansing. However, if it's moderate moving towards very runny, then give some GI tract herbs simultaneously so your animal does not dehydrate. GI Soother or ClostridEaze can be used for that, as well as herbs found in your Digestive System chapter. Remember if you get runny diarrhea, also replace electrolytes with just squeezed grapefruit juice. Then start your deworming herbs again at a much lower dose, to rule out the possibility that there is a reaction to a plant in the mix, or offer the plants one at a time to see if there is one offending plant. Ninety-nine or more percent of the time you will find it was a quick parasite die off. If it is a particular plant, discontinue using it and use something else. Until an animal has its toxin load cleaned, it is possible to have a nontoxic plant react with a chemical in their body. This happens in humans also. Get the creature real clean and the reaction will go away. That typically takes 6 months to a year to get a creature that clean, occasionally longer, but it's possible.

Part II- Body Systems and Their Support

Body Systems Emphasis

Herbalism is different from allopathy, in that we go more towards a "few in number body systems" approach, rather than a "thousands of diseases" approach when supporting the creature in its problems. So rather than learning a disease name, although that is helpful for research, it is more important for us to understand all of the body systems that are involved in a condition, and to address those; rather than just using herbs to try and control a disease or singular symptom. You will find yourself much more effective in helping your animals to wellness if you can think in a body system application rather than a condition application. I will, however, list conditions in what I consider to be the primary body system areas to make finding and working with that situation easier due to the fact that many creatures are assigned actual diagnoses by their medical practitioner. Do not forget to work with that, and other related systems as you support your creature.

Many of the herbs we use for specific systems support the body in a way that it can heal itself to its normal state of well being. Whether a system is being over active (hyperfunction) or under active (hypofunction), often times the herbs used to support that system or organ are able to give the body what it needs to self correct.

Cleansing and Nourishing Emphasis

Cleansing and nourishing was covered some in Part 1, but I want to reemphasize these foundational truths here. Really, all we do as Vitalists is to cleanse and nourish. Period. Now how that looks will be different depending on what areas of the body are involved and whether we are supporting the body in an acute or chronic condition. Remember that if you cleanse and do not nourish with the proper herbs, you can only expect partial results. If you nourish with herbs, but fail to cleanse, that won't get you as much progress as you were hoping for either. As mentioned previously, a proper healthy diet is the third piece to that triune puzzle. Put all three together and you have a good opportunity to observe what to me sometimes borderlines on miracles! After all, who can expect their medication to assist them if they only take 33% of the dose they are supposed to take or not take it consistently? If you are not getting the results you are looking for, then examine your herb plan and see that you are covering the diet, the cleansing, and the herbal nourishing portions, along with the correct herbs, proper dosages and timing for your situation, and your herb efficacy. Often somewhere in that list is where I will find my mistake. Also, be sure you are covering all of the systems that need supporting in a particular issue. If you still are not seeing progress, please do get a diagnosis or assessment to make sure you are covering everything to help that animal heal itself.

Cleansing must be done in proper order. The first part of the body to consider is the health of the digestive tract, especially the stomach/stomach compartments, small intestine and large intestine areas. I am simply amazed, by looking at irides (plural for iris, the colored portion of the eye) with iridology, at how many of our pets and stock have a toxic bowel area! For the pets, that is not so hard to understand. Most of our cat, dog, reptile, fish and small rodent friends in developed countries eat packaged and processed foods like most of their owners. Organic or not, most of it is processed and packaged and dead food. Our livestock and horses though were a surprise to me. Even though our stock usually is consuming large amounts of roughage in the forms of pasture, browse and hay, I am seeing many irises that show toxicity in the bowel and intestinal areas. That got me to start thinking… We have herbicides and pesticides in the hay and grain. Then consider the molasses in grains and sweet feeds, that is not black strap (third refining) and is very high in refined sugar. Then consider genetically modified corn and soy and soon to be available alfalfa. Vaccinations, grooming products, fly sprays, chemical dewormers (even daily feed throughs!), barn insecticidal spray mists, and the list goes on. No wonder the stomach and colon are compromised! In cleansing, the reason we address the bowels first, is that we need to know that we don't have any reduced motility in the bowel. We need them eliminating the food they ate yesterday, today, with at least two bowel movements per day. Animals that eat more frequently should defecate even more frequently, the average being one bowel movement per meal, so in grazing and browsing livestock that ought to be multiple times per day. The stool or manure should be somewhat formed, but not hard and dry. It should not be watery or running, except in cows where it is somewhat liquid but still have some substance once on the ground.

Bovine species or other animals should always have control over the bowel movements; not just have manure leak or run from them. Whole (preferably organic) corn can be fed at one feeding to your animals in a small amount and then timed to see how long it takes for the corn to travel though their system to the manure end. In most animals you will be able to see pieces of the corn, not fully broken down in the manure. That will give you an idea of how long it is taking for them to process and then pass through their feed. You can do this with each animal and chart the results if you like, then compare that information as you work them through a program to see what progress is being made. Daily at first, then weekly, then monthly would be a good time period to consider your follow up observations. Bowel cleanses can be done and should be considered in pregnant animals, which have a tendency to constipate, especially during third trimester when they are processing their waste and the waste of their baby(ies) and often not moving around as much as before their babies start growing fast in utero. You absolutely can NOT have an abundantly healthy creature without a healthy digestive tract. It is NOT possible. If you ever pull a nugget of information from this book this is it. Bowel movements are important. Missing just one per day equates to being 7 behind in a week or 30 behind in a month. That's quite a back up in toxic, putrefying material. Now multiply that by a year. I think you see where this is going (or not going!). I am often amazed at what just this one thing will do with humans or animals. However, if you want even further results, continue on with the cleansings mentioned following this paragraph. If your animal is really sick, or very toxic, I would start any and all cleansing at half dosage, and give them several days to adjust, before gradually increasing the amount you give. This will moderate any cleansing crisis. Be sure to serve ample fresh clean water during any cleanse, so they can flush toxins from their system even faster.

If one starts to clean the liver or the blood/cells before you know that you have feed moving through the animal at the proper rate, they will not be able to move toxins out of their body fast enough, and many will be reabsorbed back into your animal, settling in areas of weakness or conditions, exacerbating the problems in those tissues. Cleaning for six months to a year is not too little of an amount of time to devote to the bowels. You simply can NOT have a healthy animal without a healthy digestive tract. So, be sure that bowel health being improved first. I'll cover herbs for that in the Digestive System section. Once they are having one bowel movement per meal eaten on a regular basis, you can add on the liver and kidney cleanse and do them concurrently with the bowels

Liver and Kidney cleanses are done next. The gallbladder gets lumped in along with the liver, in those animals that have a gallbladder, as most of the liver herbs also benefit the gallbladder. The liver cleanses can be started once you know the bowel is moving contents from beginning to end daily. Liver cleanses (and kidney) must be done before you ask the blood, cells, and intracellular (between the cells) areas to start dumping their toxic loads. The liver and kidneys also must be done before any heavy metals work is accomplished, as the liver and kidneys have to process those. We don't want to increase their workload until they have had their tune up, otherwise we can push them into problems caused by increased toxicity. As we encourage the body to release toxins, they are going to come out at a much faster rate then they went in. Technically the kidneys can be started with the bowels, as it has a direct route out of the body via the urethra and bladder, but since some of the herbs overlap quite nicely with the liver herbs, and both being major organs of cleansing, I like to lump them together in a cleanse. For animals that have been really sick or poisoned, a year is not too little time to spend here, and two years is even better. For animals that weren't off that much, that have been on a good chemical free feed and lifestyle program, from at least two generations of non chemical raised creatures, four months may be enough. I do not like to start these cleanses on first trimester pregnant creatures because the teeny starting nervous system and infantile body systems are extremely sensitive to damage from toxins.

Once you have a good amount of time into liver and kidney cleansing (at least 2 months in animals that appear otherwise healthy), then it is time to address blood/cellular cleansing. Otherwise wait until you are further into your liver and kidney program before addressing the cells. Specific cleansing organ herbs will be listed in those related chapters.

Blood and cellular cleansing is a very important step. This would be the blood stream, the cells themselves, and intracellular (between the cells). Perhaps someday you can be privileged to view blood under a microscope. Maybe you can do this with your veterinarian. I have seen mine at a conference for human alternative health that I was attending. It is fascinating. The first thing I noticed was the bright light rim around the cells! That is the 'life-force' or energy field around every red blood cell. The scriptures say that the life is in the blood. There is was. Amazing. Then you start looking at shape; thankfully mine were nice and round, and free flowing. Unhealthy blood cells can clump, RBC's (red blood cells) can be crenate or not round, they can even have white 'pus' looking spots in the center, which can be Candida albicans hitching a ride on the cell to anywhere in your body it wants to go as well as reducing the RBC's ability to carry life giving oxygen. Then you look at the fluid around the RBC's. It should be clear. Not dirty or filthy. There shouldn't be an accumulation of foreign things in there. Sorry, I'm not using technical terms, but blood work is not my area of specialty. That's where your veterinarian comes in! Anyhow, it is this filth that we want to go after, the Candida if needed, and nourishing put in place to allow those red blood cells to be their happy plump round selves with lots of life-force surrounding them. Any animal that has had a bout with anemia would definitely benefit from this cleanse. Remember, not to address this cleanse until after the bowels, liver, and kidneys are well under way. Herbs for the blood will be listed in the Circulatory chapter.

We live in an industrialized nation, therefore heavy metals is something to consider; even if you are extremely rural. If the penguins in the Antarctic can have jet fuel residues in their fat layers, then believe me, you probably do too. Heavy metals are put into jet fuels to stabilize it, which is a good thing. You don't want an airplane to back fire enroute and lose power. However, I know that we must have some scientists brilliant enough out there, to design other methods of powering these aircraft if they haven't done it already. There has to be ways, as our God has infinite knowledge. But I'll leave it there; I don't want to delve into politics. Jesus avoided politics whenever those issues were tossed in His lap, and I think I'll follow that example! It is said that nearly every female in America has jet fuel in her breast tissue. I believe it and expect similar information if those surveys were ever done on men. So how many of our animals have heavy metals in their system? Probably the vast majority. Other sources of course include grooming products, drinking water, exhaust from hauling, roadways, and tractors, vaccinations, anti-caking agents in just about anything that is an edible powder, the feed that gets rained on while it is growing, etcetera. Heavy metals cleansing herbs will be discussed in the Brain chapter. Metals can lodge in any part of the body, but the effects of them on the brain are widely documented, so I'll talk about them there. A heavy metals cleanse can be done for any amount of time, but six months would be a bare minimum if one has never been done. If you are in an area known for air or water pollution, I personally would take that to a year. If you can wait to start this until you have spent at least six months on the liver and kidneys and the blood/cells, so much the better for your creature. If you can't wait that long, then start after the bowels and liver/kidneys have had some time to clean, but start at one half or less dose for your creature on the metals until you hit the four month mark on cleansing the liver and kidneys and three month mark on the blood and cells. I also would not start a metals cleanse on a pregnant creature. We don't want those highly toxic metals being cut loose during that time period where they may endanger the unborn baby(ies). That is unless you are Divinely directed to do otherwise!

After any blood and cells or metals cleanse you will really want to re-address the liver and kidneys. Anything you release from these areas must go through the liver and kidneys multiple times to be removed from the body. To not readdress the liver and kidneys will mean that they will be impaired. I would consider another four month regimen if you really want to tune them back up. You'll learn why I like four month periods of time in the appropriate systems chapters. You can't have healthy cells or blood without taking care of the liver and kidneys. It's impossible.

Any of these cleanses can be done more than once a year as a tune up if you should desire. I like to give my breeding stock cleansing herbs before I breed them to give the conceived baby(ies) the best possible environment to grow in. I like to continue any needed program right after birthing. In our goats, this works out to a twice a year cycle. We are in a fairly clean environment where we are located. If you are in a polluted environment, such as areas that specialize in commercial farming or orchards (past or present), industrial, or heavily populated areas including the suburbs, then quarterly is even better, but be sure and avoid first trimester in breeding stock other than bowel work.

Humans replace every one of the 70 to 100 trillion cells in their body every two years. I do not know what the animal rates are, but since God creates so many things in patterns, I suspect animals would be somewhere similar. This would be with a healthy, well running system. Malnourished or less than abundantly healthy systems may take longer. I'll list the organ specifics I know for regeneration under those body system chapters.

Four Channels of Elimination

Your beloved creature has four main channels in which to eliminate toxins and waste from the body. Those are the lungs, the skin, the kidneys (via the urethra), and the liver/intestinal systems. If one system is in distress, then it is wise to be supporting the other systems, as they will be under additional stress as backup systems for the one that is not functioning up to par. So in a world where our creatures often have buildups of toxicity in their kidneys and their liver, is it any wonder we see so much lung weakness as they become over burdened, or more skin issues of all types? Please remember to consider this important information as you herb away, so that you can have more complete wellness for your creatures.

Holistic Considerations

Your creature is not just a physical being. It is also an emotional being and if we want to consider a spiritual (I believe they know who their Creator is even if they can't express that to us) being as well. After all, they are able to sense all types of things in the environment and in people that we currently do not have the ability to do.

Since I have touched on the spiritual and physical in this book, I want to take a few lines to have us consider the emotional. I think most of us have seen creatures that seem to be angry, depressed, happy, etcetera. I believe they can experience the full range of emotions we can due to the fact that emotions are triggered by biochemicals in our body which then are supposed to be broken down by a healthy liver after they are no longer needful for the situation at hand.

If we fail to address the possible underlying emotion, then the biochemical over release of these emotion creators will continue to damage or re-damage an organ that we have taken time to nourish back towards wellness. This is one of those areas where love and prayer and gentle but firm handling will go a long ways towards healing. It is interesting to note that none of the positive emotions have damaging effects to the body, but rather increase body alkalinity, stimulate the immune system and encourage mental well being.

If I see a creature with liver issues (other than poisonings) then I want to consider that anger could be involved. If it is the kidneys, then I may have an animal holding a grudge in the unforgiveness area. Don't laugh. I have seen animals that I really believe were holding grudges! Have you ever separated animals that were fighting, just to watch one of them try to restart the fight once they are put back together- even if it is days later?! I've also seen animals that I really believe were mad at me or someone else for requiring something of them they did not want to do. If an animal has pancreatic weakness, it's possible that there is some depression to support them with. The lymph system appears to be bogged down by apathy and the pituitary gland seems to not handle emotional pain very well. Continual fear can be very hard on the adrenal glands which often will also impact the kidneys that they hitch a ride on. For creatures with lung issues sometimes survival issues can come into play, as in rescues or creatures that have had a previous mean or neglectful owner. These concepts are taught in Holistic Iridology™ and it is simply amazing to me how these hit right on for people when I do iridology reports for them. I won't know what the issues have been, but they will, if not immediately they will as they further consider what it is they have buried. So I list these here just for your consideration. See if their personality parlays into some of their issues. Or if you know their personality profile you may want to support the related organs that could be being affected. Animals that are often stressed will have overall body acidity, which negatively impacts them everywhere. For these animals I will point you back to the cleanses, including extra blood support.

Medication Responsibilities

Sometimes there is a temptation for people to take their creatures off of daily medications once they start working with herbs. Let me caution you here. You must NEVER EVER remove a medication from your creature that their body has been taking in just one day, or just one week. To do this could put your animal's system in a state of shock or cause additional damage, sometimes even death. I've had people tell me that they have done this, and have 'seen' no effect of doing this. Now I know that they did not question nor view microscopically each cell in the body to see if they were put under undue stress or additional damage from a quick drop in medication. Just because you did not view the damage, does not mean it did not occur to the detriment of your beloved creature. Though medicating is not something people who read this book are into, do not err in the opposite direction of forcing the body through a quick change. If your goal is to see if your animal's medication can be reduced or eliminated, here are some things you can do.

First, get them in a good cleansing and nourishing whole herb program and improved diet.

Second, work with your veterinarian to see what kind of a schedule you can come up with to slowly reduce medications as the animal's well being improves. This may require regular lab work to monitor progress so that medications can be properly readjusted. If your animal is on a time release type of medication, you must NEVER alter the medication, or a lethal overdose could result. If they are on a non time release medication, your veterinarian might give you permission to start slowly removing tiny bits of the medication to reduce its size or they may be able to prescribe the drugs in a smaller dosage so that they can be easily reduced on schedule. Extra care must be taken if an animal is on medications for heart, pancreas, mental conditions or thyroid issues. These definitely require close veterinary monitoring.

Now that I've scared you, please know that it is often possible to have an animal gain enough health and even abundance of health to be able to reduce or remove medications. However, do it RESPONSIBLY. You and your veterinarian as a team are the only ones on this planet that can decide the best way to go about this for your creature. Certainly pray for guidance too! If you do get them off of medications, or even just reduced, remember to address additional cleansing to help them remove drug residues from their system. If they remain on some form of medications then cleansing will be a daily routine to support the organs that are dealing with daily synthetic insults and increased acidity to their tissues.

Chapter 14- Brain

What an amazing creation is the brain.   Much larger in ability than the most complex of computers, running all of the body systems simultaneously 24/7, even when your pet is sleeping! Their language storehouse (all of us with animals know they have language- we just don't always understand them), and where emotions are processed.   The brain is continually receiving and disseminating information via the nervous system from every structure of the body, and continually recording all of that information in its memory. Even those premeditated tricks they pull on us are originated in the brain.   It's all there! Are you tired thinking about it yet? Then this chapter is for you!

Concussion

I'm not sure why we don't ever hear people mention concussions in creatures, but they certainly do happen. ALWAYS, ALWAYS, ALWAYS consider these as acute situations if you see any symptomology. If your creature hits its head hard, falls hard, gets kicked in the head, or is an a vehicular or other accident with a fast change in gravitational force, it certainly can receive a concussion due to the brain crashing into the skull.   If you witness any of the above it does not harm to give a dosage of cayenne to minimize any possible bleeding (bruising) that may be taking place.   I recently suffered a mild concussion when I was launched off of a horse and I was amazed at how much of a difference an oral dose of cayenne made in just seconds in my mind 'clearing up'; even immediately eliminating the mild 'halo light' effect I was seeing. It still took a few days for the mild headache and mentality that was not quite 'feeling' right to clear up, but the quick change with the cayenne was amazing. Remember also, that as in a stroke, the faster we can minimize any possible bleeding we will be able to reduce pressure on that delicate organ that otherwise would have been there. Symptoms can range from mild like mine were, to severe including excruciating headaches, memory loss, vision disruption, vomiting, severe personality changes and more. Besides cayenne, consider getting them on tissue building herbs such as are discussed in the Epidermis chapter. You will also want to consider oxygen promoting herbs such as wheat grass, raw fresh apple, gotu kola, marshmallow root (does double time as it is also a powerful anti-inflammatory herb), thyme, eucalyptus, and Lobelia inflata. Pair those with ginger, cayenne and/or rosemary for some nice circulatory stimulation and antiphlogistic (anti-inflammatory support) and you have a nice system of support going. If there is a head injury, also suspect a cervical spine (neck) or other spinal or shoulder injury at the same time. See the Skeletal System chapter for those issues.

Disability

Disability in the brain has many sources. Toxins introduced to their dam, especially during first trimester, can damage the delicate brain tissue as they can any tissue. Mechanical damage from accidents can occur. Dry fevers allowed to go too high for too long can also fry brain cells. Medications and vaccines can play a role in adverse effects to the brain. Animals, believe it or not, due to their SAD (Standard American Diet) human owner similarly packaged and processed diets are even subject to strokes. Venal tissue weakness can play a role in strokes as well. Damage from toxins from poisonous creatures or plants or industrial chemicals have neurotoxic effects. The good news is that like all tissue in the body, brain tissue will try to regenerate back to its DNA, if allowed to do so. How are you going to allow it to do so? You already know the answer C_____ and N_____! Yes, Cleansing and Nourishing, starting in order. Additional nutrients I like to use are: powdered greens mixes, nettle, gotu kola, wheat grass, barley grass, alfalfa, spirulina, organic raw unfiltered apple cider vinegar, and kelp. Physical injury to the brain can also be addressed with topical salves, like Wounderful!, ReBuilld or Dr. Christopher's Complete Bone and Tissue Formula (not for equine/camelids, as it contains black walnut). It takes about one year to rebuild a brain cell for cell for one. For moderate to severe damage or toxin buildup, you will need more than one cellular regeneration to get to optimum wellness, as the cells won't be able to repair to one hundred percent health in one regeneration. Creatures with damage from chemicals may not gain complete health, but will certainly improve with time. Just keep at it. Don't give up!

Fevers

Obviously fevers heat up the entire body, but it is their effect on the brain where we become most concerned. If the brain is baked for too long, disability or death may occur.

Fevers show us that the body really IS functioning. For every degree in temperature that the body raises, the immune system including manufacture of more macrophages, ramps up exponentially. Therefore to reduce a fever that is below dangerous levels is a serious disservice to the body. First, it lowers the body's own created ability to annihilate viral, bacterial, or microbial invaders just from the temperature alone. It also slows the body's ability to increase white blood cells to go after the warring microbes. People often also fail to recognize that it is that fever, in part that helps make us or our creature miserable, causing us to rest more. Remove the fever and watch the creature activity level go up; only to watch the health decline further. A high fever promotes rest so that nearly every ounce of energy beyond the vital operations to go towards that battle.

When one grabs at the chemical over the counter resources to combat a fever, the NSAID family as they are called, they also do the body a disservice. They may reduce the fever back to a safe level, but they also cut off the macrophages ability to communicate with the T Helper and T Killer cells and vice versa. I'm not sure that is the result we are looking for. Some safe ways to bring down a fever that is going too high follow. You want to reduce the fever slowly, as it is a rapid change in body temperature that can bring on seizures. This is whether the temperature is going up or down fast, not usually the temperature itself.

Hydrotherapy foot, neck, head, body is an age old and very useful aid. It can be as simple as soaking the feet of the animal and putting wet cool or cold towels across their back. You can wrap cool or cold wet toweling around their neck as well. Remember to change the toweling as it heats up. If it is the hot time of year, consider shaving the animal with a size five blade, if it won't stress during the clip job. Even if all you can get is the topline (back) and neck areas; this will help. They can also be led into a warm to cool pond or bathtub. Remember not to shock them with a large temperature change as you want to lower the fever back to safer levels, not break it and end its immune system support.

The Accessible Pet, Equine and Livestock Herbal

I want to discuss the difference between wet and dry fevers. In a human, a dry fever is dangerous at 105 degrees. A dry fever is what you have when you are lying on the couch or in bed. However, a wet fever can safely go to 107. Please consult with your veterinarian or other experienced resource to determine what is too high of a temperature in your creature. Each animal will have its normal. Outdoor temperature will affect the normal range and each species has their own normal range. Sometimes even a family line will run a degree hotter or colder than others, and young stock tends to be warmer than mature stock.

It has to be a WET, very wet fever. How wet? First you start with one of your favorite projects- a catnip tea enema or two to clean that very sick creature's toxic fecal matter out and start some internal soaking from the back end into the colon. The 150 pound creature soaks in a hot bathtub and consumes about one quart of catnip tea (to encourage sweating) over a 45 to 60 minute time period. Wet outside and wet inside. Then you pull your creature out and wrap them in a cold wet sheet and put them to bed or stall rest under a toasty layer of old natural fiber blankets to let them sweat toxins out of their system quickly. I know it sounds backwards from what we get taught (doesn't much of this book sound that way, though?), but it gets the immune system really moving, and the moisture protects the brain. It won't go too high in an infectious condition as long as you have sufficient internal and external moisture. If there was a head injury or medication involved that impacts the brain, then the body may go too high on the fever. Exercise GREAT caution in these situations and look to other methods in this section. Also, animals with blood sugar problems and pregnant creatures may not be able go through this procedure safely. In those cases proceed with the yarrow or catnip tea drenches to try to encourage high amounts of sweating to help them lower their body temperature in a natural way while at the same time trying to blow out toxins through the skin. Still keep them blanketed and look at the Immune System chapter for more advice on working with fevers. For those that have heard of the 'Cold Sheet Treatment', this is what you just read about.

Eucalyptus essential oil or peppermint (not for very young stock) can be diluted at 60 to 80 drops per quart of water, with ¼ cup of raw apple cider vinegar in it, shaken and sprayed on the animal to help it reduce temperature. Catnip tea can be given to increase perspiration of the animal, as can yarrow tea.

Willow bark is where aspirin was originally distilled from. Don't mistake this for today's aspirin though, which is synthetic, a NSAID, and of course not whole herb. Give the normal dose of willow tea hourly, until the fever is at a 'safe' level. Remember you want some fever to benefit the body's immune system response and so the animal will rest.

Listeriosis

Listeria bacterium normally occurs in the soil. The problem with this comes in if your animal ingests some from the ground, or mixed in its feed. Moldy hay or badly prepared silage or haylage can allow Listeria to proliferate in the mold. In cattle often more than one animal will be affected, because of the way they tend to indiscriminately pull feed into their mouths as a group. More picky eaters, such as goats and sheep, often will only have one animal coming down with it, so if you have a cow vet, they may not recognize the Listeria problem in the smaller stock as they often will be looking for multiple animals with a problem. If the Listeria bacterium cross from the blood into the brain stem, you may just find yourself with a severe fight on your hands to save your creature. If you note an animal head pressing on a wall or fence, or circling, with an unusually high fever or possibly drooling, this is a condition you want to be sure and rule out with trained help. If they become recumbent (down, unable to get up) it's much more difficult to turn them around, but not impossible. Remember, it's not too late until it is too late. Further into the condition a tell tale sign, (according to Mary C. Smith, in her book; Goat Medicine), is when their head starts to pull in towards their flank. You may be able to straighten it out, but their head will go right back against the flank. Eyes may become rolled into their head and convulsions may set it, as they did for our girl. Please consult proper veterinarian books, websites, or your veterinarian for a more complete list for assessment for your creature if you suspect this condition. Remember this thought for any condition I discuss in this book.

Progress may be SLOW, but progress can come. It may take days, be prepared for a long haul if you catch them once they are down. We did save a down doe once, before I had formal herb training, so used a drug route. If I had this problem today, these are the things I would do in my herd. First, get your animal right side up if it is down. This may mean stacking straw bales against it or dragging it against a wall. They will not be able to stay upright by themselves once they are down and will bloat or loose gut motility and die. I had to sleep with my dairy goat in twelve degree weather. Lots of straw, my Carhartt insulated coveralls, hat, gloves, and wool blankets made this doable. I should correct the sleep statement. I dozed, but mostly had to stay awake and brace myself against a wall and against her to keep her upright, as she wanted to go on her side and still had occasional convulsions throwing her on her side. Keep them WARM. In this or any other more serious brain stem or stress condition they are too stressed to keep their body warm, so you have to help them stay warm. We kept wool blankets over her with plastic jugs under them filled with hot water and changed out as often as needed to keep her warm. It worked quite well. Heat lamps in barns scare me. There are too many barn fires from heat lamps resulting in livestock, facility, and equipment loss, so I avoid heat lamps in the barn at all costs.

Garlic along with other antiseptic herbs should be considered. I like HerBiotic herb mix, but myrrh, goldenseal, cayenne, thyme (low doses in pregnant animals), rosemary, ginger and even lavender can be considered. Adding ginger and/or gotu kola to the mix will help the body get more of it to the head area. Gotu kola also has the advantage of oxygenating the brain, which uses an average of 25% of the oxygen supply taken into the body. Rosemary has an affinity for the brainstem area and helps increase circulation anywhere it is used, helping your other herbs get to the area in greater quantity via the capillary route. A blend would be best, rather than relying on just one herb. Dosage would be acute of course and for something like this I'd be administering herbs around the clock the first 24 hours if possible. Don't forget to nourish yourself during this time with herbs and plant foods and cayenne! One of my favorite ways to support my animals in these situations is through hot herbal teas with raw honey and cayenne. Garlic I would start at triple the normal 'penicillin dose" of 2 cloves (not bulbs, but the thumb like sections, cloves) for a 100 to 200 pound creature. Calibrate up or down for other sizes from 150 pounds. A full sized cow will be getting a bulb of garlic each time. Lobelia inflata can be given to support them during seizures, and it can be rubbed right onto the brainstem area, as long as you don't endanger yourself getting next to a flailing animal. The herb mixes will have to be added to a liquid and be given orally, and given very carefully so the animal doesn't choke. If you can stomach tube it in, that would be safer. If you can make a very strong tea with distilled water for the first dosage they will absorb the herbs faster. Oil of rosemary, made by putting 15 drops of pure essential oil into a tablespoon of olive oil (or oil of garlic) can be rubbed into the brainstem. Three drops of pure thyme essential oil can be added to that in non-pregnant animals. Apply hourly the first day.

An enema should be considered. Your animal's digestive tract will be shut down with such an assault, so getting the colon areas cleared out will allow the body to focus even further on the threat rather than risk it wasting any energy of digestion. Make a proper infusion (tea) using some of the antibacterial herbs and enema. Remember to wear protective clothing such as raingear and boots in case you end up wearing some of the contents. Have a lot of newspaper and straw or shavings down to catch the manure and enema mix, making it easier to remove. Do this outside if possible. Once you have cleared out the manure with one or more enemas; put one more enema in with herb tea. Once in the colon their body will pull in nutrients from the infusion. If it is a smaller animal try to elevate its hips higher than its backbone to hold in this last enema for 10 or more minutes. Livestock, if upright, can either be led to have their rear legs on much higher ground, such as a hillside or mound to elevate their hips. Animals that are down, such as goats, can have a 'slant board' placed under them. A heavy board placed on the ground, such as thick plywood, with supports under one end to get a good slope. Then bed it thickly and carefully pull your animal's rear onto that so that the pin bones or tail head are elevated a few inches higher than the withers while still keeping their body upright. This can help keep the herbs in longer. Remove the board after half an hour so that they can lie in a normal position again.

Letting them fast for a day or two while you get this underway is fine, unless they are pregnant or seriously underweight. In that case, olive oil rubs and smaller olive oil enemas (1/4 cup for 100- 200 pound animals) can be given for nourishment while they are not eating. Olive oil can also be given vaginally. The body will draw it in and use it. Just apply your clean and lubricated enema equipment just inside the clean vulva and inject the oil. Antibacterial herbs in powdered form, even some pressed garlic, can be added here as well. Test your blend with your finger to be sure you did not put too many herbs in. If it burns you are too hot for that sensitive tissue. Remember to have your animal's rump elevated or it will just run right back out.

Keep your animal hydrated! Learn how to do a pinch test from your vet, and learn from them how much water must go into that animal on a daily basis to keep it hydrated. The animal can be soaked in a tub or even a warm clean pond, if you can maintain its body temperature, three times daily. You can also give body temperature enemas (always add some nourishing herbs such as raspberry or nettle) to help hydrate your animal. Stomach tubing knowledge is also very helpful in a time like this. I prefer not to give lactated ringers solution, injectible under the skin, but if I had no other way of keeping them hydrated, this is something to consider. Do not inject plain water under the skin. Never. By doing this you will introduce bacteria and pathogens that are likely to be in the water. You can make sterilized water by boiling distilled water, or purchase sterile water from your veterinarian. Also consider adding oral electrolytes daily per your vet's recommendations. I have a homemade recipe in the appendix for those that want it.

Besides the brain, you will want to supply additional nutritional support for the body as a whole. Things such as black strap molasses, cayenne, rose hips, kelp, raspberry, stinging nettle, greens mixes, spirulina, wheat grass, and nutritional yeast are helpful here. Better Daze herb mix can also be used. They can be mixed with a liquid and carefully drenched, stomach tubed, given by enema or vaginal injection.

When an animal is recumbent (down) you will need to change them over from which rump side they are resting on, and massage the areas that is has been laying on. Ginger or cayenne or rosemary in a salve or olive oil can be rubbed in to help encourage circulation. Yarrow tea can also be used as a hot, but comfortable, temperature fomentation to draw circulation out to the limbs. You will also need to set up a sling system, or for a smaller animal even pulling their rib cage up on a hay bale, several times a day to get them upright. Gently but firmly stretch out their limbs, work them as if they were walking (if they will let you), massage well, and if they can put pressure on their limbs as you support their upright position, so much the better. This is imperative for keeping their digestive tract operating, as well as trying to discourage atrophy in their muscle structure. I can't remember the exact number, but in just 24 hours of being recumbent without moving one can lose around 80 percent of their muscle mass. That happened to me in 1995 after a serious accident and it had to happen in my case. There were so many injuries that my physical therapy couldn't be started until all of the physical repairs were made, which took several days. That is a story for another book. I am here by God's grace and only by His grace.

Don't give up. I remember it took a day to see a cessation in convulsions, followed by her being able to start gaining control of her eye movements the day after that, followed by her being able to hold herself upright and return her head to normal position the third day, etcetera. So watch for little positive changes that may be all you can see at first. Also consider looking at the Polioencephalmalacea section in this chapter. Both conditions can occur simultaneously.

Metals cleansing

Heavy metals are everywhere. We live on a polluted planet. Jet fuel pervades fat tissue in creatures from the North Pole to the South Pole and all points in between. Heavy metals are in our vaccines (aluminum and thimersol which is a minimum of 50% mercury). Mercury vapors are used to 'sanitize' sterile wraps, pads, and diapers. Of course it works; nothing can live or perform well in the presence of mercury, the world's second most toxic substance. Fuel and cigarette exhaust contain arsenic, cadmium and other heavy metals. Heavy metals are rained down out of the air as it is cleansed by that source of water called rain. Right on top of our organic and natural raised foods. They are in some wells, in city water and more. Aluminum is added to decrease caking and increase pourability in things from baking soda to milled flours and is not required to be labeled. It's added to make certain material melt easier, like processed cheese 'foods'. Bodies have a hard time removing heavy metals from the system; if unaided. They were never meant to be consumed or inhaled. They affect mentality, memory, and can impact any and every organ, cell, or system of the body. Those that display alterations to their mental well being often diagnose high for heavy metals when tested, and often for more than one heavy metal.

Herbs are a wonderful and safe support system when wanting to give the body what it needs to start cleaning these out. As stated at the beginning of Part II, do not start this until the bowels are functioning well and the liver and kidneys have been attended to. Then follow up metals work with more liver and kidneys and bloodstream and cells work to help them further remove the added burden as they are asked to move out and process these filthy elements.

Some of my favorite herbs for this are cilantro (powerful!), lemon (also quite powerful), apple with the peels on and raw apple cider vinegar, distilled water (okay, not an herb, but oh so natural). Prune juice and fig juice or the fruits also help to draw toxins. Apple pectin also helps draw additional toxins. Apple and kelp can also help draw radiation and so can bentonite clay which expands in the digestive tract helping to draw toxins and helping increase motility. Raspberry and alfalfa are gently cleansing. Ideally I would work with a blend, also mixing in two or more bowel nourishing herbs for a better combination. Plan to work on metals for six to eight months MINIMUM, and much longer than that if the mind wasn't as healthy as you wanted it to be. Plan to readdress this cleanse on some type of regular basis, as our exposure is constant.

Memory

Who doesn't want their creature to have the best memory possible? What a joy to have a well trained pet or creature that is a breeze to train and wants to please! TBF Delikat, a Norwegian Fjord mare, exemplifies this. It's as if this young mare greets me each morning with, "Hi Mommy, what do you want me to learn from you today?" I am amazed at how quickly this mare learns as I start her basic training to become a saddle horse, and I feed her as I would any student, helping to enable her to give me her best focus and attention. Her irides (plural for iris) are crystal clear and clean showing me a very healthy system to work with, and it shows. I can't make this decision for anyone else, but since I practice Equine Iridology, instead of a pre-purchase vet check, I assessed her body's well being by doing a quick iris check on each eye. I did that on all of the horses I looked at, immediately recognizing any weaknesses or areas that needed attention once I got the ones we purchased back home. Of course we also walked out the horses and watched movement from every direction, physical conformation, leg checks and feeling legs and joints, hoof checks ("no hoof, no horse"), and temperament. Certainly a vet check and an iridology assessment can be done on the same animal, giving a fuller picture and would be a wise thing to do, especially if your time and financial investment seems significant to you or you are early in your learning curve for livestock information. See the Appendix if additional information on Iridology interests you.

Some of us have athletes, be they equine, canine, draft ox or other, that have large training and performance demands on them for their species. Providing the best for them will allow you to see their genetic potential perform before your eyes.

Here we are back to memory. You already know part of the deal. Cleansing, of course. The toxins have to come out of the cells to have additional room for the nourishment to be able to come in and be fully used. Herbs I love for helping the body improve the memory department are rosemary, cayenne, ginger, gotu kola, wheat grass, alfalfa, kelp, spirulina, ginkgo (given over time). Peppermint is another good herb, as is yarrow. Burdock root for blood stream support can be added as well. Nettle is another plant I love for just about everything, and helps the body to remove blockages slowly. When is that not a bad idea for the brain for anyone or anything?

An herb of particular interest to me is basil. Yep, that FRESH stuff you can buy in the produce section at the grocery store. It's also very easy to root grocery store basil in your windowsill in a glass of water with some soil in it. Or you could also plant it from seed and keep it in your window, your planters, and your garden. Harvest before it flowers, preferably in the morning just after the dew is dried off of it. Then hang it to dry out of direct light to put away for winter. Let some seed and harvest the seeds to restart the cycle. I like to think of basil as 'brainsil'. Besides being antibacterial, it aids memory, brain circulation, can assist the body in migraines, aches and pains, stress from mental and nervous fatigue and more. Add this herb to your creature's diet, starting in ¼ of normal herb dosage amounts. Start very small if your animal is pregnant and increase to half dose only; being a stimulant herb it is powerful. Don't overdo it, a little of this herbal gem goes quite a ways. You can give it as tea, but please taste it yourself first to be sure it's not too '*picante*' hot to the mouth, which is Spanish for spicy hot, as opposed to water or food temperature hot. Basil essential oil can also be used but in small doses such as five drops per tablespoon of olive oil. If the animal is pregnant, then add only two or three drops per tablespoon of olive oil applied to the brain stem area.

The Accessible Pet, Equine and Livestock Herbal

Please note that is a whole tablespoon of olive oil and not the standard teaspoon dosage.

Salves comprised of some of this herb listing can also be administered to the head and brain stem areas if desired for additional support and add some cell proliferation herbs to that such as comfrey, lavender, and pure aloe. Organic real raw honey is very nourishing. As I write this I have a dab of one drop of rosemary essential oil on my inner shirt collar (remember a pure non oily type of essential oil will not stain after it dries). I also have a bottle of basil essential oil that I am periodically taking slow deep breaths in. They really do help. You might try these if you are reading this book and want more assistance retaining information. We can't forget the 2 capsules of 40,000 heat unit cayenne I took with some food to keep my circulation going well and the yummy blueberry leaf tea with added antioxidant plants and raw organic honey. It smells as good as it tastes! Or the beautiful views of the Central Oregon high desert I'm drinking in for a few days to give my eyes a break from the lap top and to give me time to focus on and finish this project. You might also consider that soft faith encouraging music that I have playing that quietly wafts through the background. You see, integrated alternative well being methods that work together. Think and pray about these things when you assist your beloved creature. You may be surprised at what you are inspired to do.

Oxygenating

With all of the nonstop computing and managing the brain does, it is no wonder that it would like approximately 25% of the oxygen from each breath of air that comes in. This is another reason daily exercise is so important! Without proper lung development and diaphragmatic muscle development which help one take fuller breaths; the brain will be under oxygenated. Daily exercise in fresh air is the ultimate for healthy brain development in your young stock, and maintaining it in your older creatures. This is one reason why I look for wide (not over wide which may be harder for the shoulders to hold together as they age) chests and full well sprung ribs in my stock. My chickens, my dogs, my goats, my horses, and other creatures I've owned in the past- even an iguana. Any of them.   A pinched chest and narrow rib cage will never allow good growthy oxygen supporting lungs to develop for abundant well being. See the practical things that come out of your animal type and breed's conformation score sheet? Those aren't just numbers and the information is not just for registered stock!

Water, water, water. I can't overemphasize healthy clean water. A dehydrated animal with a dehydrated blood stream will not carry as much oxygen, nor get it everywhere in the amounts it needs to be. Without ample water, the nervous system (of which the brain is in control) cannot function efficiently either. If the water is not clean daily, the animal will drink enough to survive, but never enough to thrive. So before you start spending money on the best hay, best raw and sprouted feeds and herbs, please attend to your water. Even if you have to spend some money on a reverse osmosis or other system, it will be the best spent money in your feeding and wellness program.

Wheat grass juice (fresh juiced) at two ounces per 100 to 200 pound animal, two to three times a day, adds oxygen to the bloodstream. Fresh (meaning you JUST juiced it yourself) raw organic apple juice is another oxygenator. You can also feed fresh apples. Please always slice the apples. Feeding whole apples carries the risk of one slipping back and choking the animal. I've even heard of a pig dying from choking on a whole apple. Give them sides to bite onto so they can chew them first. Also, try to get organic or natural raised apples. Sure you can wash the apple, but how to do you get the toxins out of the apple that were put inside of it via the tree roots and tree vascular system? Also, how do you wash toxins off that are UNDER the petroleum wax that was applied to the apple to make it shinier? Nettle, cabbage (red is best, green is still a good choice), and kelp to support the blood's ability to carry oxygen are good features of these herbs. Gotu kola helps take oxygen to the brain, as mentioned before. Just remember, if your creature is not used to all of these wonderful very nutritious foods, start with a small amount, perhaps 1/3 of the normal amount, and work them up to their full dose. Monitor by watching their manure. If it starts getting too loose, back the nutrition down.

Polioencephalmalacea

Referred to as just 'polio' in the ruminant world, this is not the same problem as human polio. The root cause of this problem is a thiamine (Vitamin B1) deficiency in the rumen, causing it to shut down. The animal may go down, may

The Accessible Pet, Equine and Livestock Herbal

have convulsions, may go blind, and it will end in death unless you intervene. Polio can be going on concurrently with Listeriosis, so as a safeguard if I think I have polio, I also start watching for listeriosis. The beauty of herbs is I can put a few herb doses down them and find out I didn't need to. That results in some of my time and a better nourished animal. Not a bad thing. Better that then finding out too late and losing them because I did nothing.

Mold in feed is one of those culprits that can burn out the thiamine in the rumen. Also severe distress to the animal or digestive tract, including some medications can encourage this issue.

Catnip and cayenne makes a good combination and can be given singly as well. Nutritional yeast and black strap molasses are other tools to consider. All of these can be used simultaneously if wanted. If I were dealing with that here, I would be giving triple the normal amount, and give it hourly. If it is polio, they will start turning around fast. Do NOT let that fool you! You need to keep putting herbs into them for the next 24 hours to avoid a relapse. Once they are looking quite improved you can slow it down to every three hours, but keep it going.

Whenever the rumen has been though a challenge such as this, probiotics are in order to help replenish the enzymes needed for digestion and nutrient uptake by the villi (small hairs in the intestines). Probiotics I like are any raw living food. Garlic, raw apple cider vinegar with the mother in it and raw organic honey are nice choices. I avoid the processed contents of animal digestive tracts that usually come from slaughter animals in every level of health. You can also try to swipe a cud from a healthy animal then put that into your animal orally. Try not to liquefy it very much. Even squeezing the liquid out of it (wear gloves or you will smell like silage) and carefully drenching that liquid will help. Just beware of teeth and molars. This is another good skill to learn from your veterinarian or experienced herdkeeper. Look at all the fun you'll have if you put together a workshop!

Seizures

These can be unnerving to say the least. I have seen them in humans and creatures. I have had humans call me in obvious distress because they have a beloved pet that experiences seizures. The causes can be numerous. Nervous system challenges, toxins from various sources, medications, or an adverse effect of vaccinations (which can even take a month or longer to show up, but often within the same week). Mechanical damage to the head due to an injury, heat strokes, a lack of healthy fats in the diet, very high dry fevers, some conditions, and I'm sure more. A not often considered source can be a mineral deficiency, in which the head is attempting to move nutrition, with difficulty, or 'seize it', to another area of the brain. Medications, sugars, caffeines, high stress levels, low nutrition foods, heavy milkers, and too much animal protein in a diet can all demineralize the body. Animals can also be born mineral deficient if their parents or dam were not up to optimum levels when they were conceived and then grown. Then as they grow quickly their already malnourished body can't keep up with the demands of a growing body. I also wonder if ultrasounding babies in utero can make the nervous system more susceptible to damage later on. After all, if the ultrasound did any heat or wave damage to nervous system structures, that would create an area where toxins would begin to collect, ready to show up as a dis-ease or condition later in the creatures life. These statements can be true in so many conditions.

That brings us back to cleansing and nourishing. Getting the toxins out, avoiding those things and situations which demineralize, and getting the nutrition back in. Mineral rich foods include kelp, alfalfa, comfrey, kelp, stinging nettle, kelp, romaine, raspberry leaves, dandelion, kelp, cabbage, marshmallow root, slippery elm, kelp, carrots. You can choose from quite a variety of plant roots, and aged tree inner barks that are used for nutritional purposes. Other herbs that come to mind are white oak bark and pau d' arco (lapacho) tree inner bark. You also should consider some combination of blue vervain, blue and black cohosh. Along with some of these other herbs, and Lobelia, a truly nourishing program can be built. Dr. Christopher has a nice Nerve product as well for internal use. NervEaze Blend by Fir Meadow is another one.

For the actual seizures themselves, you can apply Lobelia inflata tincture to the brain stem area and give it orally. You can also feed Lobelia inflata to your animal. If you can't safely reach the head area, start by applying it to the spine area as you stay away from a jerking head and legs. Start with smaller than normal amounts; so that you don't accidentally get into the emetic effect (throw up) of the plant. If you happen to do that, note the dose, but don't get overly concerned. The clean out from the extra lobelia will actually be beneficial for your animal. Lobelia is an herb that nourishes every cell of the body and encourages the body to function correctly.

Chamomile, valerian, lavender, hops (NOT beer as the alcohol and additives will demineralize and toxify your animal, hops by themselves are not good for dogs), lettuces including wild lettuce (compass plant) and sow thistle have a calming effect on the mind and can be added to their diet. Lavender essential oil (not lavandin) can be mixed at the rate of 15 drops of essential oil to one tablespoon of olive oil and rubbed on the head two times per day. You can try adding rosemary essential oil to that. Start at one drop and over a few days increase to as many as 5 drops of rosemary in that same olive oil/lavender blend for additional brain support. For felines remember not to use the essential oils, but you can take ½ teaspoon of rosemary needles and 1 teaspoon of lavender blossoms or leaves and make small tea. Then soak that warm fomentation on your feline's skull, if they will tolerate it. Remember to roll them in a blanket if you think they will resist, but don't push them real hard as you don't want to push them into a seizure trying to help them. If that won't do, then outsmart them. Take your herbs (not your essential oils), put them in a stainless or glass heatproof bowl, then pour hot water over them and set on the ground in the room your cat is in. Remember to place it where no one will trip over it. Let the volatile oils fill the room, and your cat. Outsmarting a cat is a difficult thing indeed, but in this one you win.

Strokes

I wish this debilitating condition was something we didn't even have to discuss, but alas, just as in humans, animals can suffer stroke from various sources, such as extreme stress, and the effects of medication including vaccinations. Your first clue may be loss of ability, sometimes with just the tongue, or a face that droops on one side, to loss of movement on one side of the body. If your animal is having life support problems, such as breathing, besides looking at those chapters it does not hurt to call your veterinarian to see if they need additional life support from equipment they may have on hand. When a vessel blows in the brain it will leak blood into the area, causing pressure to the adjoining tissues as the blood fills space there really isn't room for. Consider also that the vessel blowing can be thought of as a small explosion creating additional pressure to the adjoining brain tissue, creating additional damage. Losses of ability in mentality can occur, depending on where in the brain the explosion takes place.

Cayenne is the number one plant of choice to assist the body in a stroke. The sooner you can start getting it into your animal orally, the more you may be able to help the body alleviate damage. The cayenne will almost immediately help the body to equalize blood pressure, which takes pressure off of the injury site, reducing the amount of bleed out into the brain and allowing it to close the damaged area quicker. Evidently, aspirin will cause them to bleed out longer, as it reduces the ability of blood to clot, so this is another reason to avoid this chemical. Cayenne also helps the body build elasticity to vein and artery tissue, reducing the possibility for stroke. Your animal needs to be watched to make sure that it can keep its normal body heat, as many times in a cerebral hemorrhage event they will lose ability to heat themselves, as in other times of system stress. Blanket them if needed. Don't let them get cold. The cayenne will also help them heat their body core. Keep them on cayenne- ½ teaspoon slowly working to 1 teaspoon two to three times per day with food, six days per week until all damage from the stroke subsides. Remember it takes a brain about one year to regenerate once. With a stroke, you will expect to need more than one regeneration to get the cells where you want them. Also consider adding some memory herbs, some wound care herbs, and some nervous system herbs to their daily diet. Do not allow limbs to atrophy or lose ability. Lift and move them as full rotation as you are able to, carefully but firmly to exercise the muscles and keep the joints free moving. If it's a small pet, you can do this with them on your lap if you do lap time in the evening. If needed, pay a physical therapist if to show you how they would accomplish this with a human. Tell them what you are up to and I'll bet they will take it as a fascinating project to teach you some skills in one visit. It's worth it.

The Accessible Pet, Equine and Livestock Herbal

I'm a physical therapy rebuild project. I did 4 years over a 5 year time span; even learning to walk again. They were used by God to help me gain ability I should never have gotten back by medicine's standards (THANK-YOU Dale Rudd, P.T. in Sequim, WA). Then get creative to see how you will do it with your creature. Don't forget to use some of the wonderful allopathic resources that we do have! Injury repair after an emergency has some great tools in allopathy. Give them a progress report with a photo and homemade thank-you card 'from' their 'client'. It will likely be fun and rewarding for them.

Vaccinations

Entire books have been written on this topic, and I won't attempt to cover it here. Much of what has been written applies to human shots. I challenge someone to do some similar research on livestock vaccinations. However, I expect that much of what is written will apply over to animals. After all, animals are used for testing in labs for all types of drug and product research, and many of the herbs we use for humans we use for creatures with similar reports of body assistance. Unlike human situations, there is not a federal database that I am aware of for reporting adverse effects of vaccinations in creatures. That database is estimated to be under reported by as high at 90 percent of reactions, as most doctors do not report adverse effects. I have a book listed in the appendix for those interested in learning more, before they make decisions for their human or creature family regarding vaccinations. I won't tell you what to do, but please do be informed. There are hundreds of footnotes in that book, taken from many government sources.

Vaccination ingredients can be many. They will include some type of growth medium, the protein source used to grow the bacteria, virus, or microbe in. That can be chicken embryo, egg, aborted fetal tissue, monkey kidneys and many more sources. None of which would normally make its way into your creature's bloodstream. MSG, propylene glycol, polysorbate 80, aluminum, thimersol (a 50% or higher mercury product) and many more, including the invader you do not want your animal to catch are included in these. They are then usually injected directly into the bloodstream, bypassing all of the body's safely mechanisms in the

GI tract that are there to destroy invaders that do not belong in the body. The ingredients then gain instant access to any cell in the body it should wander into, often lodging in the weakest cells of the body. If one of the foreign proteins (the egg, etcetera) lodges there, then the immune system may become involved in trying to blow out the invader, and it also starts attacking the cells of your creature that the foreign protein attached to. Even once the egg is gone, the immune system's memory may now have decided that your creature's tissue is also the enemy. Auto immune condition support is discussed in a later chapter. This is the same problem that occurs when a human body organ transplant is done. Part of the protocol is to shut off the immune system so it doesn't attack the 'non-self' new tissue. Sure, it is human. And sure, it is amazing we can do those things. But the body still knows it is not you, and tries to autoimmune it out. Some authors of medical articles have surmised that it is impossible not to cause some brain stem damage with the ingredient listing, even if it is not perceptible to us. If you hear inconsolable or high pitched crying or screeching or whining with your creature; suspect brainstem damage in process. Sometimes these vaccinations are offered in combination with several vaccines. Normally your animal would not be challenged with so many issues and toxins all at once and especially not directly into the blood stream. This increases the potential for an adverse effect. If you do have your creature get vaccinations, and you think that your animal might be experiencing an adverse effect, please see the Poisonings chapter in Part I. If they need life support, get it immediately. Avoid all vaccinating prior to conception and during pregnancy.

Possible adverse effects run the gamut from making a creature feel ill to death. Just the things you were trying to protect them from. Mental problems from mild to severe, seizures, brain lesions, asthma and allergies, paralysis, severe personality changes or lack of personality, auto immune diseases, cancer anywhere, and damage to any and every organ of the body are listed as potential side effects. The vaccines that are given as a nasal spray are linked to respiratory challenges all the way to respiratory failure in humans. Some vaccines featuring a live or modified live virus, becomes a source of infection to non vaccinated individuals or vaccine failure vaccinated individuals that come in contact with the recently vaccinated creature. This has been shown in both humans and dogs and cats. They can even shed the virus in their feces, exposing others. Again, if this interests you, see the book.

If you choose to not vaccinate (we do vaccinate for Rabies on our dogs because it is a government requirement tied to their licensing), you must have some resources and education. For one, I keep herbs on hand that are antibacterial and nourishing to support and help my creature's body fight a good fight should it contract something. I keep good nutritious food and herbs in their diet, as discussed in the herb garden and husbandry chapters in Part I, to decrease the likelihood of them contracting a problem. And I practice biosecurity to reduce exposure to problems. This is extremely important in real pervasive diseases such as Parvo.

Chapter 15- Cardiovascular System

(Heart, Venal Structure and Blood)

The scriptures say the life is in the blood. I believe it fully. Blood that is not healthy causes fatigue, lack of proper nourishment and can be a breeding ground for a wide variety of microbial, fungal, parasitic, and other entities. The venal system is just a fancy word that comprises the arteries, veins, and capillaries. The arteries take oxygen rich blood from the lungs to the body. The smaller veins return oxygen poor blood to the lungs, and the capillaries branch off into small areas to get blood, oxygen and nutrients into tinier places as well as allowing some toxins to come back out. Oxygen rich blood is bright red; and oxygen poor/carbon dioxide rich blood is darker red to bluish. Look at the veins on your hands (it's easiest if your skin is white or yellow, if not look at a pale skinned friend's hands or see if you can see some on the palms of your hands). You can probably see some blue veins returning carbon dioxide rich blood back to the lungs.

The heart muscle is the pump for the cardiovascular (cardio=heart, vascular= veins) system. Without an efficient pump, the body is oxygen deprived and nutrient deprived. Remember the brain wants 25% of that oxygen, so this is NO SMALL matter. Heart rates are going to differ according to the type and age and fitness of your animal. In a human, 60 beats per minute (one per second) is not a bad number to work towards. The less beats that are efficient and productive that a heart needs to make a day (within reason); the longer it will remain strong to do its job. At 60 beats per minute, that equates between 31,356,000 to 31,357,000 beats per year. No wonder it takes longer than other tissues to repair once a heart sustains damage. It's not like a leg where it can have some rest. It has to keep working during the repair process!

The blood will rebuild itself one full regeneration in about four months. That means that every cell in the blood stream is replaced in about four months or three complete regenerations in a year. Though much tissue in the body has that same replacement rate, I suspect it takes a bit longer for the heart due to its constant heavy workload.

The Accessible Pet, Equine and Livestock Herbal

Anaphylactic shock or anaphylaxis

Anaphylactic shock is a fancy term for a fast drop in blood pressure due to shock to the nervous and cardiovascular systems. This can result in death if the crash is too fast or too low. This condition is usually caused by a foreign substance, such as a vaccine or creature toxin. I've had two goats do this to me after vaccinating, back in my vaccinating days. To say it is quick and scary is an understatement! I also personally experienced a moderate experience with this problem in myself as a young adult, and had to yell for nursing care to assist me. Very scary! Thankfully I did not become 'another statistic'. Anyhow, with the goats, I did have my epinephrine on hand- literally on my person, when that happened and was able to bring them out of it quickly with an intravenous injection. I also have had two goats over the years get shocky, sweaty, and shaky after bee stings. In those days again I gave epinephrine. Today I would use, you guessed it, CAYENNE, especially cayenne tincture, to give the body fuel to turbo the heart back into action and circulation and equalize the bloodstream in the case of an anaphylaxis. If you can have the animal lay down to relax to allow the blood easier access to the brain, that would be a good thing. Ginger can be used after the cayenne to encourage circulation to the extremities. Then I would proceed as suggested in the Poisons chapter of Part I, and look at the Oxygenation section in the Brain section of Part II. Continue to watch your creature for a few hours in case they move towards shock again. Until the toxins are broken up in the blood stream, they can relapse.

Anemia

Anemia can be an indirect result of parasites, which depletes nutrients (especially iron) from the blood. It can also be a complication of medications, a nutritional deficiency, or the result of severe blood loss from hemorrhaging, accident, or several blood sucking parasite infestation, such as lice or Haemoncus contortus (barberpole) or other internal parasites. Iron deficiency is also something that is watched for in swine. So, besides addressing nourishing to address the anemia, you will want to address whatever the cause will be, or you may still lose your animal to anemia or a secondary problem due to a weakened body if it is prolonged.

Iron is what enables the red blood cells to hang onto oxygen to run it around to the cells and brain.

Learn FAMACHA™ technique if you gain the opportunity to do so. This is sometimes available in goat and sheep forums, but is beneficial to learn for any animal. You learn how to read the lower inner eyelid color for degrees of anemia. It is a good assessment tool to have in your tool kit. For sure add this to your list of things to learn from your vet. Remember to reward your vet for their investment in you!

Should I encounter an anemia problem in one of my animals, after I rule out the cause, I also provide nutritional support. Wheat grass is always a good blood builder, but don't stop there, as it's not anemia specific, but will help the body rebuild the blood in general at a much quicker rate than it could on its own. Some nice herbs to consider are: dandelion (powerful), kelp, nettle, cabbage, parsley leaf and root (note that parsley amy cut back milk production). Mixing some of these with unsulphured black strap molasses will give you very nice support for your creature. A good greens mix will also give additional bloodstream support, and often times wheatgrass will be combined in a good mix. You ought to plan on at least two months of support if you are consistent with two to three times per day and longer if you are not consistent. This timing is based on blood work results in human situations. Better yet, go four months which is the time it takes for the blood to regenerate cell for cell in a healthy human. Remember the blood work usually shows 'normal' health, not optimum health.

In pigs, I would opt to keep the sow and the piglets on some of the above herbs mixed with the black strap molasses rather than inject them with toxic inorganic iron. An overdose of inorganic (non living) will kill the pig. For your larger sow, you can work up to ¼ cup of the mix twice per day during third trimester and while nursing. The piglets will get nutrition from her milk. Then, as they start onto their own feed ration; add up the weight of the piglets in the pen and mix your herbs in according to that weight. Remember to up the amount to their new 'pen weight' every week while they are growing fast. See how thrifty those piglets become on this type of an iron program.

Bleeding

Anytime you run into bleeding, whether internal or external, my first choice of herb friends to grab is my bottle of cayenne. It works fastest as a tincture taken internally for internal issues, but still works very fast as a 'styptic' by pouring powder directly onto or into the wound, no matter how shallow or deep that wound may be. It has been used even for gunshot wounds. If you have an artery spurting blood, then after covering it with cayenne get a pressure on it by either putting large non toxic plant leaves on top of the cayenne, gauze (which may be hard to get off later) or even a clean paper towel. The cayenne will be an antiseptic barrier between what you put on for pressure and the injury site. If bleeding does not slow down, as it often does within about 10 seconds, then you may need to enlist the aid of a veterinarian. If the tear to the artery is too large, it may take more than the body's clotting system to close off the injury. When we have a baby goat bump a horn bud that causes heavier bleeding, besides pouring a generous amount of cayenne over it and then my folded clean paper towel or sterile gauze, we will duct tape over that to keep the wrap on good. Remember that you have to allow for circulation so don't wrap too tight, but make sure it is wrapped firmly in place. The duct tape sticks fairly well to hair and will fall off in a few days. During that time the kid goes in a separate stall with a buddy so that the others are not trying to pull the wrap off prematurely. If you get the cayenne into the eyes (try not to) it will sting, but not damage. After some flow of tears the cayenne will wash out and the eye will have increased circulation and a decrease in bacteria from the incident. I speak from personal experience. More on that later... Do watch for infection, but we have never had infection with quality cayenne as it is antibacterial also. That spans wounds on me, my husband and the stock. It is awesome! I always keep cayenne in my kitchen, barn, stock and horse trailers, vehicles, you name it.

Other herbs you can enlist as a second choice (should cayenne not be available) would be yarrow, comfrey, shepherd's purse, blackberry leaves, grape leaves, plantain, and stinging nettle. Nearly any herb that lists hemostatic or astringent as a therapeutic use can be tried. Use them fresh picked, dry, or as a tincture. Just get them on.

Wounds will be covered in greater detail in the Epidermis chapter.

Blood poisoning

Blood poisoning is usually a secondary condition started by an injury to an area that then gets infected. Sometimes these can be tricky to catch in livestock early. How many of us have found that if there is just one thing an animal can get poked on or injured on in a whole pasture, somehow it will find it! Due to hair coats, problems can get started without being caught right away. Watch for redness, swelling, or streaking, especially for a pattern that is moving from a section of limb up towards the heart. Try to find the starting point if possible to determine if there is also an injury that needs attention. This is not a situation that you can ignore, hoping it will go away. You also don't want to 'get to it later'. It will want attention now, and you will want to use generous amounts of herb, both internal at double and triple dosages, as well as applying hot, but safe temperature poultices, fomentations, and later salves to the area showing the problem. You will need to change the poultices or fomentations every time they cool down with a fresh one.

Nice herbs for this situation include goldenseal, cayenne, myrrh, burdock root, stinging nettle, marshmallow root and leaf, plantain, ground mallow root and leaf, hollyhock root and leaf. Oil of garlic and also oil of onion or an onion poultice can be used. Pick two or more herbs for a broader range of effect, if possible. See the Appendix for recipes. Lavender essential oil added to any of these fomentations or poultices is a nice additional touch. Lemon or fennel essential oil (don't use fennel EO in stock under 1 year old) blended with olive oil (15 drops to 1 tablespoon of olive oil) can also be used to help go after impurities. If your animals are exposed to full sun, then use less lemon to reduce the possibility of photosensitivity. I have used generous amounts of honey with some infused lavender on a blood streak caused by a large wood splinter in a heel. Overnight the streak was gone.

Clotting

Clotting is an important function of the body. When blood touches anything other than the interior of the venal system, a message is sent to the body to begin quick repair work; which it usually does. There are two main problems with this system.

The first would be an over accumulation of blood clots in the system. Besides injuries that create hematomas (large stationary blood clots in body tissue), there is a more insidious injury that is not as easily recognized. Remember hearing about scurvy back in the old sailing days? It has been suggested, and holds a lot of merit, that a body that is over exuberant about producing clotting is really in a very early scurvy state. Early in Vitamin C deficiency bruising and bleeding becomes much more common. If any of this damage is occurring in the venal system, then excess clotting will occur on a regular basis as small bleed out areas form. The final forms of scurvy include severe bleeding from the nose into death. We don't tend to see the severe state in the industrialized nations, but I think it shows up in earlier stages. This is less common in livestock that often tend to have access to some living green foods such as pasture and browse. However, for our pets or our stalled creatures living on nearly all processed feeds, this can be a problem. What happens in this situation is a lack of real living vitamin C in the diet, which is readily present in many living plant foods, even green ones. Did you know that when you yourself make fresh squeezed orange juice, that 60% of the Vitamin C is gone in just 15 minutes? What's that say about packaged juices? Ascorbic acid is NOT living organic Vitamin C as found in living plants. It is a laboratory product. What happens in a culture like ours where often people's only fruit intake is packaged and pasteurized apple juice concentrate? (Yuk!). How many of our pets are eating living plant foods containing organic (living) nutrients?

Besides blood building herbs mentioned earlier in this chapter, some 'antiscorbutic' herbs should be added in. These are a much safer alternative to the blood thinner products that are out there, that can cause a creature to bleed to death in even seemingly smaller injuries. Some of those are berries such as blue, straw, black and even currants. Citrus is another good source. I would not hesitate to juice some for my creatures, as long as they are not on heart medications. You'll see more detail on that later in this chapter. Other good, usually easy to obtain herbs are burdock root, cayenne, dandelion, rose hips, chickweed, flaxseed (grind it fresh each time), stinging nettle, tomatoes, wood betony, and tart apples. Since Vitamin C is a water soluble nutrient, your body isn't going to store any. They need daily access to it.

The opposite problem is having blood that doesn't clot. When I am asked about this situation so far in every incidence it has been caused by prescribed medications. Besides cleansing and working through blood cleansing and the blood building herbs listed above, alfalfa is a very nice herb to consider. It is a high natural source of Vitamin K which is required for normal blood clotting. Rose hips and stinging nettle are other nice sources. I dare you, plant some of these to keep around. You are seeing them pop up in several chapters. Grow them and enjoy them. Especially consider getting alfalfa going, before it gets hard to obtain non genetically modified seed. Remember to look for open pollinated (OP) varieties so you can harvest seed if wanted.

Electric shock

I had a friend that didn't lose animals, but shares this for education. She came to her dairy goat area to find two or three milkers lying on the ground scrambling unable to get up. This was near their stock water tank. Evidently, an electrical cord that was under the bedding had a small puncture through the protective coating. Add that to the wet bedding from the goats' drinking water and then dripping as they walked away, as well urine in the bedding, and you have this situation. The power was for livestock heaters. Please, never ever run electrical cords where animals have access to them. When I lived in a cold winter climate we threaded our tank heater cords through pvc pipe and kept all of that external to the stalls and pens. I recently heard a very sad story about goats being electrocuted while on their metal milkstands. The power for the building ran underground in that sandy soil region, and the recent heavy rains found a short in the powerline. Sad. Thankfully the owner did not touch the stands or goats or she would have been among them. Also be absolutely, positively sure that your electricity is correctly grounded. Any stock tank or similar heaters should be connected to a GFI plug that will automatically kick out if something is not right with the power. The cost of refitting to GFI plugs will easily cover an animal or two lost if you did not have one in. If you notice that your stock is not drinking water have your electrical equipment inspected. There may be a short that the animals can sense. Do NOT touch the water or tank until power has been disconnected.

After you are ABSOLUTELY sure that you are not at risk of getting shocked by whatever shocked your creature, this is CAYENNE TIME! Get it into the mouth anyway you have it. Tinctures (of course) are best, but cayenne powder in the mouth is a great first step until you can find your tincture. Then also dump tincture onto the heart and chest region. I wouldn't take time to measure, I would just dump it on and in and massage in quickly. Administer CPR if necessary. If the heart just stopped you can often get it back with the cayenne. Then check for breathing. Then giving some nervous system foods to help their nerves relax would be appropriate. Using cayenne, also catnip, valerian, hops, lavender are additional favorites of mine. Consider that the animal has internal tissue damage similar to what a burn might do, and go to the Epidermis chapter and look into oral and topical herb support for the body.

Grapefruit and Oranges

I just wanted to mention these, as both of these can affect heart medications. This is a tidbit I picked up from David Christopher, M.H., the director for the School of Natural Healing (see the appendix for more information on the school).

Heart medications are often measured quite precisely, so any food that could impact them could give you an undesirable effect. Oranges may reduce their effectiveness and grapefruit may potentiate (strengthen) their effectiveness. Heart medications are not a product that you want to adjust on your own, so keep your creatures off of these if they are on prescription heart support.

Heart Muscle Damage

Hearts can receive damage from injury, from bacterial, viral, and microbial assaults, heartworm in canines, and diets too high in animal proteins. For heartworm problems, see the Parasites chapter in Part 1.   For bacterial and viral issues, please see the Immune System chapter in Part 11.   For injuries, see the Epidermis Chapter.

Heart attacks can occur in animals. Though not as common as in humans, they are becoming more common.   Reactions to medication and adverse effects to vaccinations are some sources.   See the Epidermis chapter for injuries.   Also see the Poisonings chapter to help the body break down damage from chemical substances.   One specific herb for heart support is cayenne. Cayenne can even give the body what it needs to stop a heart attack in progress. One teaspoon of the powder mixed with some water and taken for a 100 to 200 pound animal has had amazing results. Tincture can be given and is faster. I've even heard stories good support being achieved from only being able to get a bit of powder (at a time) into the mouth. It's not ideal, but it's certainly a place to start with until you can do better.   If cayenne isn't available, then black pepper at triple dose will help. Opt for fresh ground pepper if possible, as you may have efficacy problems with the store bought pre-ground pepper. Another very specific herb for heart support is hawthorn.   Hawthorn berries have been used for millennia for heart muscle support. Its unique combination of nutrients is a bounty of well being support for that hardworking heart.   Studies have shown the leaves to be even more powerful. Feel free to tea the herbs or add them to the feed of your creatures.   Hawthorn won't harm anything. It's a very safe herb to work with.

Remember that a diet very high in animal protein (meat, milk, eggs, and etcetera) is also a diet that will slowly leach minerals out of the body. That would include calcium, which is imperative for healthy muscle (heart) strength, properly timed and strength of heart contractions, and a healthy heart nervous system to communicate with this very important muscle.   Please don't raise your pets on a large percentage of animal products. Also, animal proteins need to be raw (find healthy organic sources) to keep the Ph correct in the stomach. Processed (cooked) foods throw the Ph off.

Heavy Metals Accumulation

I cover this topic at the beginning of Part ll.   Remember, any portion of the body that becomes weak will become a repository for toxins, and that includes heavy metals. Please consider cleaning them out.

Malignancies

Malignancies make me think about the age old question, "Which came first the chicken or the egg?"   Did the cancer metastasize, or was it already in the bloodstream and at one or more locations which finally became detectable, with others following later?   The last information I had was that it takes nearly half a million cancer cells in a mass to be detectable. A pea sized accumulation is around one billion cells! I expect our diagnostic equipment in some locations is more sophisticated than that now, but surmise it to say that the cancer has to be in some larger quantity cellular mass before it is detectable.   That means that multiple masses can be in differing body locations, developing, but still will be undetectable.   Eventually, a mass is diagnosed and later said to metastasize. These 'mets' (as they are called in the medical world), I expect were already in process, but finally became big enough to become detectable after the initial diagnosis. Anyhow, I have my suspicions.

As herbalists, we believe that malignancies really begin in a polluted, acidic, often calcium deficient bloodstream.   They happen to settle in the areas that have the weakest tissue. That may be an old injury site that has collected toxins due to its acquired weakness or in areas of inherited or acquired other weaknesses.   This includes the intestines and colon that may have putrefying fecal matter attached to them. Those toxins also encourage cellular change or mutation, which can gain access to the bloodstream. As mentioned before, this also creates a literal toxic manure tea to be pulled into the bloodstream by the body. This problem is greatest at the flexures, or bends, in the intestinal system. Environmental toxins, including food toxins are thought to be responsible for perhaps 85% of the cancer out there. Vaccinations are another linked source, even though the cancer may take months to years to become diagnosed after the vaccine. Some of these even show up at the injection location.

The initial issue is a polluted bloodstream, so that is why you will find this topic in this Cardiovascular chapter. So to work with the individual area sporting the malignancy, without considering cleansing the body's bowels and cleansing organs and the bloodstream, is to not be a Vitalist. However, in this situation where malignancies can be moving so fast at the time of discovery, you will have to be very, very aggressive herbally and nutritionally if you want a shot at assisting the body to gain victory over this challenge. You have to move faster than the cancer wants to grow, or your pet will lose. Having said that, at worst you can usually see the animal gain better quality of life while it's still here, and at times it is possible to watch a miracle before your eyes as the body restores itself to well being. Remember, that just because you have 'X' diagnosis, that does not mean that all of the malignancies in the body are known. However, this doesn't change the herbal body support.

If I had this issue in my creature, I would first start them on bowel cleansing if the animal has had any processed feeds including kibble, processed grain, and etcetera, but at a bit of a faster rate. As soon as I had regular bowel movements going, I would get going on liver and kidney cleansing. If they are weak, start at half dose, but work up to full dose as soon as reasonable for your situation. As soon as you get them to full dose on the liver and kidney support herbs, then start on the blood and cells, again at half dose, working to full dose. You do not want to make your animal overly sick, but you do need to get going quickly.

If you can bathe them, then make a strong herb tea with herb choices from this section and any of the blood cleaning and support sections, and bathe your creature in that tea daily. It will help draw toxins out of the body through the skin. Don't use store bought soap, as the last thing you want to do is to add to the toxic load. It will usually be good enough just to soak them in the tea. If they are larger and the weather cooperates, then soak clothes in hot safe to the skin temperature teas and drape that over your animal. Focus especially on any areas near known malignancies. Salves can also be used after the soaks over areas you want additional herbs soaking in full time.

Bloodstream cleaning and nutritional support herbs of great value are kelp, wheat grass, alfalfa, stinging nettle, burdock root, chaparral (powerful), raspberry leaf, marshmallow root, slippery elm bark, pau d' arco, shitake and maiake mushrooms, comfrey (except where liver damage is suspected) and other herbs that have 'alterative' or 'depurative' listed as a therapeutic effect. There are many. I have listed the ones that I work with the most and tend to be more readily available. Carrot juice and fiber should always become a part of the diet in any malignancy challenge. A 150 pound creature can partake of one to two quarts per day. All animal protein foods should be eliminated, except in baby animals. It is imperative to get an alkaline, calcium rich blood supply going. Grape juice and grapes can also be used to great advantage in animals except for canines, where they may cause renal failure in some of the dog family. Salves with supporting herbs may be placed on the skin nearest the areas of known problems. Even if that is a body organ or tissue not so close to the skin, go for it with the salve in addition to oral herbal support. The body will draw it in. Medical professionals may scoff at that idea. However, the pharmaceutical companies make 'transdermal' patches with differing medications as they accept that the skin is an acceptable route of application.

Here's a note about 'escharotics'. Escharotics are sometimes available to put on malignant areas. I don't use them. My understanding is that they can be extremely painful as they help the body chase the cancer. Adding additional stress to an already stressed system is not my idea of help. Bloodroot is sometimes used and I hear that can also be painful. If you use it, use only very small amounts of it externally blended with other herbs, and do not touch any healthy skin with it. I have personally seen the body do a good job with diagnosed problems without using these harsher methods. The choice, however; is yours.

Remove as much or all animal proteins and toxins from your animal's exposure. Keep your creature comfortable and feel free to spoil on it with attention if it will accept attention. If your animal wins this battle and it is re-exposed to the diet and environmental toxins that created the problem, expect the problem to return with a vengeance. It will be a much greater challenge to get further with body support the second time. Keep their system clean, and do routine cleansing and support to keep them moving forward.

Shock

Treat the same as for Anaphylactic shock in the beginning of this chapter. In case you are reading this section in a panic. Just remember CAYENNE. Then after you administer some, catch your breath and read the earlier section. Remember to give yourself some too!

Stroke

Strokes are covered in the Brain chapter.

White Muscle Disease

White muscle is named after the pale look to the muscles during a post mortem when this condition is diagnosed. It shows up most often in young stock from birth on through usually just a few weeks to months old. Selenium and Vitamin E deficiency are both blamed for this malady. This deficiency does not allow muscles to develop to full strength as babies develop in utero. This includes the heart muscle. Babies may be born already weak and uncoordinated from lack of muscle integrity, or may seemingly grow into the situation as their body places larger demands on it then the muscles, including the heart, can handle. In baby kids, we watch for lack of muscle coordination in their tongues as they nurse as a possible indication that the selenium and Vitamin E need to be picked up a bit. If the milkers become low in selenium, we notice that the does may be a bit down on their pasterns due to loss of some tendon integrity, and also a less tight medial suspensory ligament which supports the udder to the body wall. I have had a friend that used to have goats have an issue with this in her herd at one time. An apparently healthy younger kid leapt up to play and landed dead from a heart attack because its heart couldn't handle the additional physical challenge. Births can be prolonged or difficult due to weakness in the dam's uterine muscles from deficiency. Because several regions of the United States are selenium deficient some of the feeds given are also selenium deficient. Some areas are also selenium toxic, so don't just feed it indiscriminately, though you are on safe ground with whole herbs. In those areas, you'll have to watch out for selenium rock source mineral in your well water as a potential source of overdose. Wheat is usually not fed whole, if at all, to livestock. The little wheat germ nubbin on the end of the wheat berry (seed) is a very rich source of the fat soluble nutrient Vitamin E. Wheat germ oil can be purchased in health food stores. I prefer the gel capsule kind. Because wheat germ oil is a liquid fat, it starts becoming rancid as soon as oxygen comes in contact with it, making it a hepatotoxin (liver toxin). Liquid types have oxygen touching them every time the bottle is tipped and poured. Other sources of Vitamin E include sunflower seeds (high), moringa leaf, purslane and even pansy flowers. Selenium can be found in alfalfa, in kelp (never deficient), slippery elm, raspberry leaf and pau d' arco bark. Fir Meadow also has a whole herb product called "Kop-Sel". If you are in a deficient area (check with your veterinarian or county agriculture extension office) then you will want to have an herb supplementation plan in place. Definitely keep this in mind for your working and breeding creatures. More information on White Muscle Disease is in the Raising Your Babies chapter in Part 1. Remember to support the heart muscle with heart herbs from that chapter as well.

Chapter 16- Digestive System

Every system is important in your creature, but possibly none has greater overall impact on every cell of the body than the digestive tract. As I have mentioned earlier in this book, it is impossible to have abundant health in your creature when there is toxicity or lack of full function in the alimentary canal (from mouth to anus). If a creature is unable to break down and utilize the nutrition in food, then the entire body is deprived of life giving sustenance. Cellular deterioration will occur as the cells are unable to give full attention to operations and cell cleaning activities. In humans in industrialized nations, our absorption rate averages around seven to nine percent of what we consume. We are supposed to absorb around forty percent! Look around and see the effects on our culture's lack of well being. I was surprised when I was studying pet and equine iridology how many bowel toxic creatures there are. In human iridology that is almost a given, but in pets I was taken aback. Maybe I shouldn't have been, but I was.

So the first thing I will have anyone work on, and have everyone consider with their pets and creatures, are changes to their diet and added herbal support as necessary to move the body towards proper bowel function. If your pet or creature eats processed food, and that includes feed store sweet feeds with the poor quality molasses in it, then bowel assistance needs to be considered. Your pets need to have at least one bowel movement per meal as well. Your dog should not have to strain to eliminate their waste. Their bowel movement should be controlled, but easy to eliminate. I get emails once in awhile of people commenting on their dog's bad breath (without teeth problems), smelly skin or smelly gas. What they smell is the inside of that animal. Yes, you are smelling a body polluted with putrefying waste. Clean it out. Any animal proteins that stay in a body longer than about 18 hours become toxic to the system. Keep bowels regular please. Your creature will likely reward you with a better quality of life and possible lowered care bills.

Appetite stimulants

If you feel your creature should be eating more than it is, there are some things you can do. First, make sure it is not ill. Also, consider possibilities of pain somewhere in the body or in the digestive tract. Pain often will take an animal off of feed, so try to determine the cause of the lack of appetite. Once you know the cause and work with that, here are some other things you can do.

Cayenne, a heavy laden B vitamin herb, is good for encouraging appetite. Other additions in this department would be: catnip, black strap molasses, raspberry leaf, and nutritional yeast. Several of the spice herbs can be given, such as: cinnamon, cloves, small amounts of nutmeg, and ginger. Don't go overboard on strong cinnamon or cloves by themselves in pregnant animals. Black pepper (freshly ground by you) is also a good stomachic and can encourage the stomach back into action. Slippery elm or marshmallow root, (both being mucilaginous, soothing, and mineral rich), are good to use in situations where you believe GI tract pain may be involved. Fir Meadow makes a nice blend of herbs called GI Soother for body support in these issues.

You may bring some favorite goodies to encourage an animal that is off feed. In milking stock or ruminants, such as the goats, we can't leave them in a fast very long or we risk having the rumen shut down. Besides cayenne to encourage action within the rumen, they need long stem fiber. It is at times like this that I collect a brush bouquet for goats. Hay and grass with some browse bouquets can be brought to cattle, horses, and etcetera. Plants to consider, (remembering to not let them overdo it on plants that are not in their daily diet) are: fir tree branches, alder tree stems, salal twigs and leaves, birch and quaking aspen (white poplar) branches, raspberry branches and leaves, grape leaves/branches, apple and pear branches, comfrey leaves, unsprayed rose branches and leaves, different grasses and hays. Oat straw or oat hay (with the seed heads in it) besides stimulating appetite can also be soothing to a tender tummy, so it is often a good choice. The calcium in it is also soothing to the nerves. Remember, never feed any poisonous plants such as any pit fruit leaves such as cherry, plum and apricot. Also keep all parts of black walnut trees away from your equine and camelid (llama, alpaca, and vicuna) families.

Bloat Causes and How to Relieve

Bloat can be caused from eating too much of a plant an animal isn't used to. It can also be caused by overeating on something that they are used to, such as a grain raid. Toxin consumption can cause bloat. Eating frosted legumes, such as alfalfa or clover, can cause a difficult to alleviate frothy bloat. Acidosis, or a Ph change in the stomach or rumen can also accompany this. In very bad cases this can progress to enterotoxemia in ruminants, which is covered later in this chapter.

Peppermint can be used to break up bloat and gas, and also help manage some pain that may occur as old waste comes off and out. Peppermint essential oil diluted at a rate of about 12 drops to 1 tablespoon of olive oil can be rubbed onto stomach and rumen areas in creatures one year and older. Essential oil of dill can be used in younger animals. When I have a choice, I use peppermint though. Strong peppermint tea can be made and drenched into your animal. Peppermint, besides helping the body alleviate pain, also relaxes the valves in the intestinal system, allowing trapped air the opportunity to escape. Castor oil can be used (in place of the olive oil that you mix with the essential oil) and used externally to try and stimulate some peristaltic action, which will also help punch down gas bubbles.

Your animal can also be walked if they will let you to get movement going, encouraging the release of gas. The stomach or rumen area (the rumen is on the left rear area- forward of and at the flank) can be massaged to encourage gas to break up. In really bad cases, stomach tubing may be needed to try and 'pop' the gas bubbles and help them work their way out. Frothy bloats are particularly hard to work with, so keep at it. In this case prevention is much easier than working with the problem. Because of my concern about this problem, my ruminants do not have alfalfa or clover growing in their pasture.

If you witness your animal overeating, or eating something it's not used to; please don't wait for a problem. Practice Offensive Herbalism™ and get some peppermint into them then, and then monitor them. Also see enterotoxemia in this chapter and the Poisonings chapter in Part 1. Don't wait for a problem to show itself, as by then it may be too late to get ahead of the bloat before the animal dies.

Remember, essential oils are not to be used on or even in an area where they can be smelled by your feline family members.

The Accessible Pet, Equine and Livestock Herbal

Candida

Friend or foe you might ask. Candida actually is one of the more than 400 flora types that are needed in the digestive tract. It has a very specific job and that is to uptake alcohols and sugars to the villi and into the bloodstream. The problem comes when an animal becomes severely distressed causing intestinal flora die off. The Candida, being hardier, tends to survive the experience and over proliferate. Antibiotics are famous for setting up this problem, but any severe distress or gastrointestinal distress can also set this off. Once the Candida over grows its space it gets hungry. It then will expand its territory by whipping at the villi, damaging it, and diving right into the bloodstream, often hitching a free ride on a red blood cell. This displaces the cell's ability to transfer oxygen, which is not a good thing. Then the Candida are free to ride around the body. When a Candida infection happens to show up in one area of the body, supporting the body just in chasing the Candida at that location is not enough support. You are going to want to also address cleaning the blood stream and encourage the villi to repair with nourishing herbs, such as: slippery elm, comfrey, calendula flowers, chickweed, nettle, and marshmallow root. Drinkable aloe vera juice is also beneficial, but never use the whole plant fresh gel, which is purgative.

Herbs that are specific for trying to help the body corner the excess Candida would be: pau d' arco, black walnut (not in equine/camelids), cinnamon, ginger, goldenseal, rosemary, thyme and sage. I keep feeling like I need to put peppermint into this list even though I have no hard documentation on this choice. Plan to work on this issue for at least a couple of months. Access to sugars, such as the feed store type of molasses and feeds containing that, should be limited. Unless blood building is needed right then, hold off on the raw honey and black strap molasses during this process if possible. Also be sure and feed any fruits first in the meal and only once bowel movements are moving regularly after each meal. Fruit that is sitting too long at body temperature ferments into alcohol in the intestines.

Colic

Colic can involve bloat, or it can be separate. See the Bloat section for more information. Colic is a label given for anything that causes pain in the intestinal area of your animal. It can be characterized by bloat, by the animal appearing to be in pain via mood, that "pain look" in the eyes (I don't know how to explain this, but if you've seen it you know what I mean), teeth or molar grinding in some, stretching repeatedly at the loin area indicating pain.

The colic can be from a blockage, an acidosis (over eating creating an overly acidic condition), or even a twisted gut. Blockages have several causes including: soil and hardware (metal pieces), excessively dry feed or lack of sufficient clean water to consume with feed, and some medications and anesthesia's can shut off the peristaltic action. Excessive pain can negatively impact healthy peristaltic action, as can processed sugars over time. Tumors and scar tissue from previous injuries or surgeries can also be a problem.

If the blockage is from dry feed or foreign materials such as bits of fencing or dirt/sand collecting at intestinal flexures (bends), then lubricating and moisturizing is the goal. Drenching orally and giving enemas of olive oil and herb tea can help. A 150 pound animal can take ¼ cup of olive oil, mixed with a quart of tea, orally. Always mix cayenne with the liquids to try to encourage peristaltic action as well as help the body alleviate any bleeding caused by moving foreign objects. A teaspoon of castor oil can also be added to the oral oil mix to try to help the body move things through. Great herb or herb tea choices to also give them include: psyllium, a small amount of senna, cascara sagrada, slippery elm, fresh ground flax seed, and marshmallow root. Really any of the demulcent herbs can be used, but the above choices are my favorites. Walking helps as well. Peppermint essential oil blended with olive oil (12 drops essential oil to 1 tablespoon olive oil) can be rubbed over the loin and spine area to assist in pain reduction. Arnica oil or eucalyptus essential oil can also be used externally in this way. Lobelia tincture and other nervine (nervous system nourishing) herbs can be applied along the spine to help the scared and distressed animal relax a bit.

If you suspect a twisted gut, you may need to enlist the services of your veterinarian as soon as possible or the animal will die. They can tell by blood work and other symptomology if this problem is in progress. Sometimes a gut will twist when a horse is rolling due to pain from colic. If it rolls too hard, an intestine can twist from the violent flipping back and forth action of the horse. In these cases surgery at a veterinarian hospital may be the only help and is not always successful. Don't ignore colic in its early stages.

I have had about three baby goats over the years twist guts that I have been able to reverse on my own. Whenever I'm outside and see the baby goats bouncing around, I pay attention to them. If one of them falls hard and fast and flips with it, I note the direction they flipped. Sure enough, two of these I've dealt with started the crying and loin stretching/dipping indicating to me an immediate problem. I was able to take them out of their pen, so the other babies would not be in the way. Then I set them firmly on their back, held their front legs with one hand and rear legs with the other, and rocked them firmly with a swift movement the opposite direction from how they flipped. I did this 3 to 5 times (or do as you are led), then let them up and watched them a few minutes. If they started crying and loin stretching or dipping at the loin then I gave them another round. So far I've been able to correct all of them. The third one I never saw which way he flipped (yes, it is usually the little boys) so I had to just rock him from one side to the other side on his back firmly, trusting that the intestine would want to return back to its normal position. We saved that one too. Little monsters.

Constipation

Good general bowel herbs are cayenne (of course, you will see this herb popping up all over), turkey rhubarb, fennel, cascara sagrada, papaya leaf, seed, or fruit, slippery elm, many fruits (no grape products for dogs), grated carrot, marshmallow root, psyllium, fresh ground flax (no need to grind for ruminants), figs, olive oil, water, and more. I haven't listed senna, as it tends to be too powerful and habit forming. However, if your animal is going a whole day without a bowel movement you may want to use a bit of senna to move things along a bit faster (and also look at the colic information). If it's livestock, I wouldn't even wait an entire day, as we all know they are in the habit going multiple times per day because of their higher roughage diets and all day grazing patterns. Choose a three herb minimum, and go with that.

Keeping cayenne with your mix helps the body stop any bleeding that may show up if a layer of waste comes off of the intestinal wall leaving exposed and damaged tissue. Cayenne also encourages the return of correct peristaltic action- the wavelike muscular motion in the intestines that moves food towards its outward goal. Antibacterial herbs (of which cayenne is one) are also not a bad idea to combine. Ginger will help with any discomfort or nausea during cleaning and adds another antibacterial/antiseptic choice.

Diarrhea

Diarrhea can be caused from too much feed your creature isn't used to, or toxins in the feed from molds, to synthetics. Neighbors spraying chemical herbicides along fence lines that drift into your pasture can cause a problem. A windstorm dropping branches or leaves into a field, or fall leaves blowing in, can be another source. Spring plants coming up need to be monitored for any new or unusual plants that birds or hay may import in. Believe it or not, diarrhea can also signal constipation. If there is a near blockage in the intestine, from built up old fecal matter, or foreign materials, then the solids in the manure will back up, only allowing mostly fluids to come though. So back to the bowel cleanse drawing board if you think this is the contributor. Parasite overloads are another source and needs to be ruled out. If you have a parasite load to the point of causing diarrhea, you have waited far too long to address the issue, as tissue damage has already taken place. Bacterial issues can also cause diarrhea. Please see the Parasite Chapter in Part 1 and the Immune System Chapter in Part 11 for information on those problems. You will also want to consider reading the Hepatic System (liver) chapter in Part 11.

If the stools are just a little loose, and you are confident nothing else needs to be addressed, here is an herb list to work with. Slippery elm bark or bark powder, strawberry leaves, blackberry leaves, raspberry leaves, sage (very small amounts in pregnant animals, if used at all), lemon juice, wormwood in normal dosage amounts (see the Dosaging chapter in Part 1), witch hazel, cinnamon powder,

The Accessible Pet, Equine and Livestock Herbal

grated or powdered ginger root, white oak bark, whole oats, cloves, cayenne, yarrow, yellow dock, and rosemary to name a few.

Enteroliths/Stones in the Digestive Tract

Enteroliths are probably most widely known in horses. Perhaps because they tend to live longer than other livestock types that are simple stomached. Ruminants have more efficient digestive tracts and are able to break down problematic building blocks better. These are usually accumulations of some kind of rock minerals, often calcium, in the intestinal tract. They can grow to very large sizes, even larger then softballs and often will take several years to reach such a size. Of course a stone of that size can cause a life threatening blockage. There may be just one, or there can be several ones. The horse will colic once the problem comes to a dangerous point, so if a horse colics this is something that needs to be considered. The best way to go about working with these is to practice Offensive Herbalism™ as they are a challenge to work with once they are large enough to form blockages; especially in the case of a single stone or enterolith.

Anything that decreases gut motility and stomach acidity can make an animal more predisposed to this problem. This can be caused by too many processed foods (pelleted grains or grains, hay blends with first or second refining molasses in them), a toxic GI tract; medications that affect the digestive tract, not enough exercise, and/or not enough fresh pasture access. Fresh pasture, due to the water content, has a slight laxative effect that the dry hay will lack. Also consider animals that inherit weaker digestive tracts from their dam and/or sire. This is one of the issues that can be caught in an iris exam. The exam would reveal the blockage in process, but it wouldn't be able to tell you why the blockage would be there. Still a very useful tool to catch a problem before it actually becomes one!

Alfalfa hay gets blamed for this condition as it is very mineral rich. However, with my background I suspect that it is the WATER that is the problem. The water will contain minerals that are difficult to break down and eliminate because there are no living carbon atoms attached to these, unlike in plant minerals. Just look at your coffee maker and see how fast particulate accumulates in it. I have a coffee maker to make hot water for tea. Before I used distilled water for tea, I used my good tasting well water. Twice a week I would have to clean the particulate out of my water pot. It does that inside of our creatures too, and over time that may build up into something substantial. Where alfalfa may come in is if it is pellets or cubes that are being fed. Those simply do not provide enough long stem fiber to help keep good motility of the digestive tract. They need long fiber and some of it fresh if possible. Many of these are also stabled animals that do not get sufficient exercise, which negatively impacts healthy movement within the intestinal tract. Sand or soil accumulation in the gut can also slow intestinal movement and well being, which contributes to an environment that encourages the formation of enteroliths.

If I wanted to reduce the likelihood of encountering this issue, I would reduce all of the contributory factors that are possible in my situation. I would also be giving my horses raw organic apple cider vinegar in their grain at the rate of 1 teaspoon working up to 1/8 cup for mini horses, 1 tablespoon working to ¼ cup for ponies, and ¼ cup working up to 1 cup in horses. For draft sizes and larger warmbloods one can add another ¼ cup if they like.

Contacting your vet to rule out enteroliths and the possibility of a twisted gut is a good idea. You can drench (dilute it if drenching) or stomach tube raw apple cider vinegar at the full dose every two hours, in between times that you give herbs for other blockages (see colic). If it is one very big stone, it's not likely you'll be able to dissolve it fast enough. If it is a few smaller ones, perhaps with that and walking you may. This is a decision to be made between you and your vet. Certainly I would pray and ask for guidance from above!

This is one of those situations where preventative maintenance is much better than having a problem to deal with. Your vet can tell you if these seem to be a problem in the area you keep your horse, which may be useful information for you as you build a plan to help your horse have good GI health.

Enterotoxemia

Enterotoxemia, simply put, is a condition where the flora in the intestinal tract becomes so overwhelmed that they begin to die off in large numbers, creating a toxic situation in the intestines, which goes into the bloodstream poisoning the creature. This can be caused by eating too much of something their system isn't used to, thus the caution to always take a ten day minimum when changing your creature's diet from one type of feed, food, or hay to another. This can also be caused by ingesting one of the clostridium forms of bacteria, which are gram positive. For that situation please review the section under the Immune System chapter on bacteria and gram positive bacteria.

Symptoms you may notice could be: bloat, lethargy, disinterest in feed, wanting to lie around, diarrhea (with or without blood), and vomiting. In advanced stages the kidneys will be severely damaged, which is why this condition is sometimes known as 'pulpy kidney dis-ease'.

When an animal experiences a fast flora die off you will want to help them protect their system from toxins in the blood stream, the intestines, and the kidneys. Fir Meadow makes a product called ClostridEaze which can be used here, or you can use the herbs or products mentioned in the chapters relating to each of these sections. If your animal has gotten into feed it isn't used to, such as a grain or hay raid, or even a neighbor throwing mowing or brush clippings over the fence, be proactive and get some herbs running through their system to head off any potential problem. You do not want to wait for a full blown enterotoxemia event before you start supporting their system, as that could be a fatal error.

Fur balls in Cats

See colic and bloat. This is another mechanical blockage and does need to be moved out or they can be fatal in a complete blockage. For breeds that tend to shed more and long haired breeds, you may want to do a quarterly maintenance on their bowels.

Impacted Gut

See the section in this chapter on colic. Don't wait, time is of the essence!

Johne's Disease

Johne's (pronounced Yo-Knees) is one of those controversial diseases. However, it only seems to be controversial to those that have it in their herds. This is a problem of ruminants, that is, those creatures with four compartment stomachs. There is a nearly identical issue that plagues people, with same symptom list, and that is Crohn's disease. For those that are interested one could do a Google search on Johne's bacteria/bacterium and humans and see what comes up. Approximately 80% of the dairies have Johne's infected animals in their herd (one of the reasons for the three year turnover from milk production to slaughter in dairy cows). Johne's does not always pasteurize out of the milk. It can end up infecting the pasture or facilities before one knows their creature has it. Someone can carry it from one farm to the next on their shoes. This is another good reason to practice biosecurity and one reason why I don't make it a habit to visit dairies, since I own goats. Once symptomatic (showing symptoms) one may notice increasing lethargy and a wasting away due to severe malnutrition as the intestines are progressively hardened reducing the ability of nutrition to pass from the intestines into the animal. Diarrhea may become apparent in cattle and animals that are further along into the condition. They may also begin to show hair loss. Testing can be done on the manure when the bacterium is actually shedding. Blood tests can also be done, but as of this writing are not completely accurate, so need to be used along with other observations.

This is an issue to avoid at all costs. Know where your stock is coming from and the practices of the herd owner before you bring something home from them. If I don't breed them myself, I choose to purchase buck replacements from breeders of good reputation in the industry that are also very picky about where their stock comes from. I also look for older, yet healthy animals in their herds. Herds with only young animals have not aged enough to show if the herd is infected. They may be more expensive up front in dollars, but that is infinitely cheaper than getting a problem like Johne's going in your herd. Then quarantine your new purchase and run it through a normal farm introduction protocol. Besides deworming herbs, I'd consider strong antibacterial herbs, such as a several day course of garlic, goldenseal (always give with a Vitamin B complex herb), myrrh, cinnamon (not by itself in pregnant animals in large doses), ginger, perhaps some thyme (not in pregnant animals) and the like.   If there is something in their digestive tract that I'm not aware of, I'm going to do my best to be sure that it never has a chance to make it past the quarantine pen.   Should you get this problem in your herd, run all of them through the same herbs. I'd work on possible infected animals for a minimum of four months with solid doses of efficacious herbs. Any infected animals I would quarantine and always handle last. Then you'll have some hard decisions to make- whether you want to take a lot of time to work a lot of herbs through their system, or whether you have to make a decision you'd rather not make. No one can make that decision except for you. Whatever you choose, you will need to take precautions to not affect any other ruminants. I'd also run young stock separate from older stock in facilities that have not been infected. This is not a problem to play games with and is one that the government wants reported. If you can't commit to working steadfastly at it then please consider not passing the problem on to anyone else. Your integrity is worth far more than a few bucks from a quick sale. For this and other health issue reasons, do NOT buy animals from auctions and sale yards and bring them home to an existing herd. You are asking for trouble doing this.

Malabsorption and Hypochloridia

A wild canine or feline on a raw foods diet wouldn't normally have diet negatively impact their bowel health.   Domesticated pets are usually either on a processed food diet or a diet that is very heavy into meats, unlike their meat and plant eating wild counterparts. This would include the vegetation filled paunches of their prey. Even cats eat grass and plants.   Just ask some of my plants in and out of the house! Dang.   And then there was my beautiful aloe vera plant basking in summer sunshine that a batch of our Pyrenees puppies murdered and partially consumed. It paid them back though; with looser bowels due to the amount they ate!   Our man made unnatural diets cause the stomach gastric juices to be what we call hypochloridic, or low in hydrochloric acid. This prevents them from breaking their foods down as well and does not let them utilize their food as well, decreasing the minerals and proteins that they are able to break down and utilize from what they do eat.   Please consider getting them on a proper balanced diet that includes some sprouted grains, raw organic meats, fruits and vegetables. When you make salad for you, make extra for your pet (sans the onions). When you make carrot juice, share the juice and pulp with your pets. Another very helpful thing (besides cayenne) would be to add raw organic apple cider vinegar to their diet. You can mix it in their food, or a bit in their water. A 50 pound pet would take one teaspoon, three times per day. Over time the body will use the vinegar to correct the low acidity in the stomach, and will increase the amounts of minerals and protein they obtain from their diet. You can keep them on this as a lifelong supplement. Please do not substitute with the damaging white or apple cider flavored vinegars. Also try and keep your ACV in glass containers which will not leach any ingredients into the vinegar.

Motion sickness

I am placing motion sickness here due to the vomit response that usually is our first indicator of having a pet that has this problem. Any animal, from small to large, can get motion sickness. If I had one experiencing this, there are a few things I would do for them. For that actual nausea, I would administer ginger. This can be ginger essential oil diluted at the rate of 10 drops per tablespoon of olive oil (1/2 that for pregnant animals) and using just enough to rub it on the intestinal regions. If you know they have a history of experiencing motion sickness, ginger can also be fed at least 20 minutes before taking your creature for a ride or a haul. It can be given during the problem as well. Mix a normal dosage of powder with water and give orally or mix it in their feed.

Some other things I would look at are supporting the nervous system, so look for those herbs in that chapter. You may also consider some system cleansing, starting with the bowels as always, and working through the cleanses in proper order, as listed at the beginning of Part ll. Be sure your vehicle or trailer does not smell like a new vehicle. Air them out or wash them out! Using lemon essential oil in the process helps break down some toxins. I was looking at horse trailers recently, and could not believe all of the chemical smells in the new ones with all of the padding. You sure couldn't haul me in that without me vomiting! We opted for a generic, but safe, no frills model to get away from all of that. For some animals blind folds, or blinders (also known as blinkers and winkers) on the sides of their eyes that block peripheral vision may help. After an accident I was in, any fast peripheral movement for over a year would get me nauseated quite quickly. Also remember this after any surgeries, especially those that involve anesthesia. Be sure to eliminate any chemical sources in their diet that may contribute to nausea problems.

Overweight

In my work I usually do not focus on weight, even in humans. I focus on proper foods, moderate but enjoyable exercise, fresh air, sunshine, and cleansing, and the weight tends to self correct with that. How refreshing! So look to these things as well for your pet. With my Fjordies (Fjord horses) that means I can't let them graze all hours of the day. They have a daily grazing schedule, with a bit of grass or oat hay to chew on during their non grazing time. Please knock off the packaged and processed 'food', including people 'food' for your pets. Even if you are not going to make good choices for yourself, please be sure that your pets do. After all, they are stuck with what you give them since they can't shop for themselves. People food is so full of the very addictive substance, MSG. That is what laboratories use to make fat mice for experiments. MSG will be in nearly everything processed, and has at least forty different names that indicate its presence. Do some internet research on this topic if you would like to know more.

Parasites

Parasites have a whole chapter devoted to them in Part 1. Please do attend to them. Nearly everything has them all of the time, as most creatures reinfect themselves daily. Often one is just controlling the amount of them.

Parvo

Parvo virus as found in the canine family members is beyond nasty. It's just plain evil. Vaccinations, of course, can be given for this, but that too carries risks. Besides adverse effects, vaccinating for this disease can also allow the vaccine recipient to shed the virus in their feces, infecting the premises with it. They also will be carriers during this time and can infect other canines. Only you can make decisions on whether to vaccinate for this or not. Practicing biosecurity is important. Do not let your dog have contact with other dogs if possible, nor take them to areas that are frequented by other dogs, if possible. That includes to the pet area at rest stops. You will likely find every dog disease there. Have a different plan when you travel. Do not let your puppies or dogs have exposure to dogs or puppies that have recently been vaccinated for this. It is possible for those vaccinated animals to be carrying the virus and pass it on to yours. One of our dogs brought Parvo home from the vet clinic a few years ago. Of course, every disease known to every creature may be resident there as well.

Parvo often damages the heart muscle, attacks the white blood cells, damages the intestines and hemorrhages them. The dog will become unusually lethargic seemingly overnight. If you see this, you need to jump on things now! The animal will need heart support, especially cayenne and hawthorn. Fir Meadow has a Heart Support tincture containing these and many other helpful supportive cardiac herbs. See the Cardiovascular System chapter for additional support ideas. You will want to get them on large amounts of QUALITY echinacea- triple doses hourly. Echinacea is very safe and can be given in large amounts in time of need. This will help support the white blood cells. I would also bring out the garlic, the myrrh, the cayenne again, cinnamon and ginger for the GI tract or use HerBiotic by Fir Meadow. Make a blend and give hourly. I would also add strong peppermint tea to that, which will help the body and intestines with pain and gastric distress. Peppermint tea enemas should also be given to help keep your animal hydrated. They do have a tendency to want to vomit up anything that goes down, so if you can have some of these herbs in tincture form, and add those to the enema, that would be more desirable. Elevate the back end of your dog with the last enema in the series, to help them hold it in longer. Add electrolytes to the final enema as well. Plan to repeat these four times each day. Even trickling tinctures into the mouth is helpful, as the capillaries in the gums and mouth will uptake nutrition. Keep at it, even once they start looking better. You usually will have to herb them for about three days in a row.   Give them a quiet area with plenty of rest and blanket them to keep them warm.   For several days any stress can send them into a relapse. As you start them back on food (they can have all of the raw honey water they want), start with fruit and vegetable juices (no grapes).   After a day, you can add some slippery elm bark powder to the juice, and some soaked oatmeal.   The following day you can start adding shredded carrot and other vegetables and some organic chicken broth.   Small pieces of meat can start to be introduced the day after that.   Keep them on slippery elm powder, drinkable aloe juice, or marshmallow root powder for several days, this will give the body what it needs to soothe and repair that damaged GI tract. A pinch of cayenne is always helpful in any mix, and Fir Meadow's GI Soother can be useful here. If you have one canine come down with Parvo you can safely give your others this herbal support plan at four times per day to minimize further damage before they would become symptomatic at about ten days after exposure. I would continue at that level for two weeks, minimum.

Probiotics

The intestines of your creature contain at least 400 types of flora in them that are responsible for picking up a certain nutrient or two and moving them into the bloodstream via the villi hairs.   These are the bacteria that feed your creature. You will want to feed the bacteria to keep them happy so that they can function at peak performance, enabling your creature to do the same.   Raw fresh plant foods are the preferred source for these.   Other good sources are raw garlic, raw (meaning unpasteurized) organic apple cider vinegar, and raw organic honey. There are store bought probiotics, but they pale in comparison to the hundreds of enzymes provided by real food and are often made from the stomach contents of feedlot slaughter animals.   If your animal has had any GI tract damage or any antibiotics, plan on at least a two week amount of time to build them back up. Start when the antibiotics start, and continue for two weeks past their last use. I'm not encouraging antibiotic use, but in reality there will be many people reading this book at all different levels of herb use, knowledge, and comfort levels. So if your animal has or has had antibiotics, this is for you.

Restarting a Rumen or Digestive Tract

Having a rumen or stomach shut down is scary. This can happen as an adverse effect from medications, from severe stress, or from large amounts of pain. I know in the dairy goat world sometimes people will give human diarrhea products to goats. That is a HUGE no no; there are cases of animals dying from doing that due to their loss of peristaltic action. If the function loss is from a chemical reaction, see also the chapter on Poisonings and begin detoxing right away. There is no time to lose! Get to work immediately! Also do what this section teaches.

Cayenne. Are you seeing how important this herb is? Cayenne is a good one to try and kick start a rumen or stomach/intestines back into action. Senna is also very useful here, as is cascara sagrada. Another option would be to grab a bowel cleansing herbal product and consider triple dosing it every hour, as long as you know all of the herbs in it are fine for your creature. Fir Meadow and Dr. Christopher both have good bowel products. Tea your powdered herbs and drench orally, leaving the powdered herbs in the water. Walking your creature if possible and massaging castor oil mixed with cayenne to the stomach or rumen areas may also help. If the animal is a ruminant, see if you can swipe the cud from a healthy animal (use a speculum so you don't get bit) and also carefully drench that into your animal to get a healthy flora balance going. Offer fiber foods once your creature begins to show interest in them such as: long stemmed hay, twigs, clean leaves, edible flowers and stalks, etcetera. This will also help encourage peristaltic action.

Stool Colors

Stool colors can give you some data on what you may be dealing with. The final decision should always be made by a qualified veterinarian and /or some lab work. Often one can send samples that have been correctly collected to a veterinarian college diagnostic lab directly. This saves the expense of a veterinarian. However, due to a veterinarian's experience, they may already have a pretty good idea of what they are seeing, which can save some valuable time that sending a sample to a lab takes. You need to do as you feel led to do in your situation. These suggestions are meant as an educational guide only. Some of these are liver only and some are intestinal. I also have these listed in the Digestive Tract chapter.

When you see dark stools, you may be seeing toxin dumping. This is very common when first starting to cleanse. It also may be a sign of older blood in the stool from further up in the GI tract, which is good to report to your veterinarian to obtain a diagnosis. This situation can be serious, such as ulceration or severe parasite damage, but can be handled herbally if that is your choice, once you know what is going on. Sometimes dark stools are also liver oriented, as it lets go of excess toxins.

White stools can be caused from chemicals such as ingestion of chemical fertilizers. Definitely consider the Poisons chapter in Part 1 if you see such a thing. This happened to a dog that a friend of mine had. The neighbor had 'helped' her with her yard by applying chemical fertilizer to it that the dog then ingested. Come to think of it, just about a half year later this dog died from kidney failure and kidney cancer. Were those related? We don't know, but I certainly know it DIDN'T help! Cat's can lick this, or anything chemical off of their paws. Fertilizer and chemicals can mistakenly end up in processed feeds & grains due to computer or mechanical failure at feed mills. Be aware. Often your creature will not be feeling or looking well in this situation either. Don't wait to see if they get better, but jump on GI, liver, kidney and blood support immediately, also making sure they are staying properly hydrated through the process. I would continue the cleansing for AT LEAST one organ regeneration, unless your animal had a moderate or greater symptoms. In that case a year is not too small of time to help them restore themselves. White can also present itself if the body is moving gallstone material out. This will usually be in lumpy or stone like material. Note that horses do not have gall bladders. If you suspect the feed is a problem, perhaps you bought a new bag or switched types or brands, then save some in freezer bags and place in the freezer in case you need to have independent lab samples taken and return the remainder to your feed supplier letting them know what happened.

Green lumps may show up once a stagnated gall bladder or liver begins to clean out soft to hard bile stones.

Yellow and orange sometimes surfaces with liver cleansing, as more serious synthetic toxins are coming out of the system. Make sure your creature has GOOD functioning bowels during this problem and lots of access to clean drinking water.

Runny yellow may be a Salmonella problem. Taking a sample to your vet (in a container they provide) for a diagnosis is not a bad idea along with herbal antiseptic support at the acute level. Kat likes to use GI Soother and HerBiotic in these situations. Quarantine the animal and burn affected bedding. Don't wait for lab results to get started with herbing, by then you will be too late to help them. The lab report will give you information that may help you with future problems.

Runny grayish white stools may be Cryptosporidium. This is a time to use acute levels of herbs similar to a possible Salmonella problem along with getting a sample to your vet for confirmation. Quarantine the animal and burn affected bedding. You need to know if your animals have this problem (as well as salmonella and other bacterium issues) in their environment so you can be on the offense with the remainder of your herd, flock, or kennel.

Red stools may indicate fresh blood close to the anus. This also can be serious (injury, cancer, parasites such as coccidia and other causes) and one should consider having a veterinarian investigate to gain some useful information, so they know how to work with the situation. Carefully given enemas of water and cayenne should help stop bleeding. Cayenne can also be given orally, preferably by tincture, but giving the powder diluted in a liquid is also acceptable. One teaspoon of cayenne added to the liquid for a 100 to 200 pound creature would be a good starting place. Feeding or giving demulcent herbs will help the body soothe the area as they move through. Of particular interest here would be slippery elm bark, as more of that should reach the anal area than plant leaf sources. The body will also use the capillary route to help soothe the area and for that drinkable aloe, marshmallow root or leaf, slippery elm bark, mullein leaf, and comfrey can be good sources. These herb powders or drinkable aloes can also be mixed with warm water and gently given by enema. If the problem is close to the anus, salves applied around the anal area can also help the body repair the tissue. If parasites may be a concern, please see that chapter in Part l. Do NOT ignore this problem or plan to 'get to it later'. You might not get later.

The Accessible Pet, Equine and Livestock Herbal

This section is only meant as a stock keeper's guide and in no way replaces the evaluation of a veterinarian. Certainly feel free to employ their services to get a diagnosis.

Twisted gut

See the section under Colic. Start on this problem immediately including getting professional help if the animal is larger than you can personally carry.

Ulcers and Leaky Gut

I think these should be called "Owcers". Not to make light of this very serious issue; I've heard many excruciating stories about this issue. Causes can be from medications, including over the counter types, from antacids, antibiotics, pain relievers, undue stress, or anything that makes the stomach hypochloridic or that changes its Ph level. Under acidy can allow bacteria to eat a hole in the GI. An improperly functioning gall bladder can contribute to this problem in the intestines. If the Ph neutralizing bile does not meet the hydrochloric acid as it enters the small intestine, then overly acidic material can damage the tender tissue, creating a painful ulcer there. Antacids reduce stomach acidity, which allows bacteria which would never survive the normal hydrochloric acid level to have the opportunity to damage the stomach wall or enter the intestines, causing damage there. Processed feeds, contributing to a less than healthy stomach, also may contribute.

You can go the fast route or the slow route in your body support for this issue. Cabbage juice, fed for at least two weeks, often has good results. To get fast results, one can give 40,000 heat unit cayenne several times a day for one or two days. My preference is to go the fast route, due to the pain level this condition is noted for. One teaspoon of cayenne mixed in a liquid and given orally for that 100 to 200 pound creature is what is called for. That would be ¼ cup by the time you get to average sized horses (950 to 1250 pound ranges). Use just a large pinch for small pets. You can mix it with just enough water to make it easy to drench orally. Just so you know, though I've never had an ulcer, I do take cayenne orally. It is hot. It does not damage. And I'm a wimp! Slippery elm, drinkable aloe, or marshmallow root powder can be fed for the next few days, after you are confident that the ulcer is taken care of. You will know by your animal's change in attitude, appetite and energy. GI Soother is a good follow up product to encourage the body to heal the damaged tissue properly.

Underweight

Please see the chapters in Part 1 on Rescue animals and also Parasites. Also be sure and rule out diseases specific to your creature that can cause chronic underweight situations, and chronic,"walking" pneumonia.

When you cleanse an animal and get it on a good diet, sometimes they will go underweight in the process of getting healthier, as bad tissue is broken down and taken out faster than new tissue is replaced. This happens in humans too. As long as they are otherwise healthy, don't fret. Just monitor them and add a few more calorie types of herbs.

Some nice nutritional support would include: olive oil (one tablespoon for that 100 to 200 pound creature), organic brown rice, carrots, organic cooked potatoes, organic steamed winter squash, mullein leaf powder, calendula seeds, sunflower seeds (check very carefully for mold), flax seed freshly ground up for single stomached animals, and flax seed left whole for ruminants.

Wet or Moist or Cracked Paws

This is a "back to the drawing board" for the bowels type of issue. Clean and nurture the bowels, and switch your creatures back to a raw diet. Also be sure and check that there isn't a secondary problem going in the form of a fungal infection. See the Candida section for fungal issues. Give the herbs orally with the bowel program and put herb tinctures or salves on the problem feet.

Chapter 17- Ears

Ear Drum Damage

Work with ear drum damage just as you would any physical damage to the body. See the Epidermis chapter. You'll want to apply salves all the way around the ear that help the body heal tissue, and give oral herbs. Do not put herbs in the ear with a perforated ear drum.

Ear Wax

An over accumulation of ear wax can cause problems with lessened hearing and it can encourage infections as natural ear drainage is reduced. Animals with very small ear canals, like LaMancha dairy goats, are subject to this problem. I have narrow ear canals myself, and encounter this problem periodically.

If your animal will let you do it and they have a tight ear canal, you can hold a ear candle upright to them and candle some of the wax out. The candle has to be well seated so a good vacuum will result. It always amazes me how much wax and residue I get out of my ear when I do this. It is amazing how well I can hear afterward! You will want to get specific instructions on candling from a website or company that makes them. It will take about 15 minutes to candle one ear, one time. Sometimes an ear needs to be candled twice in a row. Make sure you do this in a way that you can sit down and do it in a safe place, which is NOT a stall that has hay or straw close by, but rather out in the driveway or a green area. Ear cones or candles can be found online or through many health food stores.

For the rest of our creatures, the other thing we can try is to warm up olive oil, and do gentle olive oil flushes trying to loosen and wash out the excess wax. If you do not have success with this, then you may need to hire your veterinarian's skilled hands for this procedure. The last thing you want to do is damage an ear drum trying to chase wax.

Hearing Loss or Deafness

Infections, illnesses, exposure to repeated loud noise, excessive ear wax or growths, physical damage and nerve damage, are all reasons for hearing reduction or loss.

Illness should be dealt with according to guidance in the Immune System chapter. Obviously doing what you can to reduce the amount of loud noises you and your creatures are exposed to is beneficial not for just the ears, but the entire nervous system. Physical damage to the ear should also be handled as in the Epidermis chapter.

When giving herb liquids by ear, we refer to them as 'injections'. Syringes without needles and smaller, handheld drenching tools are probably are the easiest and safest to work with in these situations. Do not enter the ear, but go right to the opening when you insert the liquid. Chances are good the animal may move or jerk it's head, and you do not want to be anywhere close to the ear drum if that happens. Also, using a turkey baster or an eye dropper is risky due to the suction that comes once you let go of the rubber tops. That suction can suck an ear drum out right now.

To give that ear 'injection', tilt the animals head to one side if possible and drop some tincture in along the side so that it can run in, instead of dropping it right onto the tender ear parts. While keeping the ear opening upward, massage around the bottom 1/3 of the ear and into the jugular groove to help move the tincture further into the ear. Then you can let them up. Be prepared for them to then shake some of it on you or the surroundings, because of that, do this outside or in a location that flying tincture won't stain things if possible.

Infections to the ear can be started from something as simple as a pet or larger animal scratching an ear with a rear foot, or on something stationary, and getting dirt or other foreign material into the ear. Rarely, an insect can also die in the ear and cause problems as it decays. As long as the ear drum is not perforated, warm olive oil can be infused into the ear, and then tilting the head to allow it to run back out. Make the olive oil even better by adding lavender or tea tree essential oil to the olive oil. You can use either of these in this situation with fifteen drops of essential oil per tablespoon of olive oil. Both of these essential oils are more gentle then most others on tissue. After that a tincture can be placed gently into the ear three times per day. Try to avoid alcohol based tinctures unless you first flash the alcohol off. Also avoid vegetable glycerine (glycerites), as they tend to be sticky.

Great herbs for ear nerve support are: blue vervain, blue cohosh, black cohosh, Lobelia inflata, and valerian. You can also add hops and lavender. Make a blend of several of these. Dr. Christophers Nerve formula is a good one as well. Plan on using these herbs or herb products for several months.

Ear Growths

Ear growths can be a challenge. The first place to start is with their diet and internal cleansing. Then I would also add traditional blood cleaner types of salves to the ear area itself. Plan to work on this from a few weeks to several months, depending on the level of toxicity of the animal. If it is a malignancy, then see the Cardiovascular chapter under Malignancies.

Head Shaking

Head shaking, after you rule out neurological problems, often indicates foreign material or a bug in the ear. See if you can take a flashlight to see what it might be in there. Be careful to not get your head or face hit by an animal shaking. When working on medium to large stock, it is never a bad idea to give your head some additional protection by putting on a riding helmet. The last thing you want to do is get hit by a big strong head or neck while you are trying to assist your animal. If your animal will let you, you may need to shave the inside hair of the ear with clippers (use a size ten blade). This would make problems more visible, as well as help things to fall out easier that don't belong in there. Sometimes clipping is all it takes for your animal to eject the problem. Sometimes you can flush it out with warm olive oil.

If you discover a bug crawling around in there, then grab your trusty flashlight. Many bugs will crawl or fly out towards the light.

In either case, once the offending problem is removed, if they were mine I'd carefully do a warm olive oil and lavender essential oil flush just to help the body to avoid infection. Directions for that are given earlier in this chapter.

Infection

If you find your animal pawing at their ears, shaking their head, notice foul smells emanating from their ears, see white or yellowish pus, or whimpering as you touch the ear area, you may have an infection going on. As I have mentioned earlier, tinctures and olive oil/essential oil blends work best for ears. Some of those are mentioned previously, with more herb choices being: lavender, lemon, or tea tree essential oil, goldenseal tincture, weak cayenne tincture, oil of garlic (look for the recipe in the Appendix), rosemary (or the essential oil), myrrh, usnea, and sometimes oregon grape root. Eucalyptus essential oil can be used, but is weaker. Remember to dilute all essential oils with olive oil for ear use. Avoid the hot essential oils which can damage very sensitive ear tissue. You will need to use the item of your choice in the ear at least two times a day. Even animals with chronic ear infections for two years have responded in just two and three weeks to these methods. I had a client that was trying to work with this situation only using oral herbs. Certainly you can give oral herb support in case the infection is trying to enter the bloodstream of your creature. Remember that the ear is a body cavity. Oral use of herbs may not reach the some of the infection. So it will be important to get herb oils or blended/diluted essential oils into the ear UNLESS there is a perforated ear drum. In that case, you will have to use an essential oil blend (not on felines) and wipe that onto and around but not into the ear, so that it can soak into the area as the body draws it in. I like using DisNFect blend and HerBiotic tincture or herb mix for the oral support. Adding garlic to the oral support is beneficial; just remember your appropriate dosing for a creature.

Mites

Please see the Parasites chapter for mites, as these occur on the ear flap rather than in the working ear parts.

The Accessible Pet, Equine and Livestock Herbal

Vertigo

Animals can get vertigo. Inner ear infections are a common cause. Be sure and rule out other neurological problems. Hire your veterinarian if you need assistance deciphering those; time may be of the essence so you don't want a make a mistake in assessment in these types of issues. In vertigo, I would be watching for nausea and difficulty in walking a straight line. Possibly head shaking or ear pawing if an ear infection is going on simultaneously.

Let me tell you from personal experience, that it is not fun! It's quite unpleasant to not even move your head and still watch the world spin around followed by your stomach wanting to make the same motion. I had it for one and a half days after pushing myself too hard for several days without enough nutrition, which allowed me to succumb to a mild inner ear infection. I was very highly motivated to support my body's work in healing itself, so I got over it very fast. The key was hourly use of nervous system herbs, antibacterial herb tinctures orally and in my ear. I also took liver and kidney cleansing herbs hourly. The second day, I took them four times that day, as I could feel that I was greatly improved over day one. I hope I never experience this again.

Yeast

See Candida in the Digestive System chapter for yeast problems. For ears, a salve works nicely if the problem is on the flaps, and a tincture if the problem is further into the ear.

Chapter 18- Endocrine System

"What are endocrine glands?" you ask. Great question! These are glands that put biochemicals directly into the bloodstream to get a fast cellular communication. One biochemical that most of us has heard of is adrenaline, the hormone that creates the fight or flight response. Other important communications involve the 24 hour biological clock cycles, moods, growth and development, reproduction, multitudes of tissue functions and metabolism. These organs too, can gather toxins, form blockages, become nutritionally deficient and become areas of reduced activity. The body has a good safety net, in that most processes can be backed up by a second endocrine gland. However, this adds additional wear and tear to that back up organ, which will eventually wear that one down too. Listed below are some of the major endocrine glands, whose primary function (as we understand them today) is to place hormones into the bloodstream. Additional organs that also have some endocrine functions are the heart, liver, kidneys, stomach, duodenum and even the bone marrow. I think as time goes by we'll learn even more. Interesting, isn't it?

If your animal is on medication for any issues with endocrine glands, be sure you work with your veterinarian on monitoring medication levels. This is very important. As their body chooses to use nutrition from the herbs towards healing, medications will likely have to be adjusted.

Brain

The pituitary gland is considered the "Master Gland". If the pituitary gland is not running well, then no other gland can run at peak efficiency. Its well being influences every other gland as it oversees them. This is the gland that tends to have problems (along with the adrenals) in Cushing's disease. All of the brain foods mentioned in the Brain chapter are good for the glands in the brain. Chaste Tree berry (Vitex) is specifically nourishing for the pituitary, and mullein and Lobelia inflata are good for every gland in the body. Mullein would be three parts by weight and Lobelia inflata at one part, given orally. I would also be sure and focus on the cleanses and plan to revisit them periodically. Besides oral herbs, nourishing and cleansing herbal salves can be placed on the top of the head area. The body will pull it in to where it wants to use it.

The hypothalamus and pineal glands are also little glands located in the mid brain area. The hypothalamus works together with the pituitary and adrenal glands. It is also important in the body's use of oxytocin, a hormone used by the body for milk let down, and also one of the hormones used by the body to get the birthing process going. Dopamine is another hormone some people are familiar with that is connected to the hypothalamus. The pineal gland works with the Circadian rhythm in the body, otherwise known as the sleep and waking patterns and the other 24 hour body cycles. The pineal gland is very needful of natural light to help in it in these rhythmic cycles. That is why some people are very affected by seasonal energy and emotional lulls in the "longer night" months of the year. I believe animals can be affected by this as well. The pineal also helps the body work with melatonin, the sleep encouraging hormone. Please do not supplement with the single supplement melatonin in these issues. If you provide it for the body, the body will begin to produce even less as it recognizes the provision from an outside source. Instead, cleanse and nourish the body so that it can perform correctly. Look back to the general brain and blood stream herbs to support these organs, including the mullein and Lobelia inflata blend.

Body & Throat

The thyroid and parathyroid ("with thyroid", which is where they literally are) have some very important functions. Yet at times they are considered extra body parts and removed. These are located in the mid throat region on both sides of the esophagus. The thyroid is about walnut sized in humans with the parathyroid being smaller and piggy backing behind the thyroid. The thyroid is very important for body oxygenation, energy consumption, and metabolism rates. That's why hypo (slow) thyroid is sometimes involved in weight gain, and hyper (rapid) thyroid, as in Grave's disease, can be involved with rapid weight loss among other conditions, such as increased pressure behind the eyes. The parathyroid is extremely important in the production of calcitonin, which is responsible for building bone mass and growth, and an important component of cell replacement (all of which have calcium as a building block). Iridology is interesting when it comes to these glands. Sometimes lab work can show a 'normal' individual, but when the irides are viewed, you can see that one side is hypo, and the other side is hyper, resulting in normal lab work when the individual is not normal. If lab work is off, you can also see if it is just one side or both that are involved.

For thyroid difficulties it might be hard to beat the mullein and Lobelia inflata combination. Fir Meadow makes a salve (GlandAide) which makes it easy to apply the herbs to creatures. Slather it on two to three times per day, six days per week. Add oral herbs if you want to speed the process up. Fomentations can also be made with the herbs and applied hot and held onto the animal's thyroid region until cool, and then repeated. This is, however, only practical with lap pets, but will get faster results from the body. If the thyroid is in a slow, hypo state, then additional kelp can also be added to the diet at normal rates. If you have been giving normal rates, then you can double what you feed. If the thyroid is hyper, don't use the kelp. Remember to do some cleansing to get any toxins out that are involved in congesting the gland, so that it can keep improved performance. If it is malfunctioning, it does have a toxin accumulation since weaker tissue always accumulates them. For the parathyroid do the same thing as for the thyroid, with the addition of some higher calcium herbs to give the body some more nutrients to work with. Some of those would be alfalfa, comfrey, nettle, kelp, dandelion, and raspberry leaf. One can also use a salve on the neck area, Wounderful! would be a good choice in this situation.

We have a lot of focus on the pancreas these days. Humans are at epidemic levels of pancreatic problems, at this writing it is the fastest growing problem in the United States, and the largest health problem in Mexico. It is alarming to me to see how many of our children are at the prediabetic stages. Unfortunately, the same diets and vaccines that exacerbate this in humans do the same in our beloved creatures. Besides assisting the body in blood sugar use with glucagon and insulin, this organ is extremely important in providing enzymes which it flows into the intestines at their beginning, to aid with nutrient uptake. If the pancreas is impacted, then the liver and kidneys are always also impacted.

Feeding at regular intervals, and even giving smaller meals more often, are helpful at working with blood sugar issues. Also seriously consider removing all sweet feeds (grains or feeds containing first or second refining molasses), all processed feeds and adding high quality live plant foods to their diet. They can have BLACK STRAP molasses at half of the amounts noted in the Supplements Chapter in Part 1. Contrary to public medical opinion, they can have raw fresh carrots. For smaller animals they can be grated or pulped, and for larger animals like horses they can be fed whole or chunked. Carrots do not contain the refined or processed sugars that cause the damage to the pancreas nor do they shortchange the liver on its sugar storage abilities. Make them even more nutritious by leaving the peel ON them. If your animal is on medication remember to heed the words at the beginning of the chapter. You will need to monitor their blood sugar levels and have medications adjusted as necessary.

Herbs that are very helpful for the pancreas are cedarberries, dandelion root, Jerusalem artichoke (sunchokes) tubers, chicory root, nettle leaf and root, cinnamon, uva ursi, mullein, and Lobelia inflata. Don't forget to look at herbs for liver and kidney support. If it is very irritated consider adding one or two demulcent herbs. I like marshmallow root in this situation, as it is also anti-inflammatory.

The adrenal glands also receive a lot of attention these days. They produce cortisol, which is a natural anti-inflammatory, and adrenaline, that hormone which prepares the body for battles or quick sprints to safety. When adrenaline is being released, immunity and digestive processes can be greatly reduced. They also help to regulate pain levels in the body. These are meant to be temporary processes, but in today's high demand and/or stressful situations they can be put to task daily for hours at a time, burning them out. No wonder illness and GI Tract issues often pair up with high stress living, as that is exactly what the adrenaline impacts. How can the GI tract break down and process nutrients efficiently if it is always operating at reduced levels of function? I see this issue at incredibly high rates in human iridology readings. For animals that are under high levels of stress or performance, digestive health support will become very important as well as a higher nutrition level, often double to triple of what a more carefree lifestyle would require. Kidney health also has a great impact on these organs that ride piggy back on the kidneys. You must always address kidney well being when supporting the adrenal glands. The liver also must be healthy, as it is required to break down hormones before they are expelled from the body. If the hormones are in overdrive, then the liver (especially a toxic one) will fall behind in its ability to remove them from the system. In those cases they may be dumped into other areas of the body to surface later, such as when your creature is tired, under great stress, or in conjunction with heat cycles.

Besides a good cleansing program, mullein, nettle, kelp, raspberry leaf, and especially licorice root are good supports for the adrenals. Licorice root should be given a one week break after every six weeks of use, and used no more than six days per week. This does not give you permission to just burn them out again once your animal is functioning well. Pick a realistic work or performance schedule for your creature that includes daily rest, grooming, play and turn out time into fresh air. Make sure to support them well on a nutritional level. Please give them at least one day off per week (a Sabbath of some type) from any demands at all. You need it and so do they. You'll get more out of them the other five or six days if you give them one or two off each week and you'll enjoy the process more.

Reproductive

The prostate, uterus, ovaries, and testicles will be covered in the reproductive chapter. They are listed here because they are endocrine glands affecting the body daily, not just during reproduction.

Spleen

The spleen has several important features. Though not always thought of as endocrine tissue, it does contribute hormones directly into the bloodstream as one of its duties. Other jobs that the spleen has is recycling iron in the blood as old red blood cells break down. It breaks down red blood cells that are spent, usually at about four months of age. The spleen also removes bacteria, which are covered with antibodies. The spleen also has from 1/3 to 1/2 of the body's storage for monocytes. Monocytes are what the body uses to make macrophages and other immune system cells with. Extra blood is also stored in the spleen in case the body has a need for a reserve.

Herbs that will support the spleen are nettle, burdock, and raspberry. They make excellent support due to their gentle nurturing ability of the bloodstream. Also the 3 parts mullein and 1 part Lobelia inflata mix. Other blood nurturing herbs can be used as well. The spleen is located below the bottom of the diaphragm below the left rib cage. If structural damage is done, then tissue supporting salves can also be used on that area. Wounderful! is one blend by Fir Meadow that can be used on all species of creatures, otherwise pull out the comfrey, lavender, and aloe for some single herb choices. Dr. Christopher's Complete Bone and Tissue Formula is another very good choice. Due to the black walnut in this Dr. Christopher product, don't use it on equine or camelid family members.

Chapter 19 Epidermis/skin, Connective Tissue, Muscle, Tendon

This is a wide encompassing chapter, dealing with all types of tissue, from the largest organ of the body: the skin (nine pounds on humans), to the soft tissues and musculature that lie underneath. I've lumped them together, as we tend to use the same herbs for all of these tissues with great results as the body draws nutrition from them. It takes an average of four months to replace skin, muscle and tendon cell for cell. Remember, that if the damage was severe or the location moderately toxic, it may take more than one regeneration to get the cells to the level of health we want them.

Abscesses and Boils

These pus filled lumps can occur from bites, stings, vaccinations, splinters and even certain types of bacteria. Be familiar with any diseases that are particular to your type of animal that can form these. Some of them can be zoonotic (can be spread to people), so care in handling them should always be exercised. You also do not want to infect your facilities or your other animals with whatever may be in that lump. Caseous Lymphadenitis or CL (sheep and goats) which is a corneybacterium (can infect many types of creatures) is one of those. CL is discussed in the Immune System chapter.

On these types of issues (as long as it is not a corneybacterium type of problem) I prefer to let the body decide if it's going to push it out or break it down from within and carry it through the lymph system. This goes for knots in the udder as well. To do this, I give herbs that are antiseptic orally to help the body go after any infection that is present. Those could be garlic, goldenseal, cayenne, echinacea, Oregon grape root, myrrh, usnea, thyme, rosemary, etcetera. I also give blood cleaning herbs, so be sure to see that chapter. I give larger doses, just as if the animal were sick. Then I will take one of my favorite friends, a salve made from mullein (three parts) and Lobelia inflata (one part) and keep applying that to the abscess area. Dr. Christopher makes a good one and Fir Meadow has one called "GlandAide". Then I let the body decide which way it's going to take it. I find in the case of udder knots that the body will usually shove them out through the udder. Of course if the body does that, have antiseptic herbs or salves on hand to cover the area after flushing it to encourage wellness to the area. HerBiotic salve or even infusing some Udder Blast (both by Fir Meadow) would be good applications. It would be good if you can quarantine the animal so that you can limit exposure to whatever may be in the abscess. It's easier to sanitize one stall then a whole pen or pasture! Bedding should be preferably burned, but can also be discarded in a way that no creature will gain access to it.

Sometimes these abscesses are 'aspirated'. Unless you need to know what is in them for a diagnosis by your vet (such as in CL), it is better to not invade them with a needle and syringe. As sterile as we can make things they are still not 100 percent sterile. There is also no way to completely sterilize the skin. If we draw the material out without complete flushing of the inside of the area, infective material will be left in the area. There is also the risk of hitting a vein or a nerve during this process. Usually, an abscess left to break by being drawn will not blow out a nerve or vein. I've heard of people bleeding animals to death by inadvertently cutting a main vein under the jaw. Remember, not every animal has textbook anatomy. Different structures can be in a bit of different location on each animal.

Accidents and Predator Attacks

Both of these problems just make my heart sick. By God's grace I've never had a predator attack on my goats, but I have in years past (before owning guardian dogs) lost chickens and hand raised pet ducks to raccoons and domestic neighbor dogs. I will discuss some of the some minor accidents with the stock that we've had in appropriate sections. I've counseled people through major accidents and predator attacks with their creatures. My heart goes out to them, every time.

When you discover a problem what is the first thing you are going to administer to your animal/s? Cayenne of course! See, and I'll bet you already knew that because you are such a good student. Get it in and on areas requiring attention to give the body what it needs to control any bleeding, even if you are not aware of any bleeding. It will also help with any shock. Continue to give more as you deem it is needed. For traumatic situations, that may as often as every 15 minutes at first, and then hourly for the remainder of the day. Do pair that up with garlic and other antiseptic herbs internally and externally if you think there is any possibility of infection getting a hold. Especially for any injury that is puncture like or beyond the top skin layers. For any injuries more serious than skin level, you may desire to hire your veterinarian to assess if there may be any body organs or internal damage involved. This is especially important in any kind of 'wreck' whether vehicular, into the ground, or into a solid item such as a fence or post. Also, if there are broken bones or dislocations you will want help from someone that has a deep understanding of their anatomy to help put out of place anatomy back into place. You can also hire them to help you develop a splinting or casting system if needed. Veterinarians have good resources in these areas, as many of them deal with these topics daily. If you are remote, you might have your vet help you put together an emergency props kit of supplies that are good to have on hand in these types of situations, such as splinting supplies, gauzes, wraps, etcetera. I always keep supplies in my trailer, barn, vehicle, and house. Sometimes they've even been handy for using on me.

Remember, if it is a predator damage, try to take pictures of any culprits that may have been involved, if possible. Obtain photos of the damage to your animal or animals, and of the predators where possible. In today's age of cell phones with photo abilities, it is not as difficult as in the past. If it is domestic predators, try to keep any hair or other samples from the predator if possible, using plastic bags or gloves to harvest the evidence. DNA testing can be used for a positive identification of the culprit/s if needed. This isn't intended to be a legal guide, but do consider some things, in case you are able to get reimbursement from someone's homeowner policy for their irresponsibility with their dogs. I have a friend that asked their mail carrier about where certain suspect dogs of a certain description might live. The mail carrier was able to give them some leads that eventually panned out. Not a bad idea.

One of our incidents came about when one of our young female guardian dogs got in the pasture with our old female guardian dog and decided to move up on the alpha line by way of a dog fight. Ask your vet for proper ways to break one of these up, as the way we did it may not work for you and may get you attacked and injured.   We felt safe doing it this way since we have worked with all of our dogs from puppies and we are their Alpha dog. After my husband and I were able to drag the two apart by holding back legs and digging into the ground for all we were worth, we found we had several bite wounds and tears through the skin including some on the face, with some bleeding. Thankfully there was nothing major or anything affecting their movement.   Once having them in different pens and putting rope muzzles on them just in case they responded badly to a tender area, I then took my clippers and shaved all of the damaged areas I could find to keep them cleaner and give me easier injury access for herbing. Then I administered one of my favorites for these types of situations.   Fifteen drops of lavender essential oil per tablespoon of olive oil. Lavender has some neat herbal combinations of properties.   I was leaning on its antibacterial (antiseptic), cell proliferant (cell division encouragement for faster healing), and nervine (nerve feeding) and relaxant qualities. I had to syringe it into the holes in several areas on both dogs, and smooth it on all the skin areas around the holes. I syringed it until no more could be held. It's okay to let some flow back out, as it will help cleanse the area. They had no infections and a good response by the body for healing. We administered it several more times for the week.   Bite wounds must ALWAYS be attended to.   A lot of bacteria will come off of the teeth and go into the victim that has been bitten, so expect a nasty infection if you do nothing. I could have made this even better by adding several other essential oils in it as described in other parts of this book, or by adding and steeping crushed garlic with it.   What did we learn from this? To always run our female guardians in different pastures so they don't try to protect 'their' herd from each other.   Had I the frame of mind to grab a bunch of cayenne powder before I ran out to the dogs, that would have been put to good use throwing at the eyes and noses of the dogs.   Remember, it won't harm, but will be hot. It may have helped stop or minimize the fighting right then. The outcome would have been clearer, infection free eyes and cleaner lungs and probably less bite wounds, as we would have been able to separate them faster.

Other herbs will follow in other related sections such as wounds and bones.

Athletes

Athletes require additional nutrition to support their bones, tendons, adrenal glands, backs, legs, and mental capabilities as additional demands are made on them. After a training session, competition or a workout, it is always a good idea to apply salves or tinctures to the legs, saddle areas, lower back and any other area that takes additional strain from the work being asked of them. Doing this will speed up the recovery time for the tissues involved, and may enable them to strengthen to an even greater and more supple level than they could without the herbal nutrition. Any of the injury herbs and the Supplements chapter will help you with ideas. Don't forget yourself if you are spending extra time on your feet or in the saddle during the training session.

Bad Breath

This is a condition that you do not want to ignore! Bad breath may be telling you to check the teeth and gums of your creature for infection. If an infection is in the mouth or gums, it can put your animal's life at risk quite fast. If that is the case, antibacterial herbs and wound support herbs should be used concurrently. Tinctures work nicely here, as the area can be bathed with the tincture several times per day. Salves can also be applied to the external jaw areas nearest the problem spots and the body will draw it in, but be sure you also use tinctures or very strong infusions around the problem teeth.

Bad breath may also hint of a lung infection and you'll find help for that in the Respiratory System chapter.

Often in our industrialized society foul breath will tell you that the animal is constipated or very toxic, as you smell what their insides smell like. For those animals, visit the cleansing section at the beginning of Part ll, as well as the Digestive System chapter. Remember, it's okay to have a vet help you assess the situation if you are not comfortable doing so. As your comfort level increases, you will find you are able to do more and more with some foundation under you. Developing a good relationship with a good veterinarian is important.

Bites and Sting Toxins

Bites and stings from bugs, snakes, scorpions and more please see the Poisons chapter in Part l.

Bleeding- CAYENNE!!!

Bleeding is mentioned here for your convenience in case you are paging through this book quickly in an emergency. CAYENNE is the herb you want to grab for, and get it on and in your creature quickly at the rate of one teaspoon herb mixed with water (for that 100 to 200 pound creature) and then additional topically. More information is given in the Cardiovascular chapter. Before you read that chapter get some cayenne going. Then read. I can't write cayenne in the side margin in bright red letters, but you might. Red Blood = Red Cayenne. Maybe that will help you, so you don't even have to look it up later. Put the cayenne powder or tincture (I prefer powder) on the bleeding injury, using pressure on the injury if needed. For serious venal or arterial tears you will still want veterinarian assistance, as those will be too large to clot without some repair work by your vet. I also like to give oral cayenne. For this the tincture is faster, but you can give the powder if that is all you have. If you have time, mix it with a liquid before you drench it. You do not need to clean the cayenne out of the injury. The body will eventually break it down and use it. This is true for any of the herb powders.

Burns from Mild to Severe

Probably the worst situation I've educated on was one where a burning barn roof came down on the backs of baby goat kids that were saved from the flames. I was told that as soon as they received their Wounderful! Salve they got to work with nice results. Comfrey leaf powder (don't use the root unless you want rubber), raw organic honey, mixed with wheat germ oil makes a very nice blend for burns. Aloe vera gel (not the store bought sunburn products containing alcohol) also can be placed directly on them. Lavender essential oil can be placed straight onto burns as long as it is pure, though I prefer to dilute it with olive oil. The whole Aromatherapy (medicinal use of essential oils) industry was developed from a

French man who had shoved his hand into a container of lavender essential oil after a chemical explosion in the perfume lab he worked in. He was amazed to find the redness and pain was alleviated on what should have been a damaging burn. Any of these can be placed on first through third degree burns. I like the salve best because it blocks air from the damaged nerves which will scream with relentless pain until they are blocked from oxygen. I know in the medical profession they want air on the burns and they don't want grease. Air on a fresh burn equals PAIN. You don't want pain, as that can keep sending your creature into shock and/or shut their rumen/digestive system down giving you another life threatening problem to work on. The grease medical professionals allude to is either animal based fats or petroleum based both of which can allow infections to get established under them. Plant based fats, such as are in olive oil, mixed with an antiseptic essential oil or herbs nourish the area and are completely absorbable by the body. Small amounts of quality natural beeswax in the salve blend also provide nourishment and is mildly antibacterial to the area. Another benefit to salving the burn is that the herbal salve assists the body in keeping precious body fluids into the area, preventing the burn area tissue from drying up. This will speed healing and reduce the potential for scarring.

First, attend to any bleeding and assume that there will be shock, so administer cayenne and/or shock tea. Get the cayenne in first, and then take time to make the shock tea if wanted. The recipe is in the Appendix for you. After the cayenne; attend to the pain with a hefty triple or quadruple dose of mullein tincture. One can also use HerBamine Tincture. Do dilute the tinctures with water, carrot juice, or another liquid to reduce the sharpness of the apple cider vinegar or other carrier. You can give more tincture every 15 minutes until you see some effect. The mullein is incredibly safe, just don't over vinegar the stomach. Then carefully clean what is needed, such as burned hair stuck to the area if you can get it off without causing additional pain. If I had this going on here I wouldn't wash or rinse the tissue as the water can have microbial problems in it. Then apply your herbs or salve of choice. Once you put herbs on you are not to take them back off. You just continue to repack the area over the old herbs or salve as the body uses it up. If you want to gauze wrap it, take plant leaves, lightly blanched and deribbed (like comfrey or burdock) and place them over the herbs or salve. You do not have to take these off but you can pull of any of it that comes off easily. If

The Accessible Pet, Equine and Livestock Herbal

some of the leaf sticks to the wound, leave it there and herb over the top of it. Then gauze over the leaf or leaves. If you gauze directly over the burn/herbs themselves you will cause great pain to your creature as you pull fresh cells off of the wounds every time. Gauze sticks to burns, will pull off new forming cells and will cause scarring. Using the blanched leaves over the burn and salves will keep that from happening. Herbs used right from the beginning and applied often will allow the body to discourage scarring. If tendons are damaged, it's okay. They too will be healed by the nutrient rich body. Keep at it. Scarring is also a sign that the body did not receive the nutrients it needed to do a correct tissue repair, similar to the calcium deposits left behind on broken bones.

Have no fear if you are dealing with crushed bones, bones that are normal but visible from deep wounds, or missing sections of bone. The body does want to heal those. Provide it with nutrition and watch how it was designed to repair. Amazing. For areas that have healed incorrectly consider putting them on an herbal program for as long as a year. Often the body will be able to correct a misalignment.

Clipper Marks or Cuts on the Skin or Udder

None of us ever intends on giving our animals a rash or 'raspberry' when we clip them. Eucalyptus essential oil (15 drops) diluted in olive oil (1 tablespoon) is a nice aid. The body will use it to lessen the damaged areas and also help the body with pain relief. Often your marks will be gone by the following day. Any of the other injury herbs or salves can be used also, or instead of, the eucalyptus. Be sure and have antiseptic herbs mixed in with them.

Cuts require a bit more help. The lavender essential oil, with olive oil or oil of garlic blend with lavender added is a favorite. So is the Wounderful! salve. I know I mention that salve a lot. That's because I use it and keep jars of it everywhere! My amazement never ends at what God puts in these plants for our benefit.

Some nice skin herbs are mullein, chickweed, calendula, marshmallow root, and slippery elm. All of them are soothing to touchy tissue.

Dysplasia

This is a sad topic to me. I think it's something we've done as a society to our faithful canine friends. Hip dysplasia is a term used for damage to the hip joints causing disability in dogs. It will usually show up in the larger breeds as opposed to the smaller breeds. Hip and ball sockets can be malformed, deteriorate or there can be improper conformation of the rear leg angle and how it attaches to the pelvis. This is another good reason to learn proper dog conformation. Even dogs that get hip certified can still begin to fall apart when they are older.

So what can we do to try and change this? Plenty! By now you should know that an herbalist never gives up. First, that dog ideally would come from parents that haven't had hip problems. Genetic weakness to a structure can be passed on, as they can in any body tissue. Even if you find later that there was a parental or sibling hip problem, I'll still give you a game plan.

First, consider that your growing puppy needs exercise daily. That means romping, bouncing, jumping and running. If you can't provide that for it, reconsider getting a dog of that size. Without proper resistance the body will not build as strong of joints. It also needs to have strong muscles and tendons to help hold all parts of the body better into place.

Throw away the puppy food. I mean it. We have raised a few Great Pyrenees dogs and that was a piece of advice that was given to us with our first puppy. Those high protein puppy foods encourage these large dog breeds to grow too fast. That encourages weaker joints. Our Pyrenees are supposed to live to about eight years of age. Our first one died a couple of years ago at 12 ½ years old and was actively guarding until she passed away in her sleep. We found her next to her baby girl goats that were her job to protect. We have an eight year old right now that acts like she is about two or three for activity level. Do what you can do to get them on a balanced raw food diet. Juliette Bairacli-Levy has great recommendations in her dog care book and I have many sprinkled throughout this book. Prior to about the 1960's people normally fed their dogs home prepared foods instead of feeding store bought foods for them. They lived longer then too. They also had fewer vaccinations and less health problems. If your animal already has dysplasia, start nourishing them as for a broken bone and a wound, and also start with cleansing, and see where it goes. As long as the hip can stay in its joint during the process, you should see improvement. Don't stop until you have normal movement, then feed nourishing herbs at a reduced rate to give the body tools to continue to support the area through life. Anytime you are trying to get the body to build bone, limit the amount of animal protein they eat. Animal protein causes the body to dump minerals from the bones and tissues at a greater rate than they intake from the animal products. Definitely do not feed them any animal protein that is not organic and really try to have only raw available for them, such as raw goat milk. The non organic animal products will likely have growth hormones in them, which will probably exacerbate the problem.

External parasites

Please see the Parasites chapter in Part 1 for this topic.

Fistulous Withers, Poll Evil, Bursa Problems

The bursa is the fluid filled sack in between joints including the vertebrae. They are meant to nourish and cushion the inner joint areas. When they get filled with bacteria, or suffer a blow causing structural damage, we can have problems here. Sometimes they will burst leaking their precious cushioning fluids.

Your focus will be with structural repair and with antiseptic/antibacterial herbs. Again, I like salves as they are easy to use with animals. If bacterium is involved, such as in poll evil or fistulous withers, exercise caution and quarantine your animal. Occasionally brucella (brucellosis) can be found in these. Horses with this issue should have no access to dairy stock. Don't forget internal herbs so the capillaries can speed nourishment to the area from the inside. I always work from every direction that I can.

One more item you may want to consider; to have healthy bursa you must have a well hydrated animal. Access to clean fresh water all of the time is essential. Dehydrated bursa become brittle and easier to damage.

Foot rot

"Oh, can you smell that?! Ick!" Sometimes foot or hoof rot is fungal, sometimes a yeast, and sometimes bacterial and with it can come an offending rotten smell. Either way I like a lavender essential oil and oil of garlic blend for this. You can make up other blends with your essential oils. Choose from myrrh (say expensive!), rosemary, thyme (not for pregnant creatures), tea tree, cinnamon, cloves, peppermint or sage. Don't use sage in pregnant animals. Peppermint should not be used on creatures less than a year old. Have fun blending! Keep any of these blends to 12 drops of essential oil total per tablespoon of olive oil. The rosemary, tea tree and lavender you can take to 15 drops total essential oil, not each. One can also use Udder Blast if they have it on hand.

Clean the hoof well. Trim away any excess dead material and remove the infective material from the stall. Then pour the oil blend onto the affected areas. Hold the hoof up as long as it is comfortable for you so the excess blend can sit in the area longer. Then let the foot or hoof down gently; don't just drop their feet and let them clunk onto the ground (or onto your foot). Then keep them in a dry stall or location. You don't have a dry one? Then be prepared to deal with this problem over and over and over again. It's easier to have a dry pen to put them in and change your husbandry so you don't have to play this game often; it will get old.

When trimming, or having horse hooves trimmed, be sure they trim the edges of the frog in the heel area so that the grooves are completely exposed on both sides of the frog. That reduces muck from getting jammed up in there that would unable to come out easy. On goats and other stock, if you notice the hoof tip starting to pit carefully trim it back so there is no hole to pack mud into. This will allow it to grow back healthy. Don't cut very far back though. If you do quick them (cause them to bleed), toss some cayenne powder on the bleeding area. If it still bleeds, then cayenne it, wrap it with gauze and vet wrap and leave that on. If it's bleeding badly, you may need to cauterize it with a disbudding iron or other hot tool. Get advice from your vet if you have never done this. You do not want to cause further damage doing it incorrectly. Cayenne has never failed me, however. It is my first hemostatic herb choice in this situation since it also helps the body reduce pain and is antiseptic in an area that is exposed to all types of bacteria.

The Accessible Pet, Equine and Livestock Herbal

Founder

Founder is a problem of hooved animals. Essentially founder comes from a toxic response causing decreased blood supply to the hooves, causing tissue in them to die as they are starved to oxygen and nutrients. There is also a 'road' founder which is caused by heavy concussion to the foot. Often it is from eating too much feed. That can be from a grain raid, from increasing rations too quickly, such as alfalfa or grain, or from a gradual overeating that some horses do on unlimited pasture access. If you see fat building on a horse's neck at the crest area, the time to get them off of pasture was yesterday. You will have to restrict their grazing time until they are back to normal weight, and even then you will need to monitor their turnout time. We have to limit turnout time with our Fjords and our other mini draft mare, as they are very hardy and will get fat very easy, so they are on a daily turnout schedule as opposed to free choice pasture.

The toxin release will cause decreased foot circulation, as mentioned above. Then the sensitive tissue (laminae in horses) around the hoof bone (coffin bone in horses) becomes less supported and may rotate. The degree of rotation determines the future usefulness of the horse. In a severe situation, the bone will come through the bottom of the hoof. If buying a horse, try to avoid previously foundered horses as they will be more susceptible to that and lameness issues unless you are just buying a yard ornament that you can monitor. Look for flattened hooves and horizontal rings on the hooves. Also watch for misshapen feet. We do have one mare that may have had a founder history. She came to us with a strange dimpled concave look from the center of her front coronet bands to the bottom of her hoof. Her hooves were also too steeply angled. With herbal support much of that is now grown out with normal appearing hoof and close to normal hoof angle in its place. I just saw this mare cantering and bucking in the pasture for the first time. It has been 10 months since we bought her and started her on her herbal nourishment program. All good signs for sure. My farrier told me about a donkey in California that is surviving and getting around just fine without coffin bones. That seems insane to me, but I don't have any reason to doubt my farrier. I know there are crazy situations out there. So, if the animal is not in uncontrollable pain, then I say go for it. There is quite a bit of information on the

Internet in English and in German (probably more European languages too) about restoring foundered hooves, even bad ones.

In goats, their feet may swell and it is often in the front feet only. They may or may not become lame and may even try to walk on their knees to avoid using their painful feet. As you trim their feet over time, you will find old purple to red bruising growing out. We have had a couple of these when we used to start lead feeding our goats, as we had been taught, just two weeks before they kidded. That is too short of an amount of time to get heavy producers up to full feed. See the Pregnant Creatures chapter in Part 1 for more information on when to lead ("leed") feed and why.

All of the same wound herbs apply to founder. Start the oral herbs at a slower rate, as your just foundered animal will be more sensitive to changes, but the salves or external herbs can be put on full dose. Also please address cleansing to the liver and kidneys and blood. If your animal foundered due to feed, you will have to back the nutrition level down. For horses, that means more mixed grass hay (not the high protein types that I think are problematic) and less graze time and less alfalfa; also reduce their grain. If they are on a sweet feed, consider replacing that with some whole oats with a bit of black strap molasses to it. I have a horse chow recipe in the Supplements Chapter of Part 1 that I make for my mares. For my goats, I've successfully gotten back onto their normal feeding programs later without relapses. For herb mixes I personally like to use kelp, Wounderful salve on the coronet band and hoof (I brush it on with a paintbrush) and BetterDaze. If they have any pain, or discomfort or if the founder is new then I also use A-King Joint support- a combination of pain support and anti inflammatory herbs.

Frostbite

Ears, teats and tails are the most susceptible in frostbite, especially in young, brand new, or underfed animals. That includes stock that is not getting enough hay to generate enough internal heat during a cold snap. Paws and feet can also have a problem if animals get wet or have to stand in snow for long amounts of time.

Never rub a frostbitten area, as you will further the cellular damage and do not allow the frost bitten creature to walk on limbs that have suffered frostbite. If you must walk them, get them to where you are going to work them or keep them before starting any support. You can NOT have them move on limbs that are starting to thaw. I know that may be easier said than done, but do your best and trust God.

Administer cayenne and ginger orally every fifteen minutes. You can also soak the ears or other parts in very warm (not hot) tea with ginger or yarrow or rosemary (or all three) in it, which will encourage circulation to draw to the ears. When you need a break from soaking, salves can be gently put on the areas. Your goal is going to be to encourage circulation and then tissue repair. The regular tissue repair herbs are great; add ginger and/or cayenne to those. Oral nutritious herbs also help a lot, such as: ginger, cayenne, nettle, dandelion, comfrey, kelp, white oak bark, slippery elm, carrot. You can glean more herbs from the other sections if you like. You just may watch the body repair those tissues, even if they already have turned black! Remember to also consider pain, especially during the thaw process and while nerves may be regenerating. Mullein is one of your best friends for pain. See the Nervous System chapter for nerve support.

Gangrene

You are thinking, "There's herbal support for gangrene?!? No way!" I'm going to tell you, "Yes way!" Remember that until the creature is dead, its cells will want to repair to its DNA.

Gangrene is tissue death that continues to spread. It is often started from an infection after an injury. Sometimes limbs are amputated from this problem. This is most common with diabetics, who over time may lose feeling in their limbs. At that point they don't feel infections or injuries and may not take proper care of them. For those that haven't heard of it, this is called 'diabetic neuropathy'. Supporting the body in gangrene will also provide some support for that problem.

Your first homework assignment is to carefully clean the area involved and keep it dry. Then apply an assortment of the following herbs: goldenseal, myrrh, mallow root or leaf, peppermint, hollyhock root, marshmallow root or leaf, cayenne or Fir Meadow's HerBiotic salve. Pick three or four of these and try to include marshmallow root in the mix, due to its reputation for helping the body to renew hardened damaged 'dead' tissue. Also, don't forget about oil of garlic. Cayenne is an important part of your blend, as besides being antiputrefying it will stimulate circulation to the area. Ginger and yarrow can also be used to draw circulation to the area once you know you are on top of the infection part. The area can be soaked in a hot (but safe temperature) strong yarrow and or ginger tea, before being dried and applying other herbs. Two to three soaks per day would not be too many. If the gangrene is in a very serious condition you will want to try to do an all day soak, changing the tea out every half hour with fresh tea to try to arrest the problem now. HerBiotic salve can also be used, once out of the acute danger stage.

Udders can go gangrenous. I've been told to watch for blue and purple marks showing on an udder. If you see those get a vet diagnosis, but don't wait for the vet to come out to get started in case this is what is going on. Due to the rich blood supply in the udder (300 plus gallons of blood run through a goat udder each day), infection can spread fast and kill the animal within hours of the bruising showing up. In that case, take your herb list and give it orally in double or triple doses each hour with a double dose of raw garlic (4 cloves each hour for a 100 to 200 pound animal) and also put hot compresses soaked with your herb list tea on the udder. You can salve it thickly when you need a break, but then get the fresh hot compresses going again right over the top of the salve. Adding extra cayenne to the salve will help drive it into the body faster. This is one of the few situations where you do not get to go to sleep until you have your creature turned around. The next day if your animal is out of the woods, you can drop down to herbs three or four times a day. For something this scary I'd want to herb them a full ten days minimum. Then you can give udder support per the Milking Stock chapter in Part 1.

Goat/Cow Pox, Pustules, Pimples, Acne

The Accessible Pet, Equine and Livestock Herbal

Goat pox can happen to any creature, but since I'm in the goat industry that's the term I'm using. Usually it is a combination of uncleanliness and bacteria. Staphylococcus bacteria, which reside on the skin, are common place here. Many times what happens is a doe will lie down on straw that was urinated on, which irritates and weakens the udder or tummy tissue so that it succumbs to a problem. Besides keeping the facilities clean and dry, and keeping the udder or skin clean here are some things you can do. Can you guess any before you read on? Try, I'll bet you'll do well!

This is another nice time to whip out your favorite bottle of lavender essential oil and blend it with some oil of garlic and by now you remember the dose I like to use. If not look it up in the Appendix. Wounderful! Salve is nice, as is calendula, myrrh, usnea, even some strong onion blended with olive oil. Herbs to encourage the body to heal the tissue would be comfrey, calendula, slippery elm bark, lavender and aloe vera (fresh gel from your plant). Thyme essential oil (not for pregnant animals) can be used at 12 drops per tablespoon of olive oil and rosemary or eucalyptus essential oil at 15 drops. MammarEaze salve by Fir Meadow also is good body support in this condition. Do what you can to keep an animal dry and clean so that you never have to work with this issue.

Hair loss, Growth, Shine

There is almost nothing more pleasing to me then when people compliment us on how shiny our animals' hair coats are. We don't use coat conditioners, as I know that an animal with a truly healthy system and good feeding and herbal supplement program will be healthy from the inside out. The cells have no choice but to have happy hair follicles growing out beautiful thick shiny hair.

It is alarming to me, the number of contacts I receive because of animals with large areas (even whole bodies) of hair loss. Sometimes I get contacts because of stubborn areas of hair loss. Sometimes people will be told to use cortisone creams for these problems, and sometimes they help for awhile, only to have the problem resurface. Long time cortisone use will thin and damage the tissue it is used on, so is not a good long term plan. Issues I would consider if I saw this in one of my creatures would be several. Ringworm comes to mind and I have seen some strains that cover large sections of the animal. Sometimes patches of hair starts coming out. If coupled with other problems, including ruminants that waste away, make sure you learn more about Johnes disease. The root issue I start looking to in any skin issue is the liver and kidneys for toxicity. If the kidneys are behind in their abilities, then the skin will have to try and eliminate what the kidneys can't. That will increase their burden as well as skin toxicity, encouraging skin tissue weakness. A less efficient liver will also run additional toxins through the body, which the skin will also be forced to try and deal with. So the weakened skin becomes susceptible to all manner of issues. To get to the root of the problem, please consider longer term cleansing of eight to twelve months for those valuable organs.

Herbal salves are nice to use to nourish the skin. I like Wounderful! and also Dr. Christopher's Complete Bone and Tissue formula (this salve is not for equine/camelid use). Herbs you can make strong teas with to put in their water and herbs/supplements you can feed that will be beneficial are: some of the B Vitamins helps such as catnip, cayenne, black strap molasses, kelp, and nutritional yeast. Other very helpful herbs are aloe (topically only), lavender, comfrey, white oak bark, nettle, chickweed, dandelion, calendula, and marshmallow root. Take at least three herbs from this list and start nourishing. Rosemary will stimulate hair follicles and yarrow is always nourishing for skin and hair. You can use these as the hot rinse water if washing your animals, as well as soaking a towel in the tea and draping it over your animals for a bit. Essential oil of rosemary can be diluted with olive oil and rubbed into the skin at the rate of fifteen drops to one tablespoon of olive oil.

As mentioned in the Husbandry chapter in Part 1, dry brushing is also a good habit to get into. Start very gently and avoid any skin with breaks in it. If you have ringworm going, be sure to not spread it to other animals (or yourself).

Be sure your animal is on a good parasite program. Animals with a lot of parasites can also have unthrifty hair or skin, as the parasites steal nutrition and add their toxic waste to the system. Hair sometimes will look rough, dry, or bent/barbed ends in these cases.

Sometimes animals will have fading in their coat color that has not been caused by the sun. These same animals may have hair thinning or loss around the eyes, ears, bridge of the nose, and/or their tail end. In goats this can result in the tail sometimes having a fish tail appearance. If I see all or many of these things going on at the same time, I begin to consider that their system may be asking for more copper. But not just any copper; their body wants organic or living copper. This would be copper as found in whole plant foods which would have the carbon atom attached to it making it fully usable to your creature and will not build up in the liver. Liver toxicity from products where the copper is inorganic (derived from rock/hard mineral sources) can be deadly as these types can build up to lethal levels in the system. Even sheep need a small amount copper, BUT the right kind. Not the kind in most store bought mineral supplements that don't come from whole plants and not from copper that leaches into their water from copper pipes or wells containing excess amounts in high copper areas. Herbs of interest would be cabbage, lettuce, Jerusalem artichokes, pumpkin leaves, fennel seed, and brigham tea. Brigham tea twigs need to be 3 years old to be at the right stage of use. Fir Meadow makes a mix called "Kop-Sel" that helps nourish the system with higher amounts of copper and selenium. The fun thing with the herbs in this product is that they help the body rid itself of stored inorganic copper too. Remember, supplementation for minerals from whole plants needs to be on a daily basis, as your creature is not going to store extra for later use.

Hives/Itching/Poison Oak - Ivy

I'll put these together. Hives is usually the response of an allergic response, so see the Immune System chapter for more on that. To help bring comfort in itching, I grab for chickweed, mullein, plantain, or lavender. We've had excellent results with Dbug Salve by Fir Meadow, which has chickweed as one of its ingredients. Dr. Christopher has a Bites and Stings salve that is nice. We've also had people using Wounderful! Salve for comfort in poison oak and ivy. Again, the herb list I gave above is helpful for those. If you are in the country and run into an itching problem on a creature, grab and chew some chickweed, mullein or plantain leave and put the fresh 'poultice' on the problem area. I like the salves, because I can stick enough on to help for hours and because not all animals will let us just hold herbs on them forever (nor do we want to unless they are a lap pet!).

Hot Spots

See the Hair Loss section above, as well as the Allergy section in the Immune System chapter and combine the information. Wounderful! salve can be used on the actual hot spots to provide comfort until you help the body take care of the cause.

Joint Ill/Naval Ill

This condition can cause lameness in the joints. It is usually attributed to bacteria crawling up the brand new baby's umbilicus into the system where it later settles into the joints. I would support the body as if it were an infection with oral antiseptic herbs (see the Immune System chapter), antiseptic herbal poultices or salves (such as HerBiotic) on the affected joints. It is a good plan to read the Birthing chapter in Part 1 for herbs you can use that will both nourish your baby, as well as help the body disallow these bacterial invasions. Remember, even 'clean' pasture births still happen in an imperfect world abundant with bacteria.

I would do the same thing in a Mycoplasma invasion, which can be started from the baby drinking infected milk.

Lameness

Lameness has many causes. A couple of bacterial causes were mentioned previously. There are other bacterial causes, especially as secondary infections from a tissue injury to a joint or joints or even in a foot. Failure to warm up your working animal before moving into hard work can set your creature up for an injury causing lameness. Founder of the feet, already covered in this chapter, can cause lameness. Dislocations (where you will want vet assistance) can do that. Sore feet, navicular feet in horses, slipping, twisting a leg, hurting the back, and more, can give you a lame animal.   Take time to have your veterinarian teach you how to check for limb damage by assessing angles, sizes, heat, correct posture, how everything matches up with the other side that is healthy, etcetera.

Mudscald/Scratches/Greasy Heel/Rainrot

All of these have some things in common: an area of skin that doesn't want to heal, sometimes hair loss, and in the first three sometimes lameness.   They usually have less than ideal cleanliness involved with moisture resulting in fungal or bacterial involvement.

Mudscald, scratches, and greasy heel are the same condition, but may differ in location.   Greasy heel of course is in the heel or lower foot area.   Mudscald and scratches are on the lower leg, fetlocks or pasterns.   Most often these show up during muddy conditions when the animals are not being cleaned nor have clean dry situations to stand or be in.   The mud traps a microbe underneath it on the skin and it begins to breed in the moist 'incubated' against the body temperature of the animal.   Look at the Hoof rot section for ideas on working with this.

Rainrot is often a combination of a microbe and moisture combined with dirt on the animal's skin, usually on the upper body or back areas.   Humid wet conditions will contribute to this.   I will also refer you to the hoof rot section for help in this area.   If you are blanketing stock, such as horses to keep them dry, be sure those blankets come off every day and the animal brushed to encourage the skin to breathe well again.   Do not keep wet blankets on animals.   You may have to have two, as we do, to rotate them to be sure we have a dry one for each animal that is blanketed.   If you have a fungal problem going on, consider filling a quart spray bottle with ¼ cup of raw organic apple cider vinegar, distilled water and 80 drops of your favorite antibacterial essential oil.   Use that to spray the underside of the blanket to reduce opportunities for fungal and bacterial things to proliferate. Some of my blankets are homemade (for my goats) and most of my horse blankets have been purchased used in the 20 to 40 dollar ranges and then well laundered.   It doesn't have to get expensive to keep them protected. It sure beats having to deal with some of these problems!

Navicular Syndrome

Navicular is a horse term for a problem with the navicular foot bone in the horse. This bone is located between the triangle shaped coffin bone and the pastern bone. It is subjected to a lot of stress as the horse moves, especially in horses with poor foot conformational traits such as small feet for their size, long feet with low heels, or upright angled feet or pasterns (as opposed to a normal 45 degree angle in feet and pasterns). Horses may stand a bit off instead of keeping their feet squarely under them, may be sore in the feet at the beginning of exercise, may shift weight from foot to foot, or just be outright lame. Improper trimming or shoeing can contribute as well.

I think some of our breeding programs have caused this as well. There is a reason an animal as heavy and hard worked as a horse needs nice sizable hooves. I always encourage people to learn what good sized feet look like when horse shopping.

Another contribution brings us back to that ever so important nutrient, water. An animal that is dehydrated has a protection system built into its body. Rather than the body depriving the bone marrow of moisture needed for red blood cell production, it will hold it back from the joints of the individual, allowing the joints to become dryer. Dry joints are not supple and can start to erode over time. Think of the animals that have to work hard without regular watering throughout the day. Just when their bodies are stressed the most and needing regular small drinks of water, many are deprived. These times correspond with additional weight and stress on these navicular and other foot and leg joints. Think about it. I would also remove any sweet feeds from their diet that has the wrong kind of molasses in it (see the Supplements chapter in Part 1). Those refined sugars are dehydrating your animal. Instead use black strap molasses if you want that in their feed program. You will have to add it yourself.

If you are working with this issue, you would supply herbal nutrition consistent with giving the body what it needs to repair any tissue area. Look into the broken bone section. Salves can be put along the coronet band or on other affected areas. Some salve can even be put brushed into the bottoms of the grooves on each side of the frog. The whole hoof can be conditioned this way if you desire, just for general maintenance. Remember to also give the oral herbal supplements listed in the bone area. I would also want to have ginger in their diet as this encourages circulation to go to the extremities. That circulation carries with it nutrition from the herbs you feed them.

If you have a horse with smaller feet or whose parents or siblings have had problems with this, be sure to keep them on a good herbal nutrition program along with good hydration in the form of fresh clean water. It's never a bad idea to salve the coronet band of every horse after a ride or workout. Well nourished hooves and feet will serve you and them well.

Open Wounds

Please remember to always support the body for shock with any wound, no matter how insignificant it seems. So the first thing on your list is cayenne. I remember the time I had a blood pressure drop from a dumb tiny slice on my pinky finger from a drinking glass that burst while I was washing the inside of it. It hit the nervous system just right, so to be safe, remember your cayenne. Talk about feeling like a wimp, but sometimes that nervous system will try to call the shots no matter how small the damage.

If it is bleeding, as long as the animal isn't obviously shocky and as long as it is not a lot of blood, go ahead and let it slowly trickle a minute or two while you get your cayenne prepared. That is the body's way of cleansing the area from any microbes or filth that may have entered the wound at the time of damage. Then administer the cayenne both orally and onto the area if needed. Carefully and gently cleanse the area if it is still dirty and make sure no dirt remains. Olive oil can help soften and dislodge that. You can have your vet teach you how to flush and assess wounds. I flush them with olive oil with lavender essential oil mixed in it. Then I pack with dried powdered herbs or salves. Don't clean out the old herbs unless there is some dirt on them, and then just remove the dirt. Otherwise just pack new salve or herbs right on top of the other herbs as the body uses them up and cover with a leaf (see Burns) and gauze and tape or wrap if desired to keep the area clean. Combine antibacterial herbs like: cayenne, goldenseal, oregon grape root, myrrh, usnea, pressed garlic in olive oil, raw organic honey, black walnut leaves or hulls (not for equine or camelids), echinacea, lavender, rosemary, plantain or thyme (always with olive oil, as it can be hot). Select a mix of three and see what they do. You will also want some herbs that the body will use to repair tissue with. You might select two or three of these as well. Comfrey, nettle, lavender, aloe, white oak bark, slippery elm, marshmallow root and goldenseal all would be nice choices.

Of course I like HerBiotic salve and Wounderful! salve as they are quick and easy. Also, never underrate oil of garlic mixed with lavender essential oil for this type of a problem. I've had a friend use this when it's all she had on hand to help a dog that had been run over by a car. This dog had a deep enough wound to reveal bone. I mentioned this incident earlier in the book. That dog is alive and well and fully functional today and healed itself without any evidence of infection during the process.

If an animal is moderately toxic inside, you may see a healing crisis when you start working with a wound. This is a problem we are seeing with more horses then I thought I would. However, now having studied equine iridology I find that we have a high number of toxic horses, so am no longer surprised. Sometimes after salving or herbing an injury for awhile, the hair in the area starts coming off. What is happening is that the cells in that area are starting to feel real good, so as in other cleansings, they start blowing extra toxins through the area. Sometimes the chemicals coming out burn the hair follicles. Keep internally cleansing your animal, or start cleansing if you haven't, and they will eventually quit blowing toxins as long as you aren't retoxifying them at a fast rate. The hair will come back after the toxins are out and the follicles repair. I've also seen this in pets, if they are reacting to an herb the area may get red from increased circulation.

Another healing crisis sometimes happens with wounds that do not completely heal due to an underlying resistant bacteria or microbe which has taken up residence in the area. Once antiseptic herbs are introduced some of these will start pushing out copious amounts of pus. Monitor your animal. As long as I don't see fever, lethargy, disinterest in feed, or other symptoms of illness or systemic infection that your vet can instruct you in, I don't get concerned as I understand what is going on in this case. However, you must monitor your animal closely. Once the issue is fully pushed out of the body, the area will finally be allowed to heal. I've heard of creatures finally healing after a year or more of no progress on a wound, once herbal nutrition and cleansing was added to their diet.

The thing about having a farm with a moderate amount of animals, is that it provides me with an active lab to keep my mind and hands fresh when working with conditions. Though overall they are very healthy, with this many animals we do experience different situations first hand. And my husband and I sometimes provide situations ourselves, mostly injuries as you have read about a few.

Nail Cracking and Sand Cracks in Hooves

This problem is sometimes experienced in pets, but also can be a problem in hooved animals. The root of the problem is that not enough nutrition and/or hydration is making it to the nail beds or coronet band to enable to them to be well nourished. Other things that contribute are filing the tops of the nails or hooves. Sometimes farriers will do this to get a prettier looking hoof; however, they just removed the protective layer over the hoof that helps hold in vital moisture which assists with having a pliable, flexible hoof. The same goes for painting dog nails, horse and livestock hooves with polish. That junk does three things. It adds toxins to the creature (and you as you breathe the fumes), it strips moisture out of the nails or hooves, and it blocks permeability so that oxygen can't penetrate the material. Even though the material is supposedly "dead' tissue, I don't want to reduce light or oxygen contact with it. We all know you can quick (cut too short and cause bleeding) nails or hooves, so there is living tissue not far under the surface. Also, I have seen cracks respond to salve treatment in areas that should not be possible if indeed the hoof material was 'dead'. Just because there are no nerves right near the surface does not mean the tissue isn't living.

So we go back to the drawing board. Cleansing to get the toxins out that may be blocking abundant nutritional uptake and additional nutrition, as mentioned in the Supplements chapter in Part 1. Salves can be massaged into the nail beds or coronet band of the hoof to super nourish the areas responsible for building the new nail or hoof. Ginger can also be added to the diet to encourage circulation to the limbs. Also consider some of the Circulatory system herbs for the blood stream, which for some reason is not getting enough nutrition to where it needs to go. Hooves or paws can be soaked in the Open Wound section herb infusions combined with ginger or yarrow or rosemary to encourage nutrition to soak in faster. Often if the nails/hooves are having problems, the hair coat will be too for similar reasons.

Old Scars

Treat these just like wounds. With persistence you can get these to heal back into normal tissue. However, expect it to take up to a year with a clean animal that is nutritionally sound.

Pain Purposes

Pain has two purposes. I think most of us get taught as children that pain is a messenger to the body to us to let us know that something is wrong. That way we know to address a problem.

The other purpose is one we don't hear about, but is just as important for herbalists. In allopathic medicine nutrition is not usually the focus, so pain during the body's healing process is managed by blocking it with medication, which also negatively impacts the immune system. This second purpose allows us to know whether we must increase the amount of herbs we need to be using for the situation or if we can begin to reduce the amount as the body repairs. So once mending is under way, you are going to monitor your dosages by your creature's pain level. If they are still hurting, increase the herbs used or the number of times you give them. Of course, increase the herbs within reason as you do not want to start a severe acidosis or enterotoxemia event going. If you animal is doing great, then you can reduce the number or frequency of the herbs given.

While there is structural damage you will not be able to cover additional pain completely. That is the type of pain that comes when tissue pulls on a broken or damaged area. That is a good thing. You do want your animal sore so that they still guard the area protecting it from further damage until it is structurally sound.

The Accessible Pet, Equine and Livestock Herbal

To take all of the pain away is a disservice and invites additional damage from overuse.

If your animal is experiencing severe pain, such as in emergency c section surgery which cannot be considered a normal injury, I have allowed the vet to use a drug for the pain for a first and second dose and then I take over with pain herbs. The surgery and some severe accidents can be beyond the ability of herbs to cover nerve pain. However, there are many stories of accidents that were fully covered by extreme herbal nutrition right at the beginning. Use your judgment.

Great pain herbs are mullein which does not have a toxicity level other than overwhelming the digestive tract with too much of a "new to your animal" plant. It also does not affect mentality, and all this time you thought it was a rotten weed to get rid of! Poppy seeds (including California poppy- do not use store bought as they may be chemically treated) can be used at ½ of regular herb dosage which would be ¾ of a teaspoon for 100 to 200 pound animal 3 to 4 times per day. I would not use poppy seeds if your animal is on any medications. Cayenne fights pain in three different ways. I'd have to dig up my class notes to remind myself how it does it, but it does. You can use it with the mullein to potentiate the mullein. If the pain involves the head, the limbs, the digestive tract or the reproductive organs then you can also use some ginger with it to help circulate the mullein to those areas. I'm not sure I'd want to potentiate the poppy seeds, but I would be comfortable using them along side of mullein.

I have a personal story that taught me how to feel the level of pain verses the amount of herbs to use. I was busy juicing with my Champion juicer on beautiful fall day and did not know that the bottom guard plate was not on correctly. I ended up losing the very top of my middle finger in the blink of an eye. After looking at it and throwing cayenne powder over it to stop bleeding (which it did in scant seconds) I gathered my thoughts. I was by myself and didn't want to get shocky. As dumb as that sounds it doesn't always take much. And this was a bit more than much and I somehow manage to do things like this when no one else is home! Sound familiar? I hope not. So next I took some cayenne mixed with water orally for shock support. Then I took a large spoonful of raw honey (not for diabetics) to also help my system pick up. Then I considered how much this was going to hurt once my body figured out what was going on and hit my mullein tincture I had recently made. I took a full ¼ cup of it since it was raw apple cider vinegar (ACV) based and I'm used to raw ACV. The cayenne also helps support the body in pain, but the mullein does an exceptional job. That was in the morning. I then applied a large amount of salve (yes Wounderful!) onto it, wrapped it and did milking and feeding chores and other things I needed to accomplish that day. As long as I didn't bump it I was good to go. That is until about 9 hours later when the mullein wore off and my finger began to throb, ache and complain. I took some more mullein and by the next day the oral and topical nutritional herbs were supplying what my body needed. I never had nerve problems or any scarring. If you look closely you will see the groove marks that the juicer made in the meat of the finger as a reminder to me to respect my juicer.

My new mare, the fanciest one of course, managed to rip her nostril pretty good on some fence when she was getting used to her new surroundings. I think it was her first time away from her sister and her birth home. Anyhow, I let it bleed a bit to clean itself. I found myself staring at a ¾ inch by 1 inch tear all the way through the nostril with a right angle turn to it and a large gap that I could have stuffed my finger though. I could not believe it. In just two weeks it was nearly healed with the salves and her horse chow nutrition mix that is listed in the Appendix. So far there is no scarring. At first I was not able to get the salve all the way into the tender wound. In those instances, I always make sure I had a good amount smeared near it on side of her face just below the nostril, so the body could still draw it in to use. In the beginning, I also poured an essential oil wound blend I threw together with olive oil two times into the area when I couldn't touch it. The blend? Olive oil, garlic, and lavender essential oil. I have not seen any sign of infection. I LOVE this blend. You may have figured that out, as you see it sprinkled through the book.

Proud flesh

Proud flesh is a sometimes horse problem where leg injuries will have strange scarring or tissue build up over an injured area. Proud flesh can adhere to tissue and tendons underneath causing less ability in movement for the animal, so it is not desirable. Work with this as you would an open wound, and keep putting herbs on

The Accessible Pet, Equine and Livestock Herbal

it for several months to a year for larger masses and include cleanses especially working up to blood cleaning herbs.

Saddle and Harness Sores

Work with saddle sores as you would other wounds. Also remedy the cause which is improper fitting or dirty saddles, pads, blankets, collars, surcingles, etcetera. A poor rider that bounces a lot instead of moving with the horse can also add stress to an already stressed area. Contrary to the belief of all the marketers out there that make risers and other pads to help poorly fitting tack work out better, these are not in the long term best interest for your horse. Your saddle should be able to fit the horse correctly without anything under it. The pads are merely to provide some overall cushion in western or pack saddles and in all saddle types to keep the saddles clean. Please find proper fitting tack. The Midwest Fjord Horse Club has made an excellent ten dollar DVD on how to fit various tack items of several disciplines to your horse. It is very worth the tiny investment and applies to any horse breed, not just Fjords. Do a search for their website. It would be good for every 4H group, Pony Club, and Equestrian team to own one of these. I'm saying that as a former horse 4H leader.

Soft Tissue Damage including Severed Tendons

The Open Wound directions will apply here. I have seen tendons completely repair, even when sections have been missing. Splinting may be needed to support the injured area so that the damaged area can heal.

We had a doe that had the tendons literally ripped off of her knee from a hard sideways hit by another doe. When we found her and helped her get up, the front leg would swing at the knee completely unhindered in any direction it wanted to go (ick). We did not splint her correctly as her knee could not bend during the healing process; piano type hinges would have been helpful. As a result she does not use that leg correctly, but use it she does, even jumping on the milkstand. We help her off of it, although she will come off by herself if she has to wait for us. Since it was a front leg, she still successfully carries pregnancies to full term and gets around real well. However, I wish we had splinted it in a way that would have allowed some proper knee movement yet with complete leg support. We also had a paint filly many years ago who had severed a tendon on her pastern from the metal siding on a barn. We had the veterinarian put the tissues back together as best as he was able, and then we really increased her dam's nutrition. As the filly received the nutrition internally via her dam's milk, she repaired her tendon to the point where we sold her (with disclosure of the injury) into a show home. There was no sign on her body or in her movement that there had ever been an injury. Proud flesh was never a problem in this situation.

Sprains and Strains

You will want to address these as you would Open Wounds. I'll share a couple of stories with you. Hopefully you'll never experience these, but if you do, you will have your own stories to share as the body tends to respond very fast to herbal nutrition in these situations.

I have a friend whose alpine goat kid (the prized one of course!) got her front leg caught in the gate of the pen at state fair. I was the one who noticed it and got the baby out of her situation. Then I found the owner and told her what had happened. It had only been a couple of minutes, but upon checking her we already found a very hot fetlock joint and the kid not wanting to use it. This kid was due for the show ring the following morning and it was already afternoon. She started her on Wounderful! salve at the injury location. By the next morning there was no sign of swelling or lameness and the kid got to show.

I have told you that I am my own lab to practice on at times. Last summer I severely sprained my right ankle, which has already been though some serious accidents. After getting my baby doeling pile off of me (I fell in the goat pasture and they thought I was playing with them) I quickly crawled to the gate and pulled myself up. Then I made a serious error. I walked on it the 80 or so feet to the house. I never should have done that, but it makes the story better. I got to the house and crawled to the garage where my crutches were. I was now off of that ankle. Again, I was home alone. My husband was out of the country and I had summer chores including milking and feeding to do until he was back home.

Praise God for awesome neighbors! Several took turns helping as I directed from my wheelchair. I started soaking that foot and ankle in hot comfrey infusions with the comfrey leaves left in. I very thickly coated it with, you guessed it, Wounderful! Salve (comfrey, rosemary, lavender, calendula) and was taking 100 herbal capsules per day with similar herbs in them (companies are not allowed in the United States to put comfrey in oral products, but you can add comfrey yourself if you are sure of the state of liver health of the recipient). By the end of day one that ankle was all kinds of angry colors along with being over twice normal size.   I was completely off of that foot for ten days other than some crutching and aircast support. By day eleven I was back on it for limited amounts of time.   Another week had me on it completely.   Often these things will keep people messed up for around six weeks, so I'll put another notch on the wall for herbal nutrition.   I was asked by a few people if I had it x-rayed.   No I didn't.   I was comfortable with what I was doing with it and it would not have changed what I was doing with it.   I also have had beyond a lifetime's supply of x-rays and other scans from a serious accident sixteen years ago and prefer not to increase my exposure. See the broken bones chapter to read about some things to assess when you for sure need outside trained help. If you want outside help or a 'picture' of the injury, please feel free to do so. Only you can decide that for your situation. Do as you are led, just as I have the freedom to do as I was led. If you have a huge amount of swelling and bruising (those can indicate breaks) you may feel more led to get some more help. You need to make sure any joints are not displaced or broken which may require pinning back into place.

I recently had a soft tissue injury to my inside knee area. It was about one inch thick by four inches by five inches. My body had the swelling out overnight and integrity to the joint in just a day (it was slopping back and forth sideways). Of course I kept working with it so it would heal beyond just barely healed.

Don't get overly apprehensive about swellings. First, they let you know a problem is happening. Second, that is the body's way to build a cast of pressure to help hold the area better to lesson further damage. However, do start supporting the body immediately if you find these so they don't become chronic lameness issues. That may include splinting or partial casting.

Lord willing I'm done with injuries, but they do offer the opportunity to see firsthand how herb plans support the body. I hope these stories help you.

Tying up

Tying up is a phrase given for moderate to severe muscle tightening in horses that creates pain and affects movement, most often in the rear legs, rump, or back. This is more likely to happen in the weekend warrior type of horse, or to horses that are worked hard without proper warm up or cool off time, which involves walking and a warm up progression through the gaits with bending exercises, if your horse does them before going to work. Then they should have sufficient time to walk afterwards until their respirations and body temperature return to normal. Plan your riding time accordingly. Nutritional deficiency can also contribute to this problem and you have plenty of information now to work on that area. You can place any of the bone or wound salves or herbs onto the areas. A really nice thing to do for muscles, is to use a few essential oils to increase circulation and decrease pain to the area, allowing the area to loosen up naturally. For that you can use some olive oil and some essential oils per tablespoon of olive oil such as ginger (10 to 12 drops), rosemary (15) or a bit of cinnamon (10, not for pregnant animals) or cloves (10). Eucalyptus (15) and peppermint (12, only use peppermint for animals over one year of age, which they should be in this situation) essential oils help the body to reduce pain and these also will increase circulation to the problem areas. Use no more than 15 drops of essential oil total per tablespoon of olive oil total unless you have additional education in them. If there is heat to the area, the last two will help the body to reduce heat there as well. Alternating hot and cold compresses will help after the first 24 hours. The hot should be on around twelve minutes and the cold about four. This helps 'plunge' the area and can move the tissue, like a massage.

Urine Scald

Urine Scald on the mammary system or other parts of the body. Animals with incorrect conformation, or some male animals during breeding season who will routinely urinate on themselves to become more attractive for their ladies. Eventually that can burn the tissue, making it scab up and be raw.   When I get this in a male goat in rut,   my favorite thing to do is to wash it with warm water and a mild homemade soap. Then I take my 15 drops of lavender essential oil and put it in one tablespoon of olive oil, mix well, and smooth that onto the damaged skin.   This blend really goes a long ways to helping the body heal the damage. Apply it every day until you see good progress on the healing.   Be careful not to scrub on healing tissue if the skin was open, as you may scrub the whitish brand new cells right back off and encourage scarring.   You can also put powdered comfrey, goldenseal, rosemary (or the essential oil), or calendula or mix any of these with raw honey on the areas after cleaning. I really love watching the synergy of the lavender and olive oil and its ease of application. This is so simple, and yet, so safe. Wounderful! salve, MammarEaze salve or HerBiotic salve, all by Fir Meadow or Dr. Christopher's Complete Bone and Tissue salve can also be used. If you live in an area that is quite a bit below freezing, you may not get to wash, as the water will freeze on the hair surrounding the scalded area. In that case, pat the area with a wet cloth if possible and then immediately pat dry and just place the olive oil/lavender blend right on it. If the oil is congealed from the cold, you can still apply it, but warm it up in your hands first if possible. Keeping your bottle of oil in an inside pocket in your coat or coveralls can also keep it free flowing. I used to live in snow country in the North Cascade Mountains. I understand the challenges.

Warts

Warts are viral in nature and tend to hang out in impure blood streams.   Your method of support then will be internal cleansing and topical herbs that warts tend to hate.   Some of those are black walnut (not in horses or camelids), tea tree essential oil (tea tree can be used neat or straight on small areas for a period of ten days) and garlic. Lemon balm is a widely used favorite in Europe for viral conditions. The essential oil is cost prohibitive, but you can easily grow this herb and include it in your oral nutritional program.   Some warts can be tied off with some fishing line to cut off their source of nourishment. You can discuss those possibilities with your vet. Of course, that does not remove the virus. I have heard of people duct taping off warts so that they can't breathe and also duct taping banana skins onto warts. I haven't personally tried these but if you do, let me know. I am currently experimenting with dabbing a bit of grapefruit essential oil on a cotton swab and putting that on a wart. It appears I am getting favorable results. Since it is not diluted, don't put it directly onto healthy skin; just the wart.

I hope this chapter was enlightening. I realize that there is a lot of overlap in here, but that is the beauty of herbs. There are so many that can be quite multipurpose and yet quite effective in system nourishment.

What a valuable part of the body the eyes are. Though other senses are very important, often your creature can adapt better with losses in those areas then in their eyes. I'm here to offer you some encouragement. Many times things can be done. Give it a shot, you just may gain a great herb story to share later!

Cataracts

Cataracts will have the appearance of a hazing or clouding over the eye. They can appear at any age, but are more common in senior creatures and will begin to interfere with vision. The eye, being a blood vessel rich organ that requires a lot of nutrition to remain healthy, is beginning to get constipated in these situations. The normal metabolic action of the cells in this area have been impaired by their inability to put off their toxins as efficiently or to absorb nutrition as well. Your goal? Eliminate toxin exposure, begin cellular cleansing and increase nutrition in the diet with living raw foods. I like eyebright, cayenne, ginger, nettle, and raspberry leaf for these situations. Fir Meadow has an herb blend called Eye See that can be used. We like to give oral herbs, such as the above listing, and make an infusion (tea) to flush the eyes with six days per week for as long as the condition persists. I also like to increase the nutrition with oral use of plants such as: kelp, comfrey, nettle, red raspberry leaf, carrot, beet, alfalfa, and/or dandelion leaves. Better Daze by Fir Meadow or Vitalerbs by Dr. Christopher's can also be used. If we are a talking about canine or feline companions, please remember to also address the bowels. Of course the liver and kidneys should be addressed in all creatures not previously cleansed.

Conjunctivitis/Pinkeye

Conjunctivitis is a fancy term for swelling (itis) of the conjunctiva of the eye. This can happen from injury or from a bacterial issue such as pinkeye. You may find an animal with an eye held shut and tearing, or reddish to pinkish in color and sensitive to light.   You may wince at what I'm going to suggest to you, but it works very well.

Take a combination of cayenne pepper and marshmallow root (or chickweed or calendula or slippery elm) and make a small strong tea and carefully strain the particulate out through a sterile (boiled) cloth.   You are going to flush the eyes with this. Remember safety for yourself and your animal as you do this. Diluted in water the cayenne won't be as strong, but it will still sting.   Cayenne really works WELL. It also increases circulation to the eye, so that the lymph system has a better opportunity to break down and move out the junk in the eye.   The other herbs produce mucilage or an eye soothing gel to comfort the damaged tissue. You may have to do two or three separate applications to see the body give you the results you want, but usually that's all it takes.

Dry

Dry eyes can be caused by mechanical injury to the tear duct, constipation or blockage within the tear duct, or as a side effect of some medications.   Eyes that remain too dry will become inflamed and damaged from the friction caused by the eyelid.   If I were working with a dry eye on my farm here is what I'd do.   For immediate relief, I would make an infusion and strain it with a boiled cloth. Once it cooled to body temperature, I would gently mist or pour it into the eyes. Favorite herbs for this would be marshmallow root, slippery elm, and calendula. You could also use a room temperature drinkable aloe from the health food store to gently pour into the eye.   I would follow this up by the same program that I would use for cataracts to cleanse and nourish this area.   If you find that there is a medication that is causing this you will want to discuss other options with your veterinarian.

Foreign Objects

We usually get two or three goats per year that get foxtail seed heads stuck in their eyes. We'll see a shut eye with tears.   It will usually take two of us to remove the offending object. One will hold the goat and one to investigate to find the foxtail

The Accessible Pet, Equine and Livestock Herbal

(sometimes you have to really look hard). Then I will grab onto it and pull it out. Sometimes only a tiny bit shows, as the rest rotates to the side of the eye. Unfortunately, pulling these barbed things out usually does additional eye damage, but they do have to come out. This year (2011) I ran into my first one that I could not extract. It was lying right against the eye itself and I just could not get a hold of it. For this one, I made a marshmallow root tea and carefully flushed the eye with copious amounts of it. When I checked the eye the next milking time the foxtail had come out on its own! Hallelujah! I could have also used hollyhock root tea or slippery elm tea (other demulcents), likely with similar results. Then you can bathe the eye as discussed in the Conjunctivitis section to help the body reduce any possibility of infection getting a hold. Usually two eye baths is all I need to have the body take away the white infection showing in the eye. Almost immediately after the first eye bath my goats are usually able to open their eyelid again showing me that the pain is under control.

My husband recently had a piece of metal get in his eye. Unfortunately it embedded, so we went to an eye specialist. Sometimes you will need professional assistance with removing objects from eyes. It will be worth every penny. Then you can take over with the herbs for the "after removal" body support to help the body avoid or clear out infection.

Infection

Just like in the Conjunctivitis section, you will make an infusion and carefully strain it to flush the eye with. This time it can be just cayenne, if wanted. The other herbs in that section will add additional nutrition, so are not a bad idea.

Injury

Seek professional advice if wanted for an eye injury, and especially if you need help cleaning it. Wound herbs from the Epidermis chapter work well here. Get plenty of them in the animal's diet. You can (and should) also take a quality herbal salve (like Fir Meadow's Wounderful! or Dr. Christopher's Complete Bone and Tissue formula) and put it around the eye, keeping it about ½ inch away from the eye itself. If the body wants the nutrition from the salve; it will draw it in and use it. It will.

Vision Loss

Should your animal begin shying from sudden movement or start losing navigational ability (running into things) you might consider vision loss as a possibility. In equine (and possibly other animals) a whitened area over the eye with veins running through it will usually indicate blindness. Should your beloved creature lose partial or complete vision, don't give up hope. We never know which ones the body will be able to reverse or improve, and which ones it won't. I would work on it just as in the cataract section, paying strict attention to making sure the animal has had its organs and cells/bloodstream cleansed. Also, be sure that its diet consists of many live raw foods. Processed foods and sugared foods (such as sweet feed grain mixes) rob precious minerals from the eyes. Carrots, grated raw carrots and carrot juice really do make excellent nourishing supplements to support the body in this problem.

Weepy

Oh how irritating! I personally have experienced this problem in myself as a residual problem from allergies I used to have. Besides allergies, medications, vaccinations, mechanical injury, and foreign objects can cause this issue. Be sure you try to ascertain the cause of the problem before working with it. Usually some cleansing and nourishing is all that is needed. If it's been a long standing problem, realize that it may take many months of cleansing and nutritional support to get ahead of it. I would also work on this situation as in the cataracts section. For allergy related problems you will want to see the Immune System chapter. For injuries to the eye causing the weepiness, see the Foreign Body section in this chapter.

Try to remove the cause of injury, if possible. Look for wires sticking out of pens or buildings and even in pasture soil, broken fencing, exposed nails, rough hay stems and the like, as potential causes. At shows, I always have to check my pens

The Accessible Pet, Equine and Livestock Herbal

for wires and protrusions. Almost every show I have to remove or change at least one such potential problem causer with wire cutters or pliers.

Chapter 21- Hepatic System: Liver and Gallbladder

Whenever I teach, I always have to educate on the importance of taking care of the liver no matter what the health condition is. Just like the gastrointestinal tract, it is impossible to have abundant health without having a clean and well functioning liver. When blood panels (which are sometimes used as a gauge for liver wellness) are used, they tend to measure what is good for average health levels and not optimum wellness levels. I have read that in some people the liver has to be down to 30% to 40% of function (loss of 60% to 70% of function) before abnormal blood numbers on the blood work are found. Though iridology can't tell you what is wrong with an organ, it can show you if there are issues going on with it at the cellular level. Anything from acute irritation to serious degeneration can be assessed with iridology. The liver is one of those organs that can be shown to be affecting many other parts of the body through iridology by the colors of the markings and the locations of them on the iris. I prefer iridology over sticking an animal with a needle to do a blood draw that may still end up being inconclusive. That, however; is my preference. Everyone has to decide for themselves how they want to manage their herd.

According to various research, the liver has been shown to have at least 500 functions. There could even be more that we have yet to discover. Suffice it to say the liver is quite important. The functions that I tend to focus on are its storage abilities of fat soluble nutrients (like A, D, E, K), its ever important job of cleaning fat soluble toxins (including poisons) out of the bloodstream, and its production of bile, which is extremely important in correcting ph within the intestines and making nutrients available to them from the foods consumed. Oils other than olive can coat and reduce the function of the liver. Please avoid oils other than olive. For those that ask, I have not found enough research on coconut oil to see if this is the case or not with that oil, which may be an exception to the "no other oil" rule. However, olive oil is less expensive, and until I can find more valid information, I'm going to side with what I do currently know, and stick with olive.

When working with the liver and gallbladder it is important to consider that this amazing organ will be a 100% new liver in just three to four months. That's right! It will replace every cell in that amount of time. Also consider that if a liver is at, let's say 50% of function, then you cannot expect it to regenerate to 95% of ideal wellness in just one three or four month cellular regeneration. This means you will need to consider many regenerations for a liver that is showing something unusual or has gone through a toxicity problem. I tend to side with four months for one complete cellular regeneration cycle, due to needing optimum health to replicate at the three month cycle, which very few creatures have today. So, for major problems you will expect to work on them for a one year minimum, with longer than that being better. Then consider one to two week tune ups quarterly to clean out the new accumulation they have acquired. As mentioned before, bowels need to be passing manure on a regular basis to start your liver support program. For cats and dogs that would mean at least one feces movement per meal eaten. For livestock that should be several times a day. Any of us that clean stalls can vouch for that one!

The gallbladder is a small organ to the rear of the liver that is responsible for storing bile produced in the liver. This bile is used to reduce the Ph of the hydrochloric acid coming from the stomach into the intestines. Bile also helps the body to break down fats in the digestive tract. In any gallbladder issues, one must also look into the health of the liver. In general, herbs used to assist the liver also assist the gallbladder. It is interesting to note that your equine family does not possess a gallbladder.

Don't ever let someone give your creature a death sentence because its liver is malfunctioning. The shortest such sentence I have heard was just two days. Can it die? Yes, of course. But don't let that thought immobilize you from doing what you can. I've had a few creature clients with such sentences that are alive and well today because their owners did something about it and they had enough time to react. The rest of this chapter is going to help you do just that.

Cleaning, Including Heavy Metals

Cleansing, cleansing, cleansing. We seem to return to this topic often- don't we? In an industrialized society, and unfortunately a world with levels of pollution, this foundation just simply cannot be ignored. If a creature is pregnant, you will want to cleanse at an extremely slow rate, if at all, during pregnancy. In those cases, you want to support the organ without actually throwing it into a full fledged cleanse or a cleansing crisis. However, if the life of your animal is in danger, sometimes one has to make the hard decision to save the dam and take a chance on forfeiting the unborn baby creatures; otherwise you may lose both the dam and babies. In that situation, you will want to also super nourish the dam to try and avoid that possibility. This is not a situation to take lightly and should be prayerful considered. Certainly it is possible for God to save the dam and unborn babies; I just feel a responsibility to make you aware of the possibilities. Remember to gradually increase the nourishment levels in a super prenatal nourishment scenario, so that you don't get an enterotoxemia reaction or acidosis.

Lemon and lime juices are wonderful for helping the body to clear out fat soluble toxins, much in the same way it helps cut grease when you use it in cleansers. Fresh squeezed lemon or lime is the best. Lemon essential oil can be used if diluted at my standard dose of 5 drops in a teaspoon of olive oil, then rubbing a portion of that for small animals and all of it for larger animals (100 pounds and larger) below the right rib area will help deliver it closer to the liver area. For a large animal like an 800 pound or larger horse you might mix 15 drops to a tablespoon of olive oil and use that amount. A large draft (1600 pound or larger, might again double that- 30 drops of essential oil with 2 tbsp of olive oil). Doing this five days on (perhaps weekdays), and two days off is an easy pattern to remember. You can do this two to three times per day. If your creature is pregnant, then once per day is sufficient. This essential oil has the possibility of photosensitivity, so in sunny climes or times of year apply in the evening only. Or use the lemon and lime juices. One half medium sized lime squeezed for a smaller animal, one medium lemon size for a medium sized animal, and 3 lemons for a large stock creature such as cattle.

Herbs used for liver and gallbladder support work the best when they are tasted, as that is where the process begins to notify the liver that it is going to be stimulated

The Accessible Pet, Equine and Livestock Herbal

into some type of action. So when you choose your method of administration, please consider feeding it in ways that the animal can taste it, such as teas added to their water, drenches that are not flavored (for example by molasses), or powders added on top of their food. Tinctures also work well. Whatever method you use you want the herbs to touch the mouth areas and be tasted, if possible. You will get a better response if you can do that.

Milk thistle is a WONDERFUL support herb for the liver. Milk thistle is thought to enable the body to protect itself from toxic or chemical attacks to the liver tissue itself. It also encourages the body to repair even badly damaged or cirrhotic hepatic organs. This herb goes to the top of my liver support list in these situations. Because it does its job so well, this is an herb prone to causing a cleansing crisis. If your creature is weak or pregnant, be sure to moderate the amount that you use. You may decide to wait until the third trimester of a pregnancy and go at a slower rate if using this herb by itself, but as always I prefer mixed blends of herbs.

In my opinion, lowly little dandelion is a huge hero in my opinion for assisting in liver support. When I have had clients that have had nothing else available to them in plant toxin situations, I have suggested they try feeding fresh dandelion leaves and flowers (especially the leaves). The nice thing with dandelion is that you will also gain some balanced kidney support at the same time. We've had some nice feedback in these situations. Then I suggest that one use a more balanced blend for follow up support for the hepatic system which has just survived a crisis.

Wormwood is another herb I have had people grab (in the form of Fir Meadow's Dworm BWW or W products) in plant toxicity emergencies involving the liver. In these situations you may get a diarrhea (among other problems- please see the Poisonings chapter in Part 1) that is not correcting with GI support herbs. Wormwood in reasonable amounts is thought to oxygenate the placenta, so this is an herb I will use during pregnancy. In an emergency I prefer to use this herb in a blend to gain additional synergistic effect, especially if I have to administer herbs on an hourly or bi-hourly schedule. Remember that giving this herb (or any herb) in insanely large amounts can find you with a thujone overdose as you get ahead of the liver's ability to process it out. NEVER EVER use or even own the essential of this plant which is considered very toxic in that highly concentrated form. I repeat, NEVER USE WORMWOOD ESSENTIAL OIL.

Turkey Rhubarb is a wonderful, gentle root to employ for general stagnation of the hepatic system. It encourages the body to produce and move bile, which in itself has a laxative effect on the system encouraging better movement and digestion in the GI Tract and reducing the opportunity for liver and gallbladder congestion. Any herb labeled as an 'Aperient' will have this gentle action. Usually the two to three year old roots are used.

Aloe vera in the form of a drinkable aloe vera juice encourages the body to replicate faster cell repairs; which includes the liver. It is also a 'Demulcent' herb which is soothing for damaged cells. Never use aloe gel straight from the plant internally as it contains a purgative phytochemical.

Lavender is another gentle but effective herb that we can classify as a cell proliferant, or an herb that encourages the body to replicate (repair) cells at a more efficient rate. Because we are not depending on this herb for cleaning it does not have to be an oral route herb, though certainly it can be. It also has anti-inflammatory and anti-septic properties which help the liver to deal with infective or damaging issues to the hepatic system. It should not be the only herb employed in a liver program, but it certainly can give a good program a more well rounded approach. I use lavender essential oils as in the lemon section (except that lavender does not have photosensitivity issues), the herb, a salve containing lavender (like Wounderful!) or added to water as an infusion. When using an essential oil is is imperative that you use Lavandula officinalis/officinale or angustifolia types. Lavandin or spike types of lavenders developed for the perfume industry are not considered efficacious for traditional medicinal use.

Other bitter tasting herbs can be used, as long as you ascertain that they are not toxic. Be sure to include some bitter herbs in the regular diet of any animal that has had liver challenges. Dandelion and wormwood, in moderate amounts, are two of these. Taste them (I dare you!), you'll see how bitter they are, and your liver will benefit from your taste experiment too.

When working with heavy metals toxicity, I like working with herbs like lemon, cilantro, and bugleweed to help the body clear those. At least once a week, you will need to work an animal on this type of a program to a good sweat. Do not work them this hard in very hot weather conditions or in cold conditions where you will not be able to dry them back off. This will help them blow some of these metals through the skin, as they are harder for the system to eliminate them through the regular eliminatory channels. Then follow that up with a nice warm bath to clean of the toxins and mucus released by the bloodstream. Adding some raw apple cider vinegar to the rinse water or sponging them afterwards will also help clear the toxins from the skin. A hot bath can be used for small animals. I like to serve them yarrow tea before the workout or with the bath. This helps their body be more efficient in blowing toxins as it helps the pores to open better.

Castor oil packs will help encourage a stagnated liver to do something about it. First apply castor oil to the skin and then place a hot, but safe to the touch, pad or dampened hot but safe towel over the area. The heat will encourage the oil to be absorbed faster. This is not a method to use during third trimester pregnancies as it can stimulate the body towards contractions; especially in a weak pregnancy. Unless the animal is a lap pet this is not a very convenient method to use, but I'm listing it here to give you options to work with until you can acquire other herbs and methods.

Dr. Christopher's Liver and Gallbladder Formula or Fir Meadow's Fresh Start formula both have many stories to allude to their wonderful hepatic system support. Salves such as Fir Meadow's Wounderful! or Dr. Christophers Complete Tissue Formula can be placed over the liver area two to three times per day, if wanted, for support beyond the oral herbs.

Jaundice

Jaundice is an issue that is usually recognized by yellowing in the sclera (not the iris) of the eye. Usually this is from a sluggish liver function that is not keeping up with the toxin accumulation in the liver, so the body begins to show the bilish accumulation in other areas. Remember that human babies that exhibit this usually have already been subjected to a plethora of synthetics by the time they are born. Toxic sources would be: a mom with an unclean liver, toxins from foods, drinks, environmental exposure and medications consumed by the pregnant mom, medications given before and during the childbirth process, chemicals (like eye washes & iodine naval dips) put on the child after birth, and vaccinations given within hours after birth. The poor child doesn't have a shot at a good happy start for their liver with all of these assaults! Jaundice is addressed by getting real sunlight exposure to the creature in question AND some bowel movements to help the body clear the toxins in the bile faster. If it's hot outside that would be in increments of a few minutes at a time, along with liver support herbs that were discussed earlier in this chapter. Be sure also that the animal has access to plenty of clean water, or nettle or raspberry or dandelion tea for additional gentle cleansing support.

Loss of Function or Reduced Function (Impairment)

For this problem the liver support herbs or products listed earlier in the chapter will become a good friend. Keep at it, as it can take a year or longer to get normal blood panels back with liver damage. My suggestion is to go at least 4 months past the normal blood panel, if not longer, in keeping with general liver cell regeneration times. Also remember to consider bloodstream and cell cleanses, as toxins the liver has not been able to process were stashed in other weaker cells.

Parasites

Of particular interest here is the liver fluke. Flukes are flat worms that usually have an intermediate host. In other words, they lived on some other type of living creature first before reaching the infective stage for their new host- your pet or livestock animal. Fresh water (pond, lake, or stream) snails are that host. If you live in an area where you see these, even if just seasonally, realize that liver fluke infestation can be a possibility as your stock ingests plant material that has snail eggs on it. Once they reach the acute stage as they tunnel through and damage the liver, animal losses can be quick and many. It can take months to years from exposure to life endangerment stages. During that time, your animals overall wellness may begin to decline and/or you may lose feed efficiency of your creature. If you experience animal loss, it is never a bad idea to have a veterinarian or veterinarian college do a post mortem to look for flukes in the liver and gallbladder. Yes, you can have a friend that butchers animals do it too, but the veterinarian will be looking for many more things than just flukes and can take tissue samples from other parts of the body if they find suspicious changes in the tissue. Iridology can be a nice tool to assess liver wellness overtime for gradual exposure and gradual liver degeneration. See the Parasites chapter in Part 1 for specifics in handling flukes. If I lived in an area prone to flukes, I would want to work my creatures through several to 10 days in a row of an herbal program at double or triple dose quarterly, if possible. Keeping stock away from natural water areas if possible and giving them daily supplements from the Supplements chapter to give them a stronger body and immune system are also beneficial.

Poisoning

Please see the Poisoning chapter for more assistance with poisoning. Any synthetic, toxic creature, mold, or poisonous plant substance can cause a severe problem. Please do NOT feed your cattle moldy hay just because 'they can handle it'. If we microscoped the liver tissue or did iridology readings on cattle that have a regular diet of this, you would get a different story. They are just larger animals, so they don't show symptomology as fast as smaller or more sensitive stock. But they will eventually. Meanwhile you may lose hardiness and rate of gain and may experience more problems in your young stock that were in utero during the times of moldy feeding (more scours, more lung deficiencies, and you name it). Please remember that if we increase the toxic load of one eliminatory organ, then the other three will gain greater stress. Moldy hay is more expensive then clean hay in the long run.

Stool Colors

Stool colors can give you some data on what you may be dealing with. The final decision should always be made by a qualified veterinarian and /or some lab work. Often one can send samples that have been correctly collected to a veterinarian college diagnostic lab directly. This saves the expense of a veterinarian. However, due to a veterinarian's experience, they may already have a pretty good idea of what they are seeing, which can save some valuable time that sending a sample to a lab takes. So you need to do as you feel led to do in your situation. These suggestions are meant as an educational guide only. Some of these are liver only and some are intestinal. I also have this listed in the Digestive Tract chapter.

When you see dark stools you may be seeing toxin dumping; often from the liver. This is very common when first starting to cleanse. It also may be a sign of older blood in the stool which is good to report to your veterinarian to obtain an diagnosis if you see this continuing or paired with other signs of your animal not feeling or doing well. Bleeding in the intestinal tract can be serious, but can be handled herbally if that is your choice once you whether that is going on. More can be read on that system in the Digestive Tract chapter.

White stools can be caused from chemicals such as ingestion of chemical fertilizers, including chemicals or fertilizers that accidentally made their way into processed feeds or grains in feed mills. Definitely consider the Poisons chapter in Part 1 if you see such a thing. Often your creature will not be feeling or looking well in this situation either. Don't wait to see if they get better but jump on liver, kidney and blood support immediately, also making sure they are staying properly hydrated through the process. White can also present itself if the body is moving gallstone material out. This will usually be in lumpy or stone like material.

Green lumps may show up once a stagnated gall bladder or liver begins to clean out bile stones from soft to hard.

Yellow and orange sometimes surfaces with liver cleansing as more serious synthetic toxins are coming out of the system. Make sure your creature has GOOD functioning bowels during this problem and lots of access to clean drinking water.

Runny yellow may be a Salmonella problem. Taking a sample to your vet (in a container they provide) for a diagnosis is not a bad idea, along with herbal antiseptic support at the acute level. Kat likes to use GI Soother and HerBiotic in these situations. Quarantine the animal and burn affected bedding.

Runny, grayish white stools may be Cryptosporidium. This is a time to use acute levels of herbs similar to a possible Salmonella problem along with getting a sample to your vet for conformation. Quarantine the animal and burn affected bedding.

Red stools may indicate fresh blood close to the anus. This also can be serious (injury, cancer, or ?) and one can consider having a veterinarian investigate to gain some useful information on how to work with the situation. Enemas of water and cayenne should help stop bleeding. Feeding or giving demulcent herbs will help the body soothe the area as they move through. Of particular interest here would be slippery elm bark, as more of that should reach the anal area than plant leaf sources. The body will also use the capillary route to help soothe the area and for that drinkable aloe, marshmallow root or leaf, slippery elm bark, mullein leaf, and comfrey can be good sources. Salves applied around the anal area, if the problem is close to the anus, can also help the body repair the tissue.

Liver for Dog or Cat Food

With what you may now know, you may understand my point of view on this food source. Though in an ideal organic world the liver would be a good source of raw food for you canine friend, please remember that we do not live in the ideal toxin free world. Even our penguins in Antarctica contain jet fuels in their fat layers. Unless your liver source comes from an animal on that has been on a liver cleansing program, chances are that you will be feeding the concentrated toxins from a degenerated liver to your beloved companion.

Chapter 22- Immune System

Our creature's immune systems are under challenge every day. Breathing in toxic chemicals, eating natural raised feed that is rained on (by rain that cleans toxins out of the atmosphere as it falls to the ground), chemical things that get sprayed on them, injected into them, and fed to them; all can have negative impact to a well functioning immune system. Stress from work and competitions, weather or losing a barn buddy also negatively impacts the immune system by causing acidity in the body. It goes without saying that cleansing is going to be part of your program in immunity support for your beloved creature.

Vaccinations are something to consider here. I am not going to dictate whether you use them or not. That is an individual's decision. However, I do think you need to be INFORMED about them. Vaccines are comprised of many ingredients. They will have the modified live or killed virus, a preservative (often a mercury derivative- Thimersol, or aluminum which are both very toxic to brain tissue), an antibiotic (problematic for those allergic to the antibiotic chosen), a carrier (what the main fluid is containing the other ingredients), an adjuvant (an ingredient meant to illicit a stronger immune system response), and the culture (usually an animal derived product, including aborted human fetal tissue in some human vaccinations). That's quite a list.

The culture in a vaccine poses some unique considerations, when considering immunity. Think about how a person, when receiving an organ transplant, say a kidney, will then need to go onto lifelong anti-rejection drugs to keep the immune system from fighting with and destroying the new body part. Now why would a human immune system fight another organ that is still human? It is because the immune system is intimately acquainted with what is YOU. When it comes into contact with something that is not you, it recognizes it as not belonging there and being a potential risk to the well being of the person. So the war begins. This system IS working. You want your immune system to recognize 'foreign proteins', virus, bacteria, spirochetes, etcetera and to wage war against such invaders to keep you well. Now consider what could happen when the culture is an egg, fetal tissue, bovine serum, green monkey kidney or whatever the choice.

That is now injected DIRECTLY into the bloodstream (or the muscle or SQ where they go to the bloodstream from there), bypassing the GI Tract where foreign proteins in a healthy GI tract would be broken down into amino acids and either taken up by the responsible flora or passed through the alimentary canal if not recognized and eliminated as manure. These 'foreign' proteins coming into the bloodstream have instant access to cells body wide.   If these foreign proteins decide to lodge into some body tissue or organ, then the immune system after awhile begins to associate the body tissue as part of the problem and begins attacking that. Welcome autoimmune diseases which are relevant in humans and becoming more common in our creatures. Wow.   To learn more one can read the heavily referenced books by Neal Z. Miller "Vaccines, Are they Really Safe and Effective" or "Make an Informed Vaccine Decision" by Mayer Eisenstein, MD, JD, MPH to learn more. This is an interesting topic, to say the least.

Many vaccinations also are 3 way to 8 way combinations. It is very seldom, that a creature in its daily wanderings will accumulate viral or bacterial agents of more than one condition at a time. Yet, in these combinations we are subjecting the immune system to fight multiple agents all at once. At the least, I'd consider that situation may be very stressful on the animal's wellness at a cellular level. If the topic interests you, do some more research and draw your own conclusions.

Immune system supporting herbs are Oregon grape root, garlic, echinacea, thyme, hyssop (never use the essential oil), goldenseal, astragalus, peppermint, ginger, cayenne and several of the hot herbs. Eleuthero and ginger are some of my favorite supports for a system that is stressed. Echinacea should not be used longer than 10 days in a row, as its effectiveness isn't good after that. But after a three day rest you can start right up with it again.

Allergies

Allergies can stem from many substances. They can be shown by upper respiratory distress, nostril discharge, coughs or strained breathing, running eyes, itching throat, ears and eyes, reduction in hearing ability, lack of thriftiness and endurance, and more. Anaphylactic shock from a food or toxic creature, like a bee sting, can be dealt with a strong dose of cayenne or cayenne tincture. Master

Herbalists like to suggest that 'food allergies' from any food or food part that should be considered normal in a diet, are nothing more than a toxin within the body reacting to a phytochemical (plant chemical) in the plant. Not to belittle these reactions as they can be life threatening. I have found that the root of allergies has always been related to cleaning the liver well and keeping the bloodstream clean and well functioning. The body will reheal itself from allergies if given enough support over enough time to do so. A year is considered minimum, but usually adequate with quarterly tune-ups. Until that year is over, do not EVEN consider exposing your animal to the problem food, and then, do it only after prayer and in extremely tiny amounts to see if there is still an issue. Do not take this lightly and you will have to use entirely your own judgment with this topic. If you do not continue with routine maintenance, then as the animal gets more toxic again expect the allergies to resurface.

Autoimmune Conditions

I covered how some of these in the introduction of this chapter. Other contributory sources are antibiotics, creature bites and sting and other physical injuries that break the skin.

Antibiotics (including colloidal silver) kill most of the flora in the intestinal tract. Candida albicans, a flora needed for sugar and alcohol uptake then takes advantage of the additional room and begins to proliferate out of balance to the other flora. As the Candida races out of control, it sends the brain messages for more foods that will give it sugar and alcohol. Thus some animals become more ravenous with their prepared and poor grade molasses containing processed grain feeds. Once the Candida gets to a point where they feel underfed, they will develop appendages onto their bodies. Then they rotate quickly and cut into the villi (the hairs that uptake nutrition into the capillaries. Then they enter the bloodstream. This 'leaky gut' problem now allows proteins access to the bloodstream that would never have access otherwise, such as what comes from animal protein foods. So this is another foreign protein problem. Candida can be a real battle to be diagnosed, as it can mimic so many issues depending on where it is lodging in the body. These are addressed by trying to starve out the Candida (eliminating sugar and alcohol causing feeds such as fruit and processed grain/pet food products) and by targeting them with antifungal herbs such as lavender, black walnut (not for equine/camelid species), pau d' arco, peppermint and others.   Fir Meadow makes a DYeast product and Dr. Christopher has a nice Intestinal Sweep product.   Use two weeks on, one week off, two weeks on until the problem is under control. Also provide good natural probiotics such as raw apple cider vinegar and garlic and raw vegetables. Wait on raw honey until the gut has rehealed. Consider using herbs in the GI section to help the body heal any intestinal damage from antibiotic use. Until those heal, animal products should not be fed to avoid having proteins entering the bloodstream via the damaged villi. That would include the feathers put in your livestock feed to elevate the non bioavailable protein content on the label. Oxygen foods would also be good, such as: gotu kola, wheat grass, raw apple, spirulina, and etcetera.   Candida 'hijacks' red blood cells and displaces oxygen as it does, leading to increased fatigue and decreased wellness. Mild exercise while the body heals would also encourage your creature to take in deeper breaths supplying more oxygen. Just be sure you don't overdo it with a recovering creature and set them back. Working up to extended walks would be perfect.

Some protozoa are said to be a factor in some autoimmune diseases. If I were working with an autoimmune disease I would certainly want to work on this factor as well. Please see the Parasites Chapter in Part 1 of this book for information.

Foreign proteins do enter the body from insect bites when insects inject a protein substance into the blood.   These would include spiders, ticks, bees, snakes, scorpions and the like. Don't ignore these situations if you get them.   Follow herbal procedures right away, as covered in the Poisoning chapter in Part 1.

Injuries which expose the blood stream can allow foreign proteins to enter. This is not so common but is possible, as in situations where one gets cut by a fence that also has horse hair stuck to it.   We all know that it seems some creatures have an affinity for finding something to get injured on, even if they live in the equivalent of a padded cell. Don't ignore injures, at the very least consider some herbal antiseptic help, such as: oil of garlic, oil of garlic with lavender essential oil added in, HerBiotic, cayenne, goldenseal, etcetera.

When working with autoimmune conditions, the sooner you can begin your herb work the much more likely you will obtain satisfactory results. This will involve correcting the issue by immune system re-education, eventual immune system herbal support so the immune system can act correctly, as well as helping the body eliminate any 'nonself' invaders. These may be via antifungal herbs, antiparasitic herbs, immune system relaxing herbs (astragalus, Lobelia inflata, and etcetera), system stress support herbs (lavender, eleuthero, hops (not in canine), nettle, and the like), antiseptic herbs, and the like; depending on what you deem to be the original cause. Plan to take at least a year to get on top of the problem.

Bee Immunity Herbs and How to Nurture Bee Immunity

This is a fun topic I get to address from time to time. "How do I get my bees to increase in their health"? Bees face the same perils as humans. Increased microwave activity from cell towers and etcetera, sugar water meals, stress from traveling sometimes hundreds of miles to have their hive placed in large commercial orchards, herbicides and pesticides sprayed on the crops that they are supposed to pollinate, airborne toxins, etcetera. No wonder they are more susceptible to mites and other bee conditions.

To bee kind to your bees, consider planting them some beneficial herbs to pollinate. Bees love thymes, rosemary, borage, oreganos, mints, sages and other aromatic herbs. Consider planting lavender near their hives, so that they gain wafts of lavender to help protect them from their enemies. Mites also hate lavender and peppermint, so these are good choices around your bee 'bedrooms'. Lavender will also tend to have a calming effect on your hive. An additional bonus is that some of the volatile oils and nutrients (fat soluble oils) from these plants will make it into your honey, increasing the benefits within this valuable product. Please always allow your bees to eat their own honey for their additional nourishment. There just isn't any good substitute for them.

Bees also benefit from gentle herbal teas as a nutrient and cleansing source. Teas made from raspberry, stinging nettle, organic non GMO alfalfa, or dandelions or any combination and added to their drinking water will help support these hard workers. Start with tiny amounts and gradually increase them to keep their water intake normal.

Bacteria

So many of these topics I am covering could and do contain whole books of information. Bacteria and bacteriology, the study of bacteria, is another one of those topics. There are thousands and thousands of species of bacteria, some beneficial and some harmful. Of the harmful types, there are also countless mutations. No wonder antibiotic therapy is so challenged in trying to develop drugs that will cover each bacteria type and mutants of that type. The good news is that herbs tend to be broad spectrum in their approach, so no matter what the bacteria; we have good system support in herbs. Herbs benefit the good bacteria while helping the body to go to task with the bad bacteria, so we get the best of both worlds with them. Just remember that if you don't use efficacious herbs, don't expect to get the result you are after in the amount of time you would expect. Some bacteria require fast action to be successful. Some favorite antiseptic herbs of mine are myrrh, goldenseal, cayenne, cinnamon, onion, cloves, garlic, lavender, rosemary, thyme, oregano, usnea, and there are a plethora of others. Note that many of these are "hot to the taste" herbs. Also remember your cleansing, immune system support and body organ or tissue support of the affected area. If I have an aquarium I would be prone to slowly introducing clean usnea moss/lichen to my aquarium to reduce the amount of gram positive bacterium that want to hang around. It doesn't extract well with water, but you will get a little effect.

For this discussion I'm going to separate the bacteria into two classes. There are other classes. You can do more research should that topic intrigue you. Gram positive bacteria take on a stain when worked with in a lab for identification. Many of the bacterial issues we encounter as pet and livestock caretakers fall in this category. Some of these are: Staphylococcus, Staph auerous, Streptococcus, Enterococcus, E. coli, Corneybacterium (CL, pigeon fever, pseudotuberculosis), Clostridiums, Mycoplasma (though not stainable), many pneumonias, and Listeria. Usnea, garlic, and myrrh are my first line of defense when I know I'm working with a gram positive problem. I support those with other powerful antiseptic and immune system herbs. I work the first day as an acute situation and move into the second day into an elevated chronic situation. I then keep at it 6 days per week depending on what the individual situation calls for. Many of those are covered in the related body systems chapters.

Gram negative bacteria can be more of a challenge, such as in pseudomonas aeruginosa or klebsiella and require one to be tenacious to battle these. These forms of bacteria in an udder have given many a dairy person woes. For gram negative challenges consider using garlic, black seed or black cumin (Nigella sativa), cinnamon (not third trimester), thyme (caution first trimester and very young stock), and ginger along with other immune system and related body system support. If it is a bacterium that they can pick up from wet bedding or surroundings (like pseudomonas) see what you can do to have your stock in contact with less wet material. I would also pair HerBiotic or herbs like that (goldenseal, myrrh, echinacea, and cayenne) to support the immune system in this type of a fight.

Mycoplasma organisms, of which there are over one hundred, lack cellular walls and are not damaged by many antibiotics, which target bacterium cell wall structures. Herbs, however, work well with these and you can garner your list from the gram positive and negative paragraphs with additional immune and body system support. Some forms of pneumonia fall into this category, including some chronic 'walking' pneumonia types.

CAE/OPP

Caprine Arthritis Encephalitis is one of the buzzwords in the goat community as is Ovine Progressive Pneumonia in the sheep community. There are caused by different retroviruses, but have similar symptoms so tend to be lumped together. Infection routes are similar to AIDS in humans, another retrovirus. Exposure to body fluids is how these are transmitted. In animals who's immunity is already severely compromised, that can be as simple as sharing a feed pan and thus the saliva on a routine basis with an affected animal, routinely breeding in the virus as it is coughed into the air by infected animals, through herd management that can involve blood- such as castrating or hoof trimming, through the milk or colostrum of infected animals to their young, and through birth fluids (either during birth or as other motherly herdmates clean the after birthing discharges). Animals do not need to show symptoms to be affected by these problems. There are good blood tests available through Washington State University (WADDL) and UC Davis to help in diagnosis of these issues.

Animals that become symptomatic should have blood testing done to check for this and other conditions. This is something that you can learn how to do from your veterinarian and then you can send the samples to the lab yourself. Symptoms may be wasting away, pneumonia, reduced milk production (below what you would expect for the genetics), hardened or congested udder at birthing that will not release milk, arthritic conditions in the joints, swollen joints, brain and mammary system lesions. Because it is considered incurable in the medical community, it is not something to ignore. However, as with other conditions the sooner you get to work on it the more likely you have a good outcome. I would use specific herbs or products to support immunity, cleansing, traditional herbal antibiotic (antiseptic) herbs, joint support if needed, lung support if needed, mammary and brain support if needed, as well as regular supplemental herbs at higher than regular doses. You can see this is not a small task. It is ideal to house and work with affected stock in a different location than negative stock and to handraise the resulting young to prevent the likely transmission of the disease through the milk. There is a plethora of information in print and on the internet for those that would like to learn more. Be careful to not let new babies ingest any amniotic fluids from each other or their dams during or after the birthing process.

Fevers

Fevers are a neat thing. Really, they are. For every degree of body temperature that the system increases, the immune system and macrophages increase exponentially to go after their invader. The body knows which temperature is needed to create a hostile environment for the culprit to gain ground on it, and thus is used by a veterinarian as part of the symptom information they collect to help them diagnose a situation. This increase in temperature causes the creature to go off of feed. This allows the body to move its energy from digestion to intruder fighting, which is a good thing. I find all of this fascinating.   When I encounter this situation, I have a useful monitoring tool to find out how my herbal support is progressing.   I will typically use HerBiotic and/or some of the bacteria body support herbs to start chasing the likely infection that is causing this fever response.   If the fever follows a vaccination or medication of some type, then I need to consider the Poisoning chapter in Part 1 for chemical poisonings along with liver, kidney, blood and brainstem support, to help remove the damaging agents quickly.   As the fever begins to drop towards normal, I know that the herbal program I am using is giving the body the support it needs.   At that point, I may reduce my herbs a bit and still monitor the temperature to make sure it continues to return back to normal.

Consider that if I were to use fever controlling herbs or substances to artificially lower the temperature, I have lost my way to gauge if I am using the correct quantity of herbs for the situation. I am also shutting off the body's tool to keep the immune system humming and cook the invader.

Make sure you do keep the animal well hydrated through oral drenching, soaking, or enemas with normal body temperature water or better yet, gentle herb teas such as raspberry, stinging nettle, dandelion, slippery elm, organic non GMO alfalfa or marshmallow root.   Also keep the animal blanketed during this time, as they will lose their ability to feel warm. Years ago I had had pneumonia in the summer from an industrial exposure and I was wearing my winter coat in the house to feel comfortable.

Head Injuries can also cause fevers, by throwing the brain's control mechanism in the brain stem off. In that case, use brain nourishing herbs and wound nurturing herbs such as found in those related chapters, both at the brain stem and orally.

Fungus and Molds

Fungus and molds can literally become a problem in any part of the body and can be associated especially with lung, liver and malignancy issues. They can however affect the body anywhere they accumulate. Some are ingested, some are injected, and some are breathed in.   I lean towards some of the hotter herbs (cayenne, garlic, horseradish, ginger, peppermint) to help the body to clear these out of the system along with additional liver, immune and blood cleaning support. And any other organ support that I may deem beneficial.

Leukemia- Feline

Feline leukemia, a form of cancer, is another retrovirus. Retroviruses are able put copies of their genetic material into the cells they infect. In effect, they 'hijack' the cell for their own use and replication. Some symptomology is similar to other retrovirus problems, such as Aids, OPP, and CAE. Symptoms may be a chronic combination of: decreased wellness, untreatable fevers, lethargy, wasting away, infections, inflammations, and diarrhea. It is spread through body fluids, such as saliva, infected feces, cat bites, and etcetera. If the cat has not progressed too far into the situation, judicious use of herbal body support can give you a happy ending. Consider serious cleansing as for any malignancy; including bowels, liver, kidneys, and blood cleaning. Also give support as in bacterial infections, immune system support, and supplementation working them up to a prenatal nourishment program. Don't forget additional support for any affected organs.

Microbes

Microbes are neither bacterial nor viral, but are single celled organisms that cause infectious problems. Your herbal toolkit will be the same as for bacteria. Often GI system support will also need to be considered. For that, I really like working with GI Soother. You can also look at the Digestive Tract chapter earlier in Part ll.

Soremouth or Orf and Blue Tongue

I am lumping these two conditions together, as they are both viral in origin. Soremouth (Orf, as it is called in Europe). Mild cases may show as just a little bit of scabbing at the mouth and sometimes nose, and are a nuisance. They can be picked up at shows or from bringing new animals into the herd. You can even walk the virus in on your clothes and shoes, if handling infected animals or walking through infected facilities. It is zoonotic, with some people picking it up from their goats or sheep via cuts in their hands. I've read that can be quite painful. Severe cases can cause severe inflammation and pain to the point that an animal will go off feed. Infected baby animals can infect their dam's udder, causing her to not feed her babies due to pain. Kids or lambs with a severe problem can starve to death due to the pain involved in trying to eat. Those will need to be tube fed. By applying the traditionally antiviral and antibacterial herbs list in a salve to the affected areas, we are doing a couple of things. One, we are encouraging the area to dry out faster and help the body to heal faster. We are also helping to reduce the pain level. Washcloths soaked in hot ginger tea and applied at a safe temperature level to painful areas can help reduce the pain also. Adding immune system support herbs and wound support herbs orally will also stimulate the body into faster healing mode. You will have to watch for secondary infections with this problem and help the body with those if you see any signs of infection, including pus or colored drainage. HerBiotic or other antiseptic herbs can be used orally and also placed on the problem area. Give every two to three hours the first day and then three to four times per day after that until the body is well into healing mode.

Blue tongue is spread by mosquito activity. They take in infected blood from a host, then land on another sheep or goat to infect them. See the external parasites section in the Parasites chapter in Part 1 to see ways to help detour mosquito activity. Blue tongue can also cause animals to starve to death due to them going off of feed from the pain involved. Follow the suggestions earlier in this section to help your creature.

Virus

There may be millions of these pathogenic microbes on the planet. Antibiotics do not work with viruses, so many times in the medical realm only supportive therapy is available. However, in the herb world, many of the herbs that are effective in body support for bacteria are so broad spectrum that they also are great agents to employ for viral conditions. Some of these to consider are: lemon balm (triple or quadruple dose the herb), garlic, cinnamon, oregano, thyme, hyssop, lemon. Some essential oils to consider, properly diluted, are: lemon (not in direct sun), grapefruit, thyme (not with young creatures unless greatly diluted), cinnamon (not third trimester of pregnancy), oregano (small doses only), ravensara (ravintsara), and Eucalyptus dives or radiata. As always, work with the first day as if you have an acute situation, then assess each day from there on when to move into chronic stage. Keeping your animals hydrated, warm and where they can rest without being bothered by other animals will go a long ways towards promoting their body to recovery. Don't forget love and prayer!

Chapter 23- Lymphatic System

We often hear about lymph and the lymphatic system. But do we know what it really is? Here is a brief summary for you. The lymph system is three times larger than the blood circulatory system. Lymph fluid is one of the body's garbage repositories. Toxins and waste and metabolic byproducts from cells, killed bacterium and virus, dead white blood cells and anything else the body determines as refuse that comes from or between the cells, flows through the lymphatic system. This system reaches cells that even capillaries do not reach, taking nutrition and oxygen to them as it does. While the circulatory system has a pump, called the heart, the lymph system has a pump called muscle movement. Exercise and daily movement are important for your creature to keep this system from stagnating with waste. Stagnated waste can allow cells & tissues to back up with additional toxins and be subject to cellular change from the amount of waste. So if you have a barn potato or lap potato, make sure some daily exercise is involved somehow; even if you have to move the limbs or creature yourself, as in a physical therapy situation. I will gently rebound on my mini trampoline with baby animals in my arms, which is probably the most effective route as every cell in the body is 'massaged' by the change in gravity with each direction change. Massage helps move lymph in the muscles you manipulate, and we have herbal assistance also. Some traditional herbal resources for lymph include: mullein, goldenseal, echinacea, plantain, poke (don't use internally), coriander seeds and barberry root bark. I think that the addition of some of the hot herbs like garlic, onion, and thyme, also helps stimulate lymph movement by thinning the fluids so they become easier for the body to circulate. Prickly ash bark or berries can be incorporated along with other herbs to help move stagnation quicker. Lemon is good for many types of blockages and should be incorporated. Blood cleaning herbs discussed in that chapter should also be a part of assisting in this situation. An unhealthy lymph system WILL result in an unhealthy creature. Keep it maintained by cleansing your creature in correct order and offering it plenty of freewill exercise.

Abscesses or Boils

See the Epidermis chapter for more information on these. Also see the following section.

Caseous lymphadenitis (CL), Pigeon Fever, Pseudotuberculosis

CL is named for its caseous or cheese like consistency where the pus from this bacterial problem has collected. Corneybacterium is the culprit in this case. This organism is highly infective and easily spread from infected animal to uninfected animals. There is a small risk of human infection, so please exercise caution if you decide to work with this problem. It is called CL in sheep and goats, Pigeon fever in horses, and pseudotuberculosis in hogs. The bacterium causes a swelling or abscess (depending on the creature type). They can be external, showing in the epidermis, or they can be internal, causing abscessing in a body organ which will prove fatal. This is another of the wasting away conditions. It can be spread easily via the milk in affected udders, through coughing, through drainage of the bacterium from abscesses that burst. This will infect the facilities for years and can be spread by walking through it, from people getting the bacterium on their hands and then touching other animals, and even birds can spread it on their feet. This is very common condition in sheep that are sheared. A shearer may run clippers through one abscess, infecting the clippers and then cut or nick the next sheep, giving them the bacterium. Because of this problem, I disinfect my clipper blades with hot essential oils and a bit of olive oil every time I get blades back from being sharpened. Many of these people sharpen blades that have been used on infected animals. If you sharpen blades for others, take care that you do not bring this bacterium home to your herd or flock or spread it to other herds from your sharpening equipment.

The medical community considers this an incurable condition. Blood tests are not always reliable in this condition. A swab taken of the material and sent to a veterinarian lab is the best way to have this diagnosed along with symptomology. Be careful extruding the sample, the material will be infective and tenacious. Extract it at your driveway that you can bleach or otherwise disinfect real well, wear disposable gloves and take other precautions.

With quality herbs, caught early, and being tenacious on your part, this condition can be combated. However, beware that while you fight this you still run the risk of infecting your unaffected animals, animals in other herds, or yourself. Also know that this will be a lengthy hard fight (likely one year) and will cost money in herbs to continue the body support. I would work with this situation as in the bacteria section earlier in this chapter along with immune system support, cleansing herbs in order, and overall body herbal supplementation. Please consider not exhibiting animals (even herdmates) with these very contagious conditions. The additional stress to your creature is not favorable to their system improvement, nor is the disregard for the wellness of other herds or flocks you could expose.

Edema

With edema we want to get lymph clean and moving and also support the kidneys. I explain this earlier in this chapter and the kidney information will be in the Renal System chapter.

Malignancies

I am putting malignancies here, because stagnated lymph is very often involved in these situations along with a dirty bloodstream. If you are dealing with a suspected or diagnosed malignancy, or cancer, you will want to work fast. This is no time to just sprinkle a few herbs on a situation once in awhile. You will be at war in this situation trying to give the body's troops every resource it can use as it fights this foe. You will need to support the body, so that it can move quicker than the malignancy can replicate. There are also diet changes that can be made that can stop cancer from growth while in the promotion (growing) stage. Also read in the Parasites Chapter in Part 1. Parasites, including Protozoa, can be contributory to cancer types of situations, as can molds. Molds can be found in the Immune System Chapter in Part ll.

If I were supporting one of my creatures in a malignancy issue, here are some things I would do. First and foremost I have to cleanse my creature, in order.

The Accessible Pet, Equine and Livestock Herbal

Don't ignore this foundational truth just because I'm mentioned it so many times. This is IMPERATIVE. The bowel movements cannot be stagnated, the liver and kidneys have to be in top working order and the blood stream and all of these other systems need to become squeaky clean. We believe that a clean, healthy, well plant mineralized, proper Ph and oxygenated blood steam is EXTREMLEY IMPORTANT when working with a malignant situation. If you do not gain a clean bloodstream and clear out any affected lymph, then this will become a continual battle that you will have to address again and again. Or, if the battle has been won, but the bloodstream becomes filthy again, plan to have this situation haunt your creature again. However, the second time the problem will be more tenacious and harder to get ahead of. It seems like cancer has a memory and works double time if it gets to a diagnosable stage again. Don't give it that opportunity. Every creature carries some cancer cells within their body at all times. A healthy immune system and well nourished clean body of alkaline Ph will keep them cleared out. Just because your creature doesn't have enough cells in one aggregation to be diagnosable, does not mean that there may not be a problem ready to brew. The last I had heard was that a malignant cell group needed to contain 500,000 cells to be diagnosable (one billion cells is pea sized). So a creature can have several groupings of 400,000 (or whatever the current number is) and will diagnose as clean for cancer. Don't let this worry you; just understand the limits of our current medical capabilities.

Live raw foods are imperative. Enzymes and probiotics supplied by these raw foods are important. Processed, sugared and cooked foods increase body acidity providing an environment that cancer, parasites and microbes thrive in. I like using carrots and carrot juice to help regain ground for creatures that have been on demineralizing processed or sugared foods. This carrot regimen is excellent support for any that are experiencing "cells gone wild" problems. For a goat sized creature, that will be one to two quarts per day after you take some time to get them used to that quantity. Pets can also be offered shredded carrot and lettuces sprinkled with kelp or carrot juice as a portion of their diet, which many like. Cayenne and garlic are important supplements. Cayenne to help move the nutrients around the body and to prolong their effectiveness and may also help the body kill cancer cells. Garlic, besides being cleansing and liquefying to lymph, also adds organic living sulphur to the diet. Paired with bitter tasting apricot seeds or kernels (do not use bland wimpy ones), you have what we consider a natural chemo system. The body pairs the laetrile in the seeds with the sulphur and turns them into chemo against only cancer cells. In healthy cells the body coverts it to B17 to nourish them. Thirty seeds are fed daily to creatures in the 100 to 200 pound range. My goats will eat them whole. For other animals, you can grind them up fresh each time in a coffee grinder or Magic Bullet™, and mix with other feeds including black strap molasses. I suspect that many of the hot herbs will be beneficial in a malignancy program. Lemon is also considered effective support. Many of the antiseptic herbs under the bacteria section can be used as additional support. Be sure that is additional support, not in place of the kernels and organs/blood cleansing support. The wound support herbs that are high in calcium will also be beneficial; as will the blood oxygenating herbs (apple, eucalyptus, thyme, marshmallow root, and wheat grass).

Subclinical infections

These are infections that are not problematic enough to give you clear symptoms like a fever, but still drag your animal down in energy and performance. Or they may be early in the illness process and will become 'clinical' or symptomatic soon. Cleansing, nutritional support (like Better Daze) and some antiseptic herbs at the chronic level, such as the bacteria herbs will be good support for your creature. Make sure they stay warm and intake proper fluid levels, and keep them where other creatures won't pester them. If they have herd buddy, try and keep the herd buddy close so they don't stress from separation anxiety (being herd bound). Raw honey is another nice support. Some of the tips from the Rescues Chapter in Part 1 will also be helpful.

Chapter 24- Nervous System

The 90,000 miles of nervous system in an 'average' person of the nervous system never ceases to amaze me. I like to compare it to wiring & electronics in a house, neatly ordered, each wire and switch being used for a specific purpose to move energy and information up and down the transmission lines. We do have electricity in us. Have you ever bumped your funny bone and felt an electric shock in there? When I work with reflexology it is quiet common for people to feel nervous system or electrical transmission go through joints or other areas of the body once the body is coaxed to open up congested areas. The brain, of course is considered the CPU or central processing unit, which much of that work taking place in the brain stem or medulla area. But did you know other areas of the body also have some of their own central wiring intelligence? The heart is one of those areas. So is the solar plexus- the area near your brisket that communicates to the middle and lower body organs. Nervous system and endocrine gland biochemicals (hormones) are more primary ways that our body communicates back and forth with itself. The irides (plural for iris) are the only visible part of the nervous system from outside of the body as the 500,000 optic nerves show the level of wellness being experienced by each organ and tissue on the 'TV screen'- the iris. Fascinating. I don't think we will ever exhaust the information to be learned about the nervous system.

Needless to say then, is that if the nervous system is congested or damaged it can have a serious impact on the well being of your creature. All of the lines need to fully open and communicating well for each cell of your creature to function as intended. Nerves that have been damaged can and do regenerate. Even nerves diagnosed as 'dead'. I have nerves on my side from a surgery after a serious accident that were 'dead' for 13 years. They were still there, but the area was numb. I introduced nervous system nourishing herbs and they began to announce their presence again. They are functioning just fine now. As long as the nerves are still there, they can heal themselves if given the right tools. I've watched too many diabetics regain feeling in their lower limbs to believe otherwise.

The nervous system should be considered in situations where the animal's mentality has changed, his gait or way of movement has been altered, or any head pressing or circling is observed. Changes in voice pitch, especially to a higher pitch, excessive drooling, cocking or hanging the head to one side, changes in eye movement and more can be hints that the nervous system is involved.

Also check for inner ear problems which can sometimes mimic nervous system problems such as loss of balance, repeated head shaking, head pressing or head banging due to ear pain or pressure. Do not forget to also consider that a stroke may be causing some of these symptoms. For that, immediately administer cayenne appropriate for your animal's size. See the Circulatory System chapter earlier in Part ll. Some creature bites or stings, as well as chemical consumption, are neurotoxic and can give you some strange nervous symptoms. See the Poisoning chapter in Part 1 for those issues. Rabies will be discussed later in this chapter and is a serious consideration, so don't ignore it. Certainly you may always hire your veterinarian and get their expert diagnosis on the situation. With these situations, it is good to know what caused the problem, if possible. It will make you able to better direct your herb project.

Circling/head pressing/staggering

These are often signs of brain stem involvement. It may be inflammation caused by injury, viral, bacterial, microbial or other problem. If you have one of these, they are usually serious and you don't want to waste any time starting to work with them. While your animal is still able to move, safely get them to their own area that will be quiet and warm with warm bedding. I say safely because if it is a large animal such as a horse, you do not need the animal falling on you. It is wise to have an extra long lead rope on them, so you can stay away from the side of the animal. Get the temperature of your creature and a list of symptoms to your vet, if possible, to get an idea of what you may be dealing with. This is a situation where you will want to pull out your Viral and Bacterial herbal helps and start getting them into your animal safely at acute levels with a triple dose for the first dose. If the animal is comatose, then you will either have to safely stomach tube or give the herbs by infusion/enema. If your animal is comatose or so weak that it can't swallow well, give a double dose of cayenne by enema. Chances are you may be able to get consciousness back as the heart receives the nourishment. You can also pour cayenne tincture close the heart area under the brisket between the front legs. You can even pour or put cayenne on the tongue and gums without getting near the throat area. My second dose may follow in 30 minutes at singular dose, then hourly after that for the first day. After the first hour, reduce the garlic to half dose. For these situations I like HerBiotic and garlic with it, because it is so multipurpose in body support. Other herbs to consider are cayenne, thyme, oregano, lemon, hyssop and most herbs that are hot. The garlic can be dropped after the first day IF your creature continues to improve. I also like to mix rosemary essential oil (SOLVENT FREE!) at the rate of 5 drops to one teaspoon of olive oil and rub that onto the brainstem (medulla) area to help support the brain. Three drops of ginger essential oil can be added to that blend to make it even more nourishing by increasing circulation to that area. Eleuthero paired with ginger herb given orally is a nice supplement for system stress. You can also make a fomentation with that and hold it onto the brainstem.

Remember to also keep your animal hydrated orally and/or with a normal body temperature enema according to your vet's recommended amount, to also support them nutritionally (make nurturing herb teas for the enemas, or oral use), keep your creature blanketed, and watch for small changes indicating improvement. Do not stress the animal too quickly as it recovers, or relapse is possible. I liken health situations to a war and battle situation. The battle may have been won as you see improvement, but the war is yet to be finished; even if you do not see the ambush around the corner. Make sure you follow through long enough to keep them on the mend.

Electromagnetic Fields (EMFs)

EMFs are all around us, and your beloved creatures too. These distorted energy impulses that zip by and through us to our cell phones, blue tooths, WI-FI and other signal receiving devices are a threat to all of our well being. Also included in this list of invisible invaders are high technology items that give off signals, such as: high definition TVs, TVs, microwaves, hair dryers, electricity from power poles, electric fencing, vehicles and the list goes on.   These fields, which are invisible and often undetectable by humans have been linked to problems with increased levels of stress, lowered immunity, increased jet lag, depression, enzyme and mineral depletion in the body, cancers, sleep issues, decreased coordination, decreased mind function, overactive mind function, imbalance in body tissues and organs, and many more conditions.   I am one of those more sensitive people that can 'feel' waves of energy run through my head when I drive near and under large power poles or get around a large number of electronic items. How do we deal with these things since they are so prevalent in our industrial world? I use EMF shields. Properly designed shields are programmed to readjust and reformat these frequencies, which in turn rebalances the Biofield in the body. Just like you can see a light band around a red blood cell in a microscope, our bodies and our creatures' bodies also have Biofields as a whole. I have one plugged into my house which covers any device that is plugged into the wall on of up to 2000 square feet (or one per circuit panel) in a single story home. If your office or home has multiple stories then you would want one per floor. I also have one plugged into my barn milkroom, and in any other building where I want myself or my creatures' exposure eliminated. I also have shields attached to my cell phone and my lap top, which is not always plugged in at home when I use it. When I'm out and about I have a necklace I wear, there are pet collars and key chain models that can be attached to halters or tack when you are home or out and about. I can immediately feel a difference in my home 'atmosphere' when I unplug my house unit from the wall. My mind feels more agitated and stressed. It goes without saying I leave it plugged in all the time! So, if you are having a creature that is having behavior or other issues that you can't quite help them get over with cleansing and nourishing, you certainly will want to consider this. I wonder how many of small nervous dogs are impacted by this problem?   I have EMF shields listed in the Appendix for those that are interested.

Fear

If your animal is losing control of its ability to control itself, fear is going to come into play. Besides the nervous system stress support mentioned above, herbs like lavender, hops (not for dogs), Wild lettuce, Lobelia inflata and scullcap are helpful for the nervous system. This is a situation where Bach flower remedies may also come into assistance. I also like chamomile (German) essential oil to dab on the hairs under the nostrils with a cotton swab. Just let a drop fall onto the swab and dab it on. Chamomile infusion can also be given. Some animals, like dogs or cats or reptiles, can decide to go into protective mode and could bite when they are fearful. Please take precautions. Some normally cooperative large animals can try to throw their weight around while scared, so also be careful of that. You do not want to leave your animal in a state of fear, as that will add additional stress on the body and will increase the challenge you have in supporting their system so that it can get well. If I have an un-well goat and I have to leave the stall or barn, then I will usually leave my jacket or sweatshirt with them. They seem to like that, and it does help them relax. Be careful of leaving things like that with animals that like to consume strange things, such as cows and sheep. In that case, if they are bonded with you, leave your human scented garment out of their pen, safely out of reach. They will still be able to smell it.

Grass tetany (hypomagnesaemia)

Grass tetany can occur in any livestock animal, including the equine species. It is often called grass staggers, as that is the primary symptom that brings this condition to attention. Early spring grass tends to grow fast once the conditions are right. Just like in herbs, the faster growth will have fewer nutrients per pound of dry matter. In this case we are interested in the magnesium levels being too low, which can rapidly cause a fatal situation. It has been reported that allowing animals to graze at night rather than daytime can lower their risk of acquiring this deficiency. Another strategy during fast spring growth may include feeding hay for an hour before turnout, so that they do not eat as much of the spring grass. It is likely less expensive to give some daily hay than it is to lose one or more animals to this problem. Also you can supply whole herbs that are known for higher levels of magnesium two to three times daily. Some of those herbs are purslane, Irish moss (Chondrus crispus), oat straw, garden beans of several types (wax, green, navy, kidney, string, and etcetera), kelp, lettuces, and stinging nettle leaf. A tea can be made of several of these herbs and can be added to their water source and the herbs can be fed with any grain or supplements that you chose to give. In a situation where you know this is what you are dealing with, I would drench a strong triple dose tea, followed by another triple dose in 15 to 30 minutes, and then hourly after that until you get the body topped back off. Then add additional supplementation to that creature. You don't want their blood levels to just be barely better, making it easy for them to relapse; you want them optimally better. As in other nervous system situations; keep them warm, calm and in a nicely bedded stall (oat straw is best in this situation) by themselves if possible. Also use precautions, so that you don't have a large animal fall on you.

Grieving and Sadness

Animals are caring beings. If they were not, you would not hear a cow bellow for hours (or days) on end after losing a calf. Or watch a dog mope when his favorite person leaves town (or the planet). Sometimes when I am out of town my husband will hold the phone to one of our animal's ears, if he is doing chores when I call. He always comments that they perk right up and start looking for me when they hear my voice. Sometimes they start talking back to me on the phone in their language. They do care.

Do take into account the distress to the nervous system and the increased acidity that will be created in the body when an animal is separated from someone, or another creature, that it loves. This is the same stress that is encountered when an animal is sold to a new owner. Spending additional time with them is ideal during these times. Talking, humming, brushing or gently petting it can go a long ways towards helping to soothe your creature. For those that won't try to eat your clothing, leaving a coat or sweatshirt with your scent as mentioned earlier, can help comfort them. If you use essential oil blends for perfume, as I sometimes do (often lavender or frankincense and grapefruit), then diluting some in distilled water and spraying it around their pen (not around felines) can also bring a comforting effect. Some herbs of comfort are going to be your lavender, Lobelia inflata, lettuces, wild lettuce or compass plant, and chamomile. Skullcap is also helpful. Lobelia inflata tincture can be dropped right along the spine and rubbed in. Sunshine and exercise are also very helpful for a creature that is adjusting to a loss. B vitamin herbs, such as cayenne (excellent choice), chia seed, and catnip are nice supports.   Eluetherococcus herb is always good in any type of system distress. I also like nutritional yeast for its B Vitamin support.

HYPP – Hyperkalemic Periodic Paralysis

I remember back in the 90's when HYPP was a buzzword in the equine community. HYPP horses have problems with proper movement of sodium in their nervous system, with leakage into their musculature affecting muscle movement.   If their nervous system stress level overloads, they can go into muscular spasms and go down. If you are leading or riding such a horse, I think you can see the potential danger. Due to this fact, horses with this issue should not be used or handled from the ground by children or people early in their horse handling knowledge acquisition.   Most of these horses trace back to a famous and beautiful heavily muscled halter stallion, named Impressive, in the Quarter horse world. A few others only trace back to his dam. Since quarter horse genetics are used in the gene pools of some other breeds, such as: Paint, Appaloosa, Azteca and other stock types, this is always a consideration when you look back into pedigrees of animals you own or are considering purchasing. UC Davis in California does offer hair testing for this condition, with the ideal results coming back to you as N/N or double negative.   H/H or H/N can be animals that exhibit symptoms or pass the condition on to progeny. Symptomatic horses will have larger than average musculature in the affected muscles due to the continual muscle contractions.

Should you find yourself with a horse with the possibility of having this problem, there are some things you can do. You will NEED to always consider your safety if you take on the responsibility of working with a horse that may have or does have this condition.   First, as always, you will want to really focus on cleansing this animal for at least a year. However, you will want to cleanse at half dose each time you add a step for approximately a month before moving to full dose.   Any fast change to their system can bring about an attack and that is what you are hoping to avoid. Next, I would be considering moderate amounts of some high calcium feed, along with other herbs to help the body strengthen the tissues that are allowing the sodium to leak.   Some herbs to consider specifically for this situation will be oat straw, comfrey, white oak bark, slippery elm bark, and kelp. Oat straw has a double bonus, because it is so soothing to the nervous system in general. In addition, salves like Wounderful! or other whole herb calcium containing salves can be placed onto the muscle groups where known problems have been; to encourage that area to repair itself faster. ReBuilld herb mix can also be fed, as can BetterDaze herb mix. I would also want to put a NervEaze salve or some of the other nervous system herbs onto musculature areas that have had problems. Lobelia inflata tincture can also be placed on muscles exhibiting problems, as long as you can safely avoid being fallen on if the horse goes down. I would also want my horse on small amounts of Lobelia inflata herb as a daily supplement. It is in Fir Meadow's Better Daze herb mix. I would plan on supplementing the horse for the remainder of its life. Even if a horse goes from being symptomatic to not being symptomatic, the tissues with the problems will still be weaker than non affected areas of the body, allowing a larger toxin accumulation and increased cellular weakness to come back to those areas. You do not want to go back into relapses after taking all of the time and effort to move them out of being symptomatic.

Horses exhibiting this problem should have whole or sprouted cereal grains such as oats and barley. They should NOT have any processed feeds which may contain first or second refining junk molasses. Black Strap unsulphured molasses added to their whole or sprouted grains starting at one tablespoon per day and working up to ¼ cup per day is another good supplement. Beet pulp probably should be avoided, due to the possibility of mold being on the beets at processing time. If your horse is in need of weight supplementation, then adding olive oil to his diet would be an excellent choice.

If it is used, an affected horse should have his training and work schedule arranged to increase at a very slow rate as it gains condition. Also, it should not be exercised at times that will place extra stress on its system, such as on hot days. Any events or travel that could place additional stress on its system that could encourage a flair up, should be minimized where possible. Daily turnout exercise in fresh air and sunshine is ideal for a horse with these issues.

Listeriosis, etcetera

Listeriosis is a situation that you will want to jump on right away. According to Mary C. Smith DVM et al. in the book, "Goat Medicine', some of the telltale signs are the circling and head pressing that are mentioned earlier in this chapter. Further into the problem, your animal may go down, may start having convulsions, may flail and exhibit rapid eye jerking. The unique sign is that their head will begin to pull towards their flank near their rear leg and eventually be into the flank as near as it can reach.   You likely will be able to straighten it out, but it will put itself right back there.   Left to itself the animal may go comatose and die, or may bloat before it dies because of it's on its side position. They also will usually have a very high temperature, in goats perhaps as high as 108 F (I have seen that in a diagnosed case). They also may drool and have partial facial paralysis, so be sure you are not seeing a Rabies case in front of you. Listeria bacteria is a gram positive bacteria that is found in soil and is also found in mold. Avoid using hay that has mold in it or having your stock eating directly off of the dirt on the ground. Polioencephalmalacea can occur concurrently with this problem if mold burns up the thiamine in the rumen. For that, you would give cayenne orally or by enema (mixed in water) with the first dose being a double dose, followed by another double dose in 30 minutes, and then hourly will be best.   They need to have herbs at least every 4 hours for a 24 hour time period with polio, in case some of the causative agent for the thiamine destruction is still in the gut when you start nourishing them.

I would follow the directions under the Circling section near the beginning of this chapter and also for Bacteria in the Immune System Chapter. You need to hit this one fast and hard, especially if your animal is already down.   You also need to keep them warm. If it is cold out, you will want deep bedding and blankets. I've taken plastic containers and filled them with hot water and set them under blankets near my goat to keep them warm in 'teen temperature' weather. You will also need to keep them upright by bracing bales or some other safe object up against them, and trying to right them if they go on their side. If you have a block and tackle and can attach it to a strong beam (or tractor or backhoe) over head and rig up some type of harness for under your animal then you can lift them a bit to get them back upright.   You will want to try and have them alternate their rest on different rump sides, so you can massage or otherwise encourage circulation to keep moving to avoid bedsores or other loss of circulation problems. Ginger or cayenne diluted in a salve and rubbed on will be helpful, as will applying a cloth soaked in the tea of either or both. Tea can also be given orally to encourage the body to good circulation. You should be able to see some progress every day. This is another condition that you will want to baby the animal for a few days afterwards, to avoid any chance of their much stressed system from trying to relapse. Heart support is never a bad idea in these serious issues.

Loss of Feeling, Nerve Death, Nerve Damage

As mentioned at the beginning of this chapter, nerves can and do regenerate if given the tools they need to do it. I like oral use of some of the standard nervous system herbs mentioned in other areas of this chapter. I also like adding Wounderful! and/or NervEaze salves to the area. Fomentations of yarrow, ginger, rosemary, probably peppermint (please let me know if you use this) a bit of cayenne or other circulatory stimulant herbs can be placed on the affected areas to help the body draw circulation out to that area. Using herbal supplements from that chapter, or a product like Better Daze or God's Greens, to help super nourish minerals to the system, would also be beneficial. Dr. Christopher's Vitalerbs would also be a nice choice.

Jealousy

I would expect proper training to have the animal learn to work with their jealous behavior in an acceptable manner, along with nervous system support herbs and proper cleansing in order to get any toxins out of the brain area. In addition, taking some quality time to spend with the jealous animal, will go a long ways towards making the situation better.

Music

Music really does nourish the soul. Or it can make the soul heavy and depressed and black. Choose wisely the music that you expose your creatures and yourself to. I prefer beautiful orchestra/instrumental, praise music, and classical types to uplift my creatures with.

Nuisance Barking

Nuisance barking is one of those situations that might give ME a nervous system breakdown, or that of your neighbors and your relationship with them. Dogs do bark. They should only give a smaller bark or few when they are excited to see you, or a larger bark when they see or smell something that they consider a threat to their or their master's/livestocks' well being. If they are barking at the drop of a hat for elongated periods of time, you have an issue you will want to work with. We have Great Pyrenees, so we understand what it is like to have dogs bark off and on at night. However, there is always a legitimate reason for their barking. Where I live that is often coyote, cougar, or bear in nature. Dogs will also get barked at until they are a safe distance from the fence. Dogs do not understand that fences are a safety barrier, so will bark at what they can see through it that gets too close for their comfort level. I like the fact that I can walk to my barn at night and not wonder if I'm going to bump into a cougar in my yard or barn. When the legitimate reason leaves, the barking should stop. For dogs that don't follow those rules on barking, there are some things you can do. Some of them may be training oriented, especially fear oriented barking, which is beyond the scope of this book, and some will be herbal support and nourishment for those overactive nervous systems that express themselves verbally.

Some soothing herbs for your favorite canine will be the cleansing program, to be sure toxins are not compromising their nervous system or brain. Also consider having raw foods in their diet, including carrots and lettuces. Yes, the dark green lettuces support nervous system relaxation. Compass plant or wild lettuce, also in the Latuca family is another choice. As is lavender, Lobelia inflata in smaller doses, Ladies slipper, and clary sage. Sometimes hormonal imbalances can exacerbate this problem, and those are addressed by liver cleansing page over to the Reproductive chapter to hone in on those problems more. Foods and herbs that clean, nourish and oxygenate the brain are also helpful. Constipated GI tracts impair nervous system health. Massage is another tool that can help your animal relax. Pressing firmly in the middle of the breast bone (not at the tip, which you could break) with your left hand, can help calm an animal down as you activate the solar plexus nerve bundle.

Working dogs need to have a job or they can exhibit neurotic behavior, including excessive barking. Please make sure they have a job that is somehow related to the purpose they were bred for. Daily exercise and fresh air is important too, for brain oxygenation.

Don't forget to consider that their nervous system may just be being overwhelmed by electromagnetic fields. Consider obtaining a shield if you think this is a possibility.

If you are all of the sudden hearing a high pitched bark, please check for an injury, bite or sting. If the dog received a vaccination (usually that day or the previous day) and they are now having high pitched barking or inconsolable whining, consider that they might be experiencing a vaccine injury to their brainstem. In that case see the Poisonings chapter in Part 1 and follow the suggestions for chemical poisoning- quickly! Also administer some cayenne in case the animal is hemorrhaging in the brain simultaneously. Please be sure to report any suspected vaccine injury to your veterinarian. Some will believe you and some will not. I can certainly collect data on those if you send the information via email. Once I have enough data, I can look to see if we can find any possible correlations and report on that later. I can do this for all creatures, not just dogs. Remember, to the manufacturers, our creatures are just numbers and statistics and income, but to us they are a part of our family with names and personalities and sometimes a part of our income.

Pacing

As mentioned earlier in the chapter, you may have a dog or other creature that needs a job. You also may have an animal that has an overactive nervous system. He also may be missing his master, or be unhappy or bored with his situation and looking for a way to get out to find a friend to spend time with (a job). From other sections of this chapter, you'll be able to cleanse and nourish and train to find what it is that your particular creature may need.

Sometimes animals will also pace when they are coming into a fever or before a seizure. In those cases, look at those sections to see what you might do to support your friend.

We also need to consider that our creatures are much more sensitive to environmental happenings such as earthquakes, tornadoes, storms and the like, and may be alerting us to an oncoming event. Please don't ignore the behavior, but make sure that there really isn't something health wise going on with your animal. And be prepared for these other types of situations.

Pain

There are two ways we can go about working with pain. One is to support the body in its ability to thwart pain directly. And the other is to help the body to relax while in pain, which will often allow the pain level to decrease. An animal that is fearful and/or tense due to pain will not heal itself as quickly as one that isn't. Some animals also risk having their digestive tract shut down if the pain is too great. If you cannot get on top of the pain for your creature, then I suggest that you contact your veterinarian for help. Some pain, such as nerves being continually pressed on by tumors, are difficult to get on top of no matter the support you try to work with. Don't forget prayer either. God does do miracles. If you don't have a problem, you can't see a miracle… Also remember that pain is an indication that you have not yet provided enough herbal support to keep up with the body's demands for resources to repair the problem. The key therapeutic terms you will be watching for as you learn herbs will be: anodyne (topical) and analgesic (oral).

Herbs to consider for supporting the body in more direct pain relief would be: mullein leaf and flower (never the poisonous seeds), arnica- external use only, wild lettuce (compass plant), cayenne and sow thistle. Lemon balm is mildly sedative and is fine for mild aches and pains. Occasionally my dairy goats will raid ours.

Eucalyptus, peppermint, and rosemary essential oils in a salve can be nice as well. By placing them into a salve, you usually will get a much longer relief period. You can combine oral use herbs along with external use methods if you like.

Herbs I would use as additional support, that tend to have a relaxing effect on tissues encouraging them to release tension and thus sometimes pain, would be: ginger, wild lettuce, lemon balm, German chamomile, clary sage, lavender, scullcap and Lobelia inflata. Certainly this would be a good use of the three parts mullein to one part lobelia blend. For lavender and clary sage one can employ essential oils blended with olive oil for a quicker response. I would love to experiment with lemon balm, but at this time the essential oil price is well beyond my pocket book, so I have to go off of the advice of others on that one as an essential oil. The other herbs can be made into a tea and drenched or fed whole, or applied as a salve.

Adding heat or moist heat to a painful area (not the first 24 hours of injury) is beneficial. Making a fomentation with one of the relaxing herbs and placing that on the tense area can be very nice. Massage and personal quiet time spent with you are also good ideas to help your creature relax, and thus, hopefully gain a decrease in pain.

Paralysis

Is an animal always paralyzed once losing ability? Not necessarily! Cleansing toxins out, getting supplemental nourishment in, and specific herbs for the nervous system as mentioned in other sections, may result in a change. If the spine is involved, then besides nervous system support you will also want to include wound or injury support to the damaged area. Make sure skullcap (scullcap) is part of your program if the spine is involved. Also hot (but safe to the touch) limb soaks for affected limbs or daily hot, but safe, fomentations will be beneficial with your choice of yarrow, ginger, rosemary, some cayenne or other circulation drawing herbs.

Seizures

As Vitalist herbalists, we believe that the brain or musculature is dealing with a mineral deficiency and the body is seizing to try and force nutrition into a deficient area. This can be caused by toxins, medications, head injuries, high dry fevers, and some viral and bacterial issues in the brain or brain stem. Lobelia inflata will nearly always relax a seizure. A few drops orally, like 3 to 5 for up to 20#, and 10 drops for a 100 to 200 lb creature. Do not panic and give at normal herb dose, or you will find its emetic (vomit) therapeutic effect, which could prove dangerous in this situation. Then go about cleansing and nourishing, focusing on nervous system and body tissue building herbal supplementation from those sections.

Rabies

Rabies is scary. There is just not a way around that thought. I know we've had some active cases of rabies in wild animals in the state of Oregon this year, as in other states. If you even suspect a case of rabies, you need to take all precautions that it is not spread to other creatures or humans, including yourself. Whether you put the animal down or try to work with it herbally, it is going to need to be quarantined. If at any time the animal could be a potential danger I personally would not want to work with it, but would put it down without head damage and have its brain tested. Once an animal has gone further into this condition the risk of danger is just too great. Contact your county health department for that information. Rabies is a viral condition that causes encephalitis (swelling to the brain stem). You may find a creature walking in circles, lethargic, wild animals without fear of humans, loss of coordination, convulsions, disoriented, irritability or aggression and/or excess drooling. This drool and all body fluids are infective, even in a dead animal.

Having said all of that, if I had an animal that was bitten or exposed to an animal that was exhibiting possible rabies signs, or I was in an immediate area where rabies was found active, I would start on this herb program immediately and have myself on it too. The animal would also be in quarantine and other people would not have access to it unless they also were on the herb program.

Since you know it is viral, you would start working with the herbs listed in the Viral section in the Immune System chapter. I also would be using HerBiotic or the herbs in it: goldenseal, myrrh, echinacea and cayenne. Garlic always comes to mind in appropriate doses for the creature you are working with. Also go to the Listeriosis section and do some of those things due to the brain stem being affected. My idea would be to try and burn it out of the system before it even had a chance to replicate. That would mean treating the first day as acute with oral herbs and topical herbs at the bite site, then a strong chronic (4x a day) after that for 2 or 3 days, then a normal chronic rate of 2 to 3x per day for ten days minimum. I would repeat this if a new case of rabies were to show up in my neighborhood. Rabies need not be a scary foe, but BE RESPONSIBLE.

Tetanus

Clostridium tetani bacterium is another gram positive nuisance. Tetanus bacteria are present in the soil and they are concentrated in equine species manure. Any mammal can be subject to tetanus, or lockjaw as it is sometimes referred to, but goats and sheep seem to be extra susceptible. The bacteria like to flourish in an anaerobic (oxygen free) environment, which is why it flourishes in some deeper puncture wounds, behind bands for castrating and sometimes under tight scabs.

You will work with this situation just like you do in any bacterial situation. If an animal is starting to lock up, Lobelia inflata tincture would be my first choice of help, followed by tinctures of lady's slipper and/or clary sage mixed with ginger. Essential oils of clary sage and ginger could also be used. Five drops of Clary sage with 3 drops of ginger in 1 tsp of olive oil. Lobelia i. is still going to be my weighted first choice. You do not want to wait until the lungs get paralyzed. Also consider that the animal will have extra stress to the lungs, if it is down, and consider additional support for them. Remember to attend to the bacteria. If you don't cover that base they will just lock up again.

Chapter 25- Renal System: Kidneys, Urethra, and Bladder

The renal system is one of the four primary routes for elimination by the body. Compromise of the kidneys will result in compromise in the well being of the entire creature. Due to their placement near the surface of the loin area, they are a bit more susceptible to injury from use and accidents then some of the other organs. I had one goat die from getting hit too hard by another goat in the kidney area. Horses tend to be somewhat prone to damage when people ride double and bounce on the area or pack extra weight over the loin region. The kidneys have many important functions, such as cleaning water soluble waste from the bloodstream and guiding it out in the form of urine. They also regulate blood pressure, blood volume, the electrolyte balance in the blood stream and blood level Ph. A diet containing a large percentage of processed foods tends to put additional strain on this organ, as does exposure to rock minerals in the diet or drinking water. Kidneys must be continually releasing their waste to the bladder to avoid fatal uremia or a buildup of urea in the bloodstream. These are incredibly important organs that we all too often take for granted. Have you noticed the large increase of people in the human population that are requiring dialysis because kidneys no longer function properly? I believe we are also seeing the same trend in pets. So here's some hopefully helpful information for you.

Cleansing

By now you ought to be very well versed on the concept of cleansing. Since these organs are constantly filtering the bloodstream of water soluble waste and toxins and we live in that imperfect world with toxins, we can't skip this basic topic. Remember that anytime we have one of the four channels of elimination below superior performance, the others will be overworked to try and take up the slack. The skin and lungs seem to be those routes that take the brunt of the excess, and also the pancreas. It is very interesting to note that in human iridology is very easy to see where poorly performing kidneys are throwing mucoid toxins into other areas of the body. Kidneys are another organ that require 3 to 4 months in a healthy creature to get one complete cell for cell regeneration. You know then that any cleansing addressing this organ structure is going to involve at least that long, and often longer if the animal is having chronic health issues. If your creature has been primarily on processed feeds, sweet feeds (grains with feed grade molasses), fly sprays, chemical grooming products, medications and the like, then I suspect you will want to do some cleansing of this organ. Sweet feeds are a double whammy due to the refined sugars which are always hard on delicate kidney tissue. The kidneys can be cleansed even before the bowels are cleansed, since they have their own elimination route, but I prefer to pair them with the liver as some of the herbs overlap. I do that with a product I call Fresh Start. However, it is not necessary to do them at the same time as the liver however.

Kidneys suffer big time from a lack of adequate, fresh drinking water. Supply plenty all of the time. In colder climes have it heated, so that your animals will intake more. In the winter during milking time, I keep a five gallon bucket of hot water and black strap molasses in it. The goats love it and it helps keep their milk up. Then they can use more of their calories for milk production instead of body temperature maintenance. My horses get hot water served with their herb mashes. They slurp it right up without any complaints. And I drink lots of non caffeine containing herb teas while I take care of them. Caffeine is another problematic substance for kidneys (and heart, nervous system, pancreas, adrenal glands, brain tissue...). The tender tissue doesn't handle it well. Thus look around at our society- look for bags, swelling and lines just below the eyes of all age groups. Enough said.

Herbs that I like for kidney distress include: juniper berries (Juniperous communis), uva ursi, dandelion, nettle, raspberry, lemon, distilled water, raw apple cider vinegar, cayenne, garlic, horse radish and hyssop.

Cystitis

Cystitis is inflammation of the bladder wall that can cause frequent urges to urinate, often with pain. There is no infection present with cystitis. It may be an autoimmune problem, or it may be in response to having to process things like refined sugars or processed/cooked feeds, which makes the Ph acidic, causing inflammation in weaker constitutions. The key to working with this issue is to adjust the diet to remove the dead foods and add demulcent herbs such as slippery elm bark, marshmallow or hollyhock roots, mallow roots, drinkable aloe, comfrey root or leaf, or mullein to the diet. TumEaze by Fir Meadow can be used, as can GI Soother if you are looking for products to try. If the problem is determined to be autoimmune, then look in the Immune System chapter for more information.

Infections

These can be excruciating. In a bladder or kidney infection, there may be frequent urination, blood upon urination (get a diagnosis), and the animal may cave at the loins due to pain in the kidney region. Infections in this region cannot be ignored, as they can become life threatening fast. Look up the bacterial herb list in the Immune System chapter and add demulcent herbs from the Cystitis section you just read and you will have a nice approach. Since kidney tissue is pretty tender, I would want to nourish it with demulcent herbs for quite some time after the problem to make sure it finishes healing. Some of the wound care herbs will also be beneficial. I want to mention organic corn silk to this section. It has centuries of use with our Native Americans with a long tract records of UTI (urinary tract infection) support. Make a tea with a generous handful of the silk and add to the drinking water of your pet or drench to your creature three times per day. When I get a hold of organic corn I keep and dry the silk for storage. Non organic corn will probably be genetically modified in the United States.

Kidney Failure

I'd like to share a neat herbal support story with you. Several years ago I purchased a beloved, 9 year old dairy goat doe, named Faith. She is the matron of my toggenburgs. She was a shy, but sweet natured gal and was a lovely example of a dairy goat, having one Best In Show win at 9 years old and finishing her permanent championship with us as a ten year old! Well, when she was 13, she began to shut down. She had even kidded for us that year and was being milked, but now, at midsummer, it was her time to go home. Into the second day of her starting to fade away, she had quit urinating. Well that just would not do for me, as I knew that would be a very painful process for her to die from uremia within a day.   So I started her on some kidney herbs to see what her body might do with them.   A half day later her kidneys kicked back in and were working once more. We still had her about 5 more days before she went to be with her Good Shepherd. But when she left here to go there, she did it with her kidneys still functioning. Faith teaches us to say it's never too late to try.   I still miss her.

Malignancies

These are covered in the Lymph System Chapter.   You must remove all sugar feeds from the diet if you are helping the body to fight with this problem.

Urine control

This does not have to be a function of age.   We should be able to expect our young and our old animals to maintain control over their urination for their entire life. Definitely focus on a good cleansing program followed by quarterly maintenance. Also consider some of the kidney herbs and some of the wound herbs to help the body strengthen the tissues in these areas that have been allowed to degenerate. Again please consider removing the dead foods from their diet.

UC/stones

UC is short for a condition labeled as Urinary Calculi or crystals built up in the urine causing a blockage in the urinary canal, the urethra.   Kidney or bladder stones are just that, mineral growths that can be from very tiny to quite large.   If you view any of these under a microscope you will see that they are quite jagged, so besides causing a blockage they are cutting at and damaging the very sensitive renal tissue.   As an herbalist, I'm going to tell you to consider the rock minerals that may be in the water you are serving, and any feed or mineral mixes you feed that have rock minerals or rock mineral isolates added to them.   Remember from the foundations chapter that this would be anything listed on the label as x mineral without saying it is from a plant source.   To help compensate for this imperfect world, distilled water and raw apple cider vinegar added to drinking water on a regular basis are going to be good friends.

How often should you keep raw apple cider vinegar going through your creatures? I tell people to look at their coffee… ahhhhh, I mean tea pots. As soon as they see any residue, which is rock mineral particulate, you would want to do maintenance on your animals. That's about every three days at our farm. Remember to test with the water they get, not water that may be filtered at your house only, but not the barn or pasture.

In UC, you may see your animal attempting to urinate (usually males) but only dripping or nothing at all. You may also see crystallite hanging from the penal orifice or surrounding hair. They may also be crying, walking stiffly or with the rear legs placed further back, or hunching at the loins. This is an emergency. If you allow this condition to go on and the animal stays backed up, the bladder will burst, usually within zero to two days.   If that happens, your animal will all of a sudden look better again as the pain is relieved, but will die a day or two later. We don't have herbs for a burst bladder.   For my 100 to 200 pound animals I will give them 60 CC's of raw apple cider vinegar or Fir Meadow's Kidney, Bladder, and Stones tincture and then follow that up every two hours with another 30 cc's (one ounce or 30 ml) until I see a good flow of pee. How long this takes depends on if there are many tiny blockages for the body to dissolve or if there are a few larger ones. The larger ones take longer. Then follow it up with demulcent herbs listed in the Cystitis section to help soothe the area and more kidney support from possible damage caused by urinary backup into the kidneys. Note to watch for this problem in the sons of animals that have had this condition. They may have inherited a smaller than average urinary canal.   Lobelia inflata or other Nervous System chapter relaxing herbs may help a tense from pain animal relax. Mullein infusion or tincture for the pain and additional demulcent benefit are also good ideas. Marshmallow root with its demulcent and anti-inflammatory benefits is also a good plan for follow up. Animals that have done this once can relapse. Please keep up with some maintenance on them. We have even had creature clients that have had emergency surgery (normally done just to keep them alive long enough for slaughter) and have done well by keeping their kidney maintenance up to date.

Those have used the Kidney, Bladder and Stones formula, which I used to call DSolve.

Infertility problems are on the increase, whether it be pets, livestock, or humans. In a way, a large percentage of these are really a mixed blessing. Just think about it. If the reproductive organs are not functioning properly because of conditions or toxic buildup, do we really want our prized next generation starting out its existence that way? These toxins and conditions make the baby/ies much more prone to birth defects or a lost pregnancy. My personal preference is to get the dam clean and well, in order to provide the best possible opportunity to have healthy babies that are able to reach their full potential with proper care. As mentioned in Part 1, ideally this program starts before they are even conceived. How does that sound to you? As always you will need to address cleansing, diet, and specific herbs to assist the body in renourishing and rebalancing the area. Remember that each of these is approximately 1/3 of the game plan to get a complete favorable result. In an ideal world, our breeding stock will have been under routine cleanses well before breeding comes into the picture. However, we don't always get that opportunity. However, if you do, definitely take advantage of cleansing your breeding stock. Your next generation will thank you!

As mentioned in Part 1, I do not consider age a factor on whether to breed an animal or not. I consider nutrition levels, wellness, ability to stay in good condition (weight) easily and ease in mobility. Age never comes into consideration and we've had several aged dairy goats continue to be productive into their teens. In humans, we never consider age a factor to the wellness of the internal infant, but plant nutrition weighs heavily in this situation.

Herbs commonly used for reproductive system support are: black cohosh, raspberry leaf, goldenseal, cramp bark, mullein, false unicorn root, squaw vine (partridge berry), sarsaparilla in reasonable amounts, ginseng, Lobelia inflata, licorice root in reasonable amounts, wheat germ oil, and blessed thistle (holy thistle). Also consider the nutritional support herbs discussed in Part 1.

Crushed or Damaged Scrotum/Testicles

This is not the type of problem you like to find in your barn, but it does happen. Please don't let anyone talk you into amputating the tissue. Once it is removed we have no opportunity to give the body a chance to renew the tissue and organs. You and I have about zero use for our nice breeding boys being castrated.

First, attend to the injury as in any injury, being careful to restrain the stud in a safe way so that you or your helpers or your stud do not sustain injury as you try to take care of this very tender area. If you need veterinarian help to safely restrain them, by all means hire your vet! Always administer cayenne for shock. Then if you need some quieting nervous system support, you might pull out lavender, hops (not for canines), Lobelia inflata, ladies slipper, or wild lettuce. Your goal now is going to be to use antiseptic herbs, such as garlic mixed with olive oil and lavender essential oil, goldenseal, myrrh, cayenne (or use HerBiotic) to give the body some tools at the scrotum to avoid infection from settling in. Then apply three parts mullein and one part Lobelia inflata by salve, and give the herbs orally either in a tea or herb mix. Or you can use Fir Meadow's GlandAide salves and herb mixes. The body can regenerate family jewels with the assistance of this herbal support.

Cystic ovaries

Cystic ovaries can be a painful issue and some can bleed. Some can 'short cycle' or get caught into recycling at intervals shorter than normal. Most are not cancer related, but a few are. There are many types, all of them involving the improper sequencing or functioning of events during a normal cycle. To get to the root of this issue, you are again going to hop onto the cleansing wagon. At the same time you are going to nourish with some of the reproductive system herbs listed earlier. Dr. Christopher also offers a Female Reproductive product that is excellent. Fir Meadow offers a Bal-Nce herb mix. Both products will require you to use them concurrently with wheat germ oil for the reproductive organs to take the fullest benefit of the nutrition. Otherwise the body's ability to work with the herbs may be significantly reduced. I prefer the oil in capsules, as it is better protected from oxygen. I also prefer human grade. If you are working with a larger animal, like a horse, you will use the liquid bottled variation fast enough to keep it from oxidizing in the bottle. You can also pour it into smaller bottles to reduce the amount of air that comes into contact with the oil as you pour it. If you cannot find human grade wheat germ oil, then you can consider using cold pressed and organic sunflower seed oil in its place. Wheat grass juice given or fresh handfuls of wheat grass can also be added for additional nutritional support.

Failure to Cycle

You are going to use the same herb and nourishment plan as for cystic ovaries. Also be sure that the animal is not burdened with parasites, is proper weight (not too thin or too heavy) and is well nourished. It rare situations you may have an animal that is not complete. In other words, they may be missing some reproductive organs and are not going to be able to be bred. Your veterinarian can determine this. It will usually be less expensive to get this possibility diagnosed rather than to keep the animal for another year with the cost of feed, time and facilities, if your only plan for them is to be used as breeding stock.

Male Performance

Male performance is covered in the Pregnancy chapter in Part 1. Please don't forget about feeding cayenne for endurance during breeding season (or better yet, all year long).

Pizzle Rot

Male animals that are on diets that are too high in plant proteins (or added animal proteins in processed grains) for their needs, can actually deteriorate or rot at the precipice ending at the end of the penis. A moderate to bad case of this can render your stud useless due to the pain involved with putting pressure on this area. Relax on his protein intake. Add some good quality regular mixed grass hay not the high protein "blow your socks off of your feet" varieties that are out there. I'll say it again, our animals need adequate plant protein, but not excessive in this excessively protein fixated culture. Also clean the area (get help if you need it to be safe). This is another area I like to clean and coat with oil of garlic blended with lavender essential oil. One half cup of olive oil with 6 to 8 lady 'thumb joint size' cloves of garlic smashed or pressed into it and aged for three days -stir well and make sure the oil is always covering the garlic and cover with a permeable cloth or paper towel to allow moisture to evaporate. Then add 15 drops of solvent free lavender essential oil (angustifolia or officinalis) to each tablespoon of oil used. Wound support herbs can be used after the twice daily gentle oil mix cleaning.

Quiet or Silent Heats

You are getting excited to breed your female creature, but she isn't giving you any signs or at least not enough to perceive that she is coming into heat. This tends to be more common in younger stock, in stock that has never been bred, and in stock not living within smelling or listening distance of an appropriate studly sire. The infamous 'buck rags', that some goat breeders use, may gain questionable results. One takes a cotton cloth, rubs it on a buck in rut, getting it as odoriferous as reasonably possible and then putting it in a sealed container. This harvest is then opened and held in front of goats that might be in heat. If you get a tail wag or a squat and pee, then you just may be catching them right and it's probably time for a drive to where the herdsire is. However, it's been reported that many does will just play with the rag (a new toy, maybe?) without ever giving you clues that they are in heat. Rats.

If you are faced with a silent heat female, then there are some herbs you can use to try and encourage a more visible cycle. You ABSOLUTELY CANNOT use these herbs if it is possible that your animal is already bred, or you may just lose the pregnancy. The process in most creatures takes two to eight weeks, as long as they are not excessively toxic (humans generally take longer- what does that tell you?) While you are waiting for the heat, do address some cleansing. You can always stop that the day she cycles and is taken to her prince. Consider adding wheat germ oil for superior body use of the herbs. I had one local gal use our CyclEaze on a Toggenburg goat in February (she had missed all the heats, as they were not obvious to her). Two weeks later she brought her over to breed in a strong heat and she had July kids! (Where we live February is well past normal breeding season for Toggenburgs). If they are out of season breedings, we cannot know for sure if the female will ovulate, but it's worth a shot if you really want to try and get the breeding going.

Herbs to consider would be: (REMEMBER NOT IF THE DAM MAY BE PREGNANT) black cohosh, blue cohosh, blessed (holy) thistle, cramp bark , false unicorn, raspberry (fine for pregnant stock, as it is a corrective/alterative), yarrow (another alterative) squaw vine (partridge berry) and fennel (also fine for pregnant creatures when in a blend). You can also add some of the herbs from the beginning of this chapter.

Short Cycling

Short cycling can be irritating. This is when an animal's reproductive hormones (usually the progesterone) get 'stuck'. Besides not breeding, the animal will have repetitive heat cycles, sometimes as short as five days apart. This is not a situation to ignore, as the longer it's not dealt with the longer it takes to try and help the body to correct it. Things to consider in this situation would be doing liver, kidney, and blood cleanses, as well as supporting with reproductive herbs. See the liver and kidneys and blood for those products and herb lists. For the reproductive part I would consider looking at squawvine (partridge berry), sarsaparilla, raspberry leaf, ginseng, cramp bark, and black cohosh. I would give them orally, and also make a vaginal bolus and get those in twice per day. Another thing to consider, is that the animal could have an infection or subclinical infection going on in the reproductive area. We'll cover that more in the Reproductive section. Remember that to get best results you will want to pair your herbs with oral doses of wheat germ oil. The human dose on the bottle will be for a '150' pound person. Adjust up or down from that. I leave the 100 to 200 pound creature at the human dose.

Uterine Infection

I handle these as any other infection. Two things tip me off to this possibility. One is a female that keeps cycling after bred, which usually also has the second clue; there may be a whitish pus discharge coming from the vulva. Those I need to clear up before I want any babies growing in that uterus! You can look in the Immune system chapter for a nice list of herbs to use in bacterial situations. I give the herbs orally and I put them in vaginal boluses, discussed below. Sometimes I also mix the herbs with olive oil and carefully give an 'injection' of olive oil with the herbs into the vagina. The body will pull those towards the reproductive organs. If the cervix is open (it will to let out pus and discharge), then consider using AI (artificial insemination) technique to get the herbs and olive oil mix right into the uterus. I like to use HerBiotic herb mix for this, but you can use your own selection of herbs if you like. I infuse and give orally every milking (every 12 hours). To speed up the process, get a third set of herbs into them sometime during the day.

Vaginal Boluses

These are easy to make and I'll mention them another time here. Take your proper sized dose for your creature of dry powdered herbs, and mix them with some gently melted (a double boiler over water is best) coconut oil until you have a pie dough consistency- not runny but still formable. Then form them into small finger sizes appropriate for your creature's vagina size, making sure you round the ends and place them on a plate or similar and refrigerate. Bag them and store them in the fridge. Put one or two of these gently into the vagina, pushing them a little ways in, two to three times per day. Warming them in a clean hand and softening any stiff edges on the insert side is a good idea. Sometimes as they cool they flatten a bit, making an edge. Smooth out that edge before inserting. You can also lubricate them with some room (warm) temperature olive oil before inserting carefully into the vagina.

Chapter 27- The Respiratory System

The respiratory system is comprised of the upper and lower systems. The upper respiratory includes from the mouth and nose to the trachea. The lower system includes everything from the trachea to the bottom of the lungs. The respiratory system is one of the four channels of elimination. As your creature exhales, any waste coming out with that is eliminated from the body. The lungs are primarily responsible for removing carbon dioxide from the bloodstream; but of course, a back logged liver/GI tract, kidneys, or skin will increase the toxic load that the body will push to the lungs to still try and remove them. Lungs are rebuilt in a well animal, cell for cell, every 4 months. So any lung challenge one faces should receive support for at least one cellular regeneration. Challenges that have been chronic for multiple months or years, will require more than one organ wide regeneration to return towards optimum wellness. Remember that lungs do not get to rest. While they are healing themselves they still must work, so progress can seem slower than other body area repairs. Also remember that every breath inhaling particulate, such as dust or smoke or airborne toxins, will irritate the already tender lung tissue that is now hyper sensitive. Because of that some symptoms, such as coughing, may take a long time in clearing. Look for progress. Do they sound better than they did yesterday, then last week? Then you know that your program is moving them the correct direction.

With lung irritations we are looking to do TWO things. Please don't ignore one for the other. First, we have to stop the invader, whether it's an inhaled issue or microbial in nature. Second, we need to help the lungs to expectorate or clear the stuff out after it's been made inert. We do not want to leave filth in the lungs waiting to become lunch for the next microbial invader that wants to set up their home. Filth in the lungs also compromises the amount of oxygen your creature can intake, which will negatively impact their brain processes, their energy, and their performance.

Some of my favorite lung support herbs are thyme, horehound, licorice root, mullein, elecampane root, comfrey, coltsfoot, hyssop, peppermint, rosemary, horseradish, eucalyptus, Lobelia inflata, pleurisy root, sage (astringency), garlic, white onion, and cayenne (but of course!).

CAE/OPP

Caprine Arthritis Encephalitis & Ovine Progressive Pneumonia were mentioned in the Immune System chapter. I mention it here again because animals that go symptomatic may have some serious pneumonia problems. Any animal that tested positive for these issues, I would want to have consuming lung support herbs as a part of their daily diet to keep the lungs well nourished along with overall system well being herbs. Besides reading those herb sections; products that may be helpful include Better Daze and Lung Support tincture. Also read the pneumonia section later in this chapter.

Remember that the lungs are a direct route to the bloodstream. Anything toxic that is inhaled is taken up by the blood stream as it circulates through the lungs to pick up new oxygen and drop off carbon dioxide. So anything polluting the lungs will gain access to the bloodstream and then to the cells of your body. The opposite is also true. Toxins that enter the blood via foods or other things ingested or through the skin will have access to the lungs, as the blood goes through the lungs. Remember that the next time you use cleaners, fly sprays or anything else that can go airborne and be inhaled by you or your creatures.

Choke

Animals can consume things that can get caught and make them choke. Sometimes they can even choke on their food, if distracted or bothered while eating. A Heimlich maneuver can be performed on many creatures. Reaching around with one or two people just BELOW the breast bone and forcefully pushing at an angle up towards the lungs can help them dislodge any item as you shove the air from their diaphragm. Take all care to not harm that breastbone, which can cause lethal puncture wounds. If your immediate Heimlich doesn't get you anywhere, get a call to your vet immediately for assistance. Cayenne can also be sprinkled on the nostrils to try and encourage some sneeze/coughing reflexes if

The Accessible Pet, Equine and Livestock Herbal

needed. Cayenne tincture can be placed along the spine or on the rib area to try and keep the heart strong, which will be under a lot of stress in an extended choke situation. If the creature goes unconscious, you can GENTLY get air into it. You do not want to blow hard, which may force the blockage further out of reach. If a strong mouth speculum is used, it may be possible to reach into the throat to try and grab the offending problem, but do not put yourself at risk of injury and do nothing that may push the object further down. Be sure if you are feeding your pets or creatures that any food chunks they are eating is half or less the size of their windpipe. Apples and other harder roundish fruits tend to be a common problem in chokes. Never feed whole apples, but always slice them into pieces with flat sides that are easy for your creature to hold and chew before swallowing. Sometimes whole apples or other hard foods slip to the rear of the throat, causing the problem.

Chronic Cough

Chronic coughs can have many causes. Some of those to consider are: allergies, mechanical irritation such as dust (air or in feeds) or smoke, chemical irritation from chemical fumes (tractor or truck exhaust, painting, etcetera), infections caused by microbes, and parasites. Remember from the introduction that it takes time for tender damaged lung tissue to heal. Until the body heals it, expect to hear some coughing whenever the tissue gets irritated from something inhaled. The intensity and severity of the coughing should improve though, as you look back every two or three days to know that you are making good progress. We don't want to artificially stop the cough. The cough is showing us that we still need to support the body, so that it can continue to help it heal or eliminate the junk it is trying to get out of the lungs, or both. The cough is a clue to let us know where the creature is in its healing progress. The amount of damage and or garbage in the lungs and the overall wellness of the animal are going to dictate how long that will take. Whenever you hear a cough in your barn or kennel, be sure to take a temperature to be sure that you don't have pneumonia or other infection brewing at the same time.

I like to combine lung herbs, such as thyme, hyssop, comfrey, mullein, lobelia, eucalyptus and coltsfoot for traditional lung support. I also like to serve demulcent herbs such as mullein, comfrey, slippery elm, drinkable aloe, marshmallow or hollyhock root, and calendula to give the cells some much needed soothing comfort. I never support the use of smoking herbs, which will cause heat and particulate damage to the herbs. Instead, take those traditional lung support herbs and give them orally. Overactive coughing soreness can be supported by giving peppermint tea or putting 3 drops of peppermint essential oil in a teaspoon of olive oil and rubbed over the rib cage. Peppermint tea is preferred over the essential oil for younger creatures.

Detoxifying and Congestion

To detoxify the lungs we have a couple of options. I encourage you to employ both. The first will be to address bowel, liver, kidney and blood cleansing so that those toxic areas don't cause a backup in the lungs. Please remember to do them in order, to avoid other problems. Also remember that the bloodstream will be running all of its toxins through the lungs 24/7, so it MUST be clean to keep a clean set of lungs.

Another route to consider is to super nourish the lungs so that they themselves (on a cellular level) can also continue to be healthy and remove their garbage every day. Pair this with a healthy lymph system, so the garbage is actually packed out and eliminated.

Steam inhalations with herbs and/or the careful use of essential oils can be used. The simplest method for me is to take 1 to 5 drops of an essential oil, depending on creature size and age, and place those in a stainless pot and pour very hot water over it and let the air be permeated by the volatile oils as they go airborne. Remember to not do this around cats. The more closed in the area can be where your creature is, the more effective. My favorite essential oils to use this way are thyme, peppermint, rosemary and/or Eucalyptus globulus combined with a cleansing essential oil such as 3 to 5 drops of ravensara, lemon, fennel or birch. With thyme, you will want to side on the smaller dosage of one drop. For very small animals or very young ones, keep the pot a distance away from them, so that

The Accessible Pet, Equine and Livestock Herbal

the thyme and other oils are more diluted in the air they breathe. You can do this 1 to 3x the first day, and once a day after that for a few days. Then give the system a three day break from them. I would combine essential oil use with cleanses and lung support herbs to increase the nutritional levels of your animals. I would not use just the essential oils.

Onion poultices are real neat. The onion literally helps the body break up congestion, mucous, increases immune system activity, encourages detoxifying and loosens and liquefies the mucoid matter making it easier to expectorate. I will take 1/3 of a large (white, if possible) onion for a 100 to 200 pound goat sized creature (3 onions for a horse size, and of course less for smaller creatures). The juicier and stronger the onion, the better it will support. If all you have are other onions, then use what you have, but use more. I always keep juicy white onions on hand on my farm. I will chop it up into smaller pieces and place it in a glass pan with a bit of olive oil in it. I toss the onion in the olive oil, put on a lid (foil is not desirable, but will work if that is all you have) and place it in a 225 degree Fahrenheit oven for 20 minutes. Using a hot pad, I take it out and see that the onion is translucent and juicy looking. It's ready for use. I then turbo the poultice by adding a few lung support herbs to it. I press two cloves of garlic for that 100 to 200 pound creature into it, and I put in ¼ teaspoon of cayenne powder and 2 drops of Eucalyptus globulus essential oil. I add a bit more olive oil just to toss it together real good. At that time I will stretch out two long strips of plastic cling wrap and overlap them, so that they make one long but wider wrap. I usually end up with about two feet of width. For a horse or other larger sized creature, you might go a third strip to get it three feet wide. I put my poultice on the center of the wrap and spread it out just a little bit. Then I straddle my goat to clamp its head with my legs to hold it (or put it on a milk stand, horse at a hitching post, etcetera) and I place the wrap under them and pull it up against their barrel, and then wrap the top of the plastic wrap over to make a 'sandwich'. Then I take more plastic and wrap two or three more wraps around the animal to hold it in place. I'll spread out the poultice a bit more by pressing on it, and make sure that the plastic does not obstruct the urination of my male animal. Then I'll put a goat coat, horse blanket or the equivalent on the creature to keep them from picking on the poultice. Keep all plastic away from herdmates that may try to pull on it or ingest it. I leave these on for a three hour minimum and sometimes leave them on longer. Do not be surprised if the onion and/or garlic are strange colors of blue or green when you take them off. Ick, that was in your creature! I call this recipe Kat's Turbo Onion Poultice. This poultice is most likely going to liquefy a bunch of junk in the lungs. Be prepared to start some expectoration support when you apply the poultice. Leaving liquid in the lungs without helping your creature to expectorate it could be deadly.

DCongest Salve by Fir Meadow can also offer nice lung support.

Expectoration

As mentioned at the beginning of the chapter, it isn't so helpful if we help the body fight a microbe or other problem, but then do nothing to help it clear the blockage. Herbs that are expectorants encourage the body to cough up the phlegm or work it up via the cilia hairs in the respiratory tract. Some of my favorite expectoration herbs include: Eucalyptus globulus, elder flowers, lavender, onion (limited in dogs), garlic, ginger, cayenne, horseradish, cloves, boneset, yarrow, elecampane root, fennel, hawthorn (leaf, berry, flower), goldenseal, and Lobelia inflata. I would use these three to four times a day. You can speed up the expectoration process by loosening up the mucous with the Turbo Onion Poultice recipe in the section above. This poultice can be used with dogs and cats for a three hour support period. In these two species I would use it only every other day, as needed. Remember that any mucous that you help the body liquefy, you MUST help it to expectorate. You cannot leave liquid in the lungs without consequences. DCongest salve can also be used with the oral herbs for additional support.

Kennel cough

Kennel cough is usually an upper respiratory problem, Please see the Coughing section for ideas. Also be sure that any potential airborne contributing issues are eliminated.

The Accessible Pet, Equine and Livestock Herbal

Lung worm

Please see the chapter in Part 1 on Parasites for information on lungworm. Remember this is a problem you can 'import' to your place from an animal infected at a location where this exists, even if your farm is too dry to normally have the problem.

Mycoplasma

Mycoplasma is a bacterium that lacks the typical cell wall of gram positive and gram negative bacteria, making it more of a challenge to fight in a creature. It can show itself as swollen knees, swollen face sides into the throatlatch and/or pneumonia. It can pass through the milk of infected individuals to their young or to others that consume the milk. It can only be cultured in the milk when the creature is actively shedding the bacterium. If I were working through this problem, I would support the body with strong antiseptic herbs, such as goldenseal, cayenne, myrrh, hyssop, oregano, thyme, or garlic (or Fir Meadow's HerBiotic blend). I would also want to use lymph support herbs like mullein, fennel, grapefruit, lemon, ravensara, onion, or garlic. For the related possible pneumonia, see the Pneumonia section.

Oxygen Support

Anytime you have a creature with compromised lungs you will want to consider some herbs that will supply the body with additional oxygen. These can come from organic apples (make raw applesauce with your blender), wheat grass juice or the plant, burdock root, marshmallow root, Lobelia inflata (remember to use at small doses), thyme, and eucalyptus. Herbs that help add additional whole herb 'living iron' to their diet include: stinging nettle, dandelion, kelp, and cabbage. Iron helps the blood carry oxygen, so is an important supplement. An overall nutritional support product such as Dr. Christopher's Vitalerbs or Fir Meadow's Better Daze can be considered also.

Pleurisy or Pleuritis

Pleurisy is the inflammation of the pleural tissue outside of the lungs. This inflammation places pressure on the lungs, and can also cause fluid buildup that can compromise the lungs, essentially drowning your victim in an advanced case. If you are working with a pneumonia that does not seem to be responding, I would also start working with this situation.

One of my favorite support combinations for this issue is mullein, marshmallow root, peppermint, pleurisy root and garlic and cayenne combined. Mullein, peppermint and cayenne help with the pain, all of them help with the lungs and pleurisy root is a specific for helping the body combat this situation. I also like the marshmallow to help the body with inflammation (ginger and/or drinkable aloe are also good). The peppermint, garlic, and cayenne all work together to support the body in infectious causes. One can also use HerBiotic combined with Lung Support tincture. This acute situation should be handled hourly the first day, then 4 times a day after that, as long as progress is being made. Additional kidney and lymph support would be good to help the body move out fluids, and can be found in those chapters. Astringent herbs would also be helpful, as they are drying to the tissues. Sage, white oak bark, oak (not black) leaves, mullein, lobelia, apple peels and bark, barberry, blackberry leaves and roots, rosemary, manzanita, red raspberry leaves, stinging nettle, yarrow, ladies mantle and many more. Taste astringent herbs when you use them, so you get a feel for them over time. Any herb that dries your mouth and even your nose a bit and tastes, well, astringent, can be used. Mullein and Lobelia (three parts mullein plus one part lobelia) is always a nice lung support blend. Always combine antiseptics with that though, if infection is a possibility.

Pneumonia

See also Pleurisy above. If you think the situation you are working with could also have pleurisy involved, then include that in your herb program.

Pneumonia is way too common in livestock (and people for that matter) in my opinion. I believe we are reaping what we have sown in this chemically polluted society. Since the lungs are one of the four major eliminatory channels, it is no surprise to me that we see a lot of problems in lungs as the other systems are compromised. I am finding that the more generations I have of goats away from chemical husbandry, the stronger the lungs are getting as viewed from the irides and as evidenced by a reduced amount of lung problems in the herd.

There are three types of pneumonia I'm familiar with. There is chemical, which is caused by inhaling something synthetic that burns to the lung tissue. There is mechanical, which would be breathing in particulate causing lung damage such as fiberglass, diatomaceous earth, smoke or dust. And there are microbial causes. The microbial causes can be concurrent with the other types, or get started due to tissue damage from the other types.

Learn from your veterinarian how to listen to lungs. You can use a stethoscope, or like me you can just put your ear against their rib cage. Listen to each side. You should hear heart noises. You should NOT hear any breathing or lung noises. If you do, trouble may be brewing. Get started now. Don't wait thirty minutes or for later that day to start. Pneumonia types of situations are nothing to play with. If you lose the lungs, you lose the creature. Having a temperature is another clue to look for, as well as them looking lethargic, possibly having hair sticking up, ears that are droopy in long eared breeds, having nasal discharge and just not looking well. They will usually also have a fever, unless they are subclinical.

Blanketing your animal when they are this ill is paramount. They will need a blanket on them to help them retain precious body heat, even it if feels warm or hot out to you. They will not be able to regulate their body heat at this time. I like mine deeply bedded in oat straw, out of drafts, and away from harassing herd mates when I see this problem. This is another one of those situations where after herbal support; if I can't stay with them I will leave my jacket or sweatshirt with them to help comfort them by my 'presence'. If they are young enough, I bring them into the house and put them where I can keep them contained and keep a much closer eye on them, as well as keep them away from temperature extremes. If they are that sick, they won't be moving around much anyways. This is one of those times where they usually enjoy being wrapped up on a warm lap, if you can sit with them a bit.

Essential oils can be a valuable tool. I like to use them initially in a problem of this nature. Dabbing a smear of Eucalyptus globulus essential oil on the hairs under the nostrils of your creature is a great initial response when you find respiratory problems. Besides dilating the bronchials (allowing greater oxygen intake), it is very cooling and soothing to the lung tissue. It is also antiseptic and will help the body to start taking care of the microbes involved in this situation, if any. The hot water steam mentioned in the Detoxifying section can be used, focusing on the thyme, eucalyptus, peppermint and rosemary essential oils. You can also add a couple drops of each of these to a Turbo Onion Poultice. You can also put 4 drops of each of these into a tablespoon of olive oil and rub that onto the rib areas. If you listened to their side, you may hear that you only need to concentrate on one lung. Then focus your oil blend there. On small animals only use 1/3 or less of that oil blend at a time. For a 100 to 200 pound animal I would use only ½ of that blend at a time. I like to reapply this every 4 hours in this situation for the first day; then 2 to 3 times per day after that for up to ten days. By then they shouldn't need the essential oil support. After a three day break, you can apply it once per day if you feel led to continue on.

Oral herbs also should be employed for body support. I like mixing HerBiotic (cayenne, ginger, goldenseal, and echinacea) with a carrot/ginger/garlic juice blend. You can also add additional lung support powdered herbs to this mix. I will take 4 to 6 large carrots and juice them. Then I juice a one inch chunk of ginger and two garlic cloves (four for the first dose) and carefully drench this into a 100 to 200 pound creature for additional support. Your HerBiotic antiseptic herbs and lung herbs can be added to this before you drench it. For additional oxygen and sweetness, you can definitely add an apple to the juicing. Cut this in half for a 75 pound creature, by one quarter for a 38 pound creature, etcetera. Try to serve this at least 4 to 6 times that first day. Eight would be even better.

Consider making a tea with a combination of lung support herbs such as hyssop, horehound, eucalyptus, thyme, mullein, licorice root and/or some other of your favorite herbs. I like to drench this tea (as hot as is safe) for additional relief and body support. It need not be a huge quantity of tea each time, but I would make it strong. Serve it before the juice, if you are juicing. You want the volatile oils in the steam to permeate the system before you add something else. Even waiting five minutes (15 is better) before adding something else orally, allows it to work deeper.

Oxygen herbs have been mentioned several times, but be sure to add one, if not two of raw apple, marshmallow root, lobelia, eucalyptus, thyme, and/or wheat grass.

Pneumonia is definitely one of those issues that you want to practice Offensive Herbalism, if pneumonia is a problem you see on your place. Lots of nutritional support, cleansing, and lung herb support added to the diet six days per week, will help them have stronger lungs then they would ordinarily have.

My recipe for Kat's Turbo Onion Poultice is in the Expectoration section. This is definitely an issue where I would be using one to three poultices the first day. Remember the animal will still be sick, just improved, so keep up the additional support so they do not relapse.

If your creature will let you rub around their ears, their neck or other areas they enjoy being rubbed on, this is a good time to do that to help them relax. Adding lavender essential oil (3 to 5 drops) to their pot of hot steam water will also help them relax. I have also gotten creatures to rest by putting a drop of German chamomile essential oil on the hair below each nostril. Just a drop is plenty. For small animals (no feline) just a smear will do. Put a teeny bit on a cotton swab and smear under the nostrils.

Relapses can happen if you do not provide sufficient rest and protection for your animal. I would give it ten days past last symptoms to start any work or training they were doing, and then work them up to it gently. If I have a milker, I will not encourage her to produce more milk until she's been well for this time. Having the milker is much more important than dealing with a relapse. If they were with the herd in the weather, you will need to wait to turn them back out in the weather, too.

Poison Ivy/Oak Inhalation

Poison oak or ivy that has been inhaled from smoke in a burn pile is going to be very uncomfortable.   Do not EVER burn these or any other fat soluble toxic plants. I would handle as for pneumonia, as they can very easily get a mechanical pneumonia from these. This will make a rash in the respiratory tract, including the lungs. I would also include mullein and plantain given as powdered or dried herbs, and also make a tea with fresh herb if you have it available (otherwise use the dry) and drench some to start with.   Also other demulcent herbs such as some of the root powders, slippery elm bark, flax seed (freshly ground for simple stomached animals) olive oil, or drinkable aloe, can be used for the body to take the nutrition to the damaged areas via the capillaries and bloodstream. Remember, all of the blood runs through the lungs, so let's take advantage of feeding herbs.

Sinus

Any of the hot herbs can help break up congestion in the sinuses.   Horseradish tends to be our favorite to work with. If it is store bought and already prepared, try to get the refrigerated, as it will have less chemicals added to it. Safely add a bit of this (1/2 half of powdered herb dose) to the mouth. You can also give some orally. If this sounds insane to you or not safe, then you can apply a few grains (a small pinch for large stock like cattle) of cayenne to the nostril or hairs three times a day. Your creature will breathe this in and sneeze it back out. What powder does go into the sinuses will help the body to start to break up the congestion. Keep this up until they no longer have this problem at 2 to 3 times per day. You might be surprised at the amount of gunk they get out.

Stories

I'll share a couple of stories here. One is mine. Another is a client's.   A few years ago a client with show ARBA rabbits was having a serious chronic lung problem in their rabbitry.   It seemed that the most genetically correct rabbits were also the ones that tended to have the weakest lungs. They were having challenges getting them raised to breeding or showing age. I want to say this was three years ago.   I had them make adjustments to their feeding program to include some supplements that I discuss in Part 1.   I also had them make gentle nourishing herb teas and include that in their water.   I had them use HerBiotic tincture, which their rabbits readily licked up, when they saw nasal or eye discharge.   I also had them eliminate all chemicals they were using to sanitize pens, feed bowels and waterers, and replace that with lavender essential oil diluted with some distilled water and raw apple cider vinegar to clean with.   The good news is that after a transition time their rabbits now live to produce and show, even the fabulous looking ones.   I expect each generation to get stronger.

Zana, a dairy goat of ours, has a story too.   As a kid she suffered from severe chronic pneumonia that I brought home from a show.   Three different times this goat was near death, with no movement and foam coming from her mouth.   The first time this happened my husband was caretaking while I was out of state.   He got some products from the vet, as he was unable to contact me and did not have time to deal with the problem herbally.   It did pull her through, but of course also allowed the problem to be stuffed further into the system.   She relapsed twice while I was home.   The first time I gave all thirty five pounds of her about 60 cc's of Heart Support Tincture, which does contain garlic and cayenne among other nutritional and traditional heart support herbs.   I picked the tincture first due to the speed it would enter her bloodstream and get to work.   Realize this is much higher than a 'normal' dose, but I was confident in the herbs and their safety level to use in this emergency.   You can't do that with all herbs in all situations.   Do as you are led by God in your situation.   Anyhow,   that bought me time to make a Turbo Onion Poultice and get that on her.   Then I took a dab of German chamomile essential oil and put that on her nostrils to knock her out.   I did not want her awake lying there in fear.   Three hours later, my little Zana Hosanna woke up, raised her head high, had light back in her eyes and was animated.   I still had a very sick baby goat to work with, but I had a very alive goat to work with.   I love herbs.   I believe drugs in her situation this time would have probably killed her.   We had one more horrible relapse that I worked with in a similar way, along with a stronger herbal chronic support regimen and I still have her today as a two year old. Needless to say she IS spoiled.

Chapter 28- Skeletal Structure

Bones take the average creature four months to rebuild, cell for cell. The bones house the formation of red blood cells in the marrow and are also the framework that the other tissues hang from. The skeleton gives stability to the parts of the body. It also dictates ability for correct movement, as incorrect bone attachments or angles cannot be changed if the issue is bone in nature. If it is tendon in nature, then those may be changeable with proper nutrition. See the Epidermis chapter and treat the tight or weak tendon areas as injuries.

Arthritis

Arthur, as some people call arthritis, has many causes. They can be mechanical such as is caused by an accident damaging a joint ending, causing it to deteriorate. It can be diet. Processed sugars (like what can be found in sweet feeds) cause the body to dissolve calcium and other minerals from the bones. Autoimmune causes, which cause perpetual inflammation to the joint, also make the list. Chronic dehydration can also cause dehydration in the joints allowing cartilage to become brittle and non lubricated joints to start incurring wear and tear. The kind of arthritis the creature has will let us know how we want to work with the situation. Feeding Fir Meadow's A-King Joint Support can be used anytime pain or inflammation is a problem in joints.   DCongest salve is also a nice option to put on the painful location.

Work with injuries just as you would any tissue damage. In fact, if an animal receives injury to a joint, it does no harm to start giving supplemental herbs in their feed, and salves to the joint, for longer than you see a problem, just to be sure an area gets well nourished so that it heals well without any doubts.

Eliminating processed foods and refined sugars, such as feed grade molasses, from the diet and adding mineral rich foods (see the Supplements chapter) will help your creature build its body back.   Additional herbal support can be found with Dr. Christopher's Complete Bone and Tissue formula or Fir Meadow's God's Greens or ReBuilld formulas. You can also make an herb list from the Supplements chapter in Part l.

For autoimmune causes, read the Immune System chapter. Cleanses, area support, and attempts to reeducate the immune system will be the goal. The earlier you catch these the better the body has a shot at correcting it.

For chronic dehydration problems, get the creature off of processed and refined sugar feeds which increases the problem. Also make sure they have a fresh, clean source of water (all they can drink) available to them every day. In colder months you may need to warm water to keep them drinking. Also, an animal with dental pain may not drink cold water well enough to thrive. Feeding kelp can encourage animal's water intake to increase and provides a nice mineral base for them to help repair joint damage.

Broken Bones, Crushed, Floaters, Chips

Broken bones

Rascal, a Toggenburg buckling, and Kat have some interesting broken bone stories to share with you. I hope you learn something from them (besides to not break bones in the first place!).

I'll start with Rascal's story, as his isn't an embarrassing one. How they do it, I'll never know. One morning we went out to do chores and there stood Rascal with his front leg hiked all the way up under him. Upon investigation we found a broken, non compound (no breach of the skin or other protrusions), but slightly turned at the point of the break to the outside causing him to toe out. No joints were involved. After giving him a large dose of mullein tincture to enable the body to work on pain support, and some cayenne for the body's nourishment in possible shock, we carefully clipped the area with a size ten clipper blade. Of course the vibrations at the exact break location caused him to jump a bit and cry. That let us know exactly the area we needed to focus on. Some people will use a piano tuning fork for that same purpose. They get it vibrating, then gently run it along the limb to see where the creature or human flinches. That's your target. Be sure and check the whole limb in case there is more than one break. Then we built a splint from flat paint sticks and electrician's tape. Once I had the precise spacing that I wanted between the two sticks, we taped them to ensure that I wouldn't have to try to repeat the spacing of each piece every time. Then I put on a very thick layer (an over ¼ inch layer) of Wounderful! salve and gauzed over that area to protect the leg from the pressure of a hard splint. The gauze also protected his body from the dye in the vet adhesive wrapping being sucked into the body by the salve. We gave him oral God's Greens mix and his normal access to alfalfa hay. For the first week we changed it only one time per day because of the discomfort to him as we handled the leg. Each time I pulled the old gauze off, it was bone dry. The body sucked in every bit of salve. By day seven he was toe touching to the ground. Day eight found him starting to use it lightly. At eighteen days we removed the splint, as he was his normal self tearing around the pen every direction. I think he was making up for lost play time. We continued to apply the salve two times per day. At day thirty I noticed that his leg was once again pointing straight forward. It had self corrected. A few days later my vet saw him, and could not tell me which leg had been broken by watching him walk. At that point, he went to a new home with a jar of salve. They only applied it a few more days before the calcium and mineral "welds" (that could be felt on the break) had dissolved, indicating the healing process was complete. If you ever see an X-ray with those denser calcification areas from a previous break, the area still is not done healing, even if it is years old. Start nourishing the body again and it will finish the process, as long as you give it tools to do so. Even osteoporosis will respond if you are aggressive enough and change the diet from bone robbing drinks and foods to nourishing ones.

Kat's toes have stories. The blonde lady can't walk and talk at the same time, or so it seems. Twice over the years I have walked into a piece of heavy furniture breaking the same little toe. The first break was before I did much with herbs. After taping it to itself via my doctor's advice and not doing anything else in particular for it, I limped around for a couple of weeks before I could get a shoe on the foot and at least walk fairly normal. For several years afterwards, it would partially dislocate if I stepped the wrong angle. It was quite annoying. Well, 2 ½ years ago I broke the same toe again on another offending unmoving piece of

The Accessible Pet, Equine and Livestock Herbal

furniture. I did not have complete herb access that time. I was in tropical region with no plants growing around that I was familiar with, and with people that didn't know anything about the local herbs. The herb store we found was a wash. They didn't even have comfrey, which I absolutely could NOT believe. But I did find marshmallow root (minerals and good for inflammation), a horse tail extract (silica to pair up with any calcium for faster building), and a couple of other things, including homeopathic arnica for pain. Darn, those little toes can sure scream if they want to. So those were my oral herbs. I did have my trusty two ounce jar of Wounderful! Salve (comfrey, rosemary, lavender, and calendula) and literally packed that toe, then taped it the best I could tape a toe covered in salve.   Even without a complete herbal plan, I still was able to be walking on it in four days in sandals.   Well enough to hike a couple miles to another health food store in town where I found oat milk (calcium!), almond milk, comfrey, nettle, and a few other things I'd been missing to speed up the process even more. By three weeks, the toe was completely healed without any of the aftereffects of the first break.   Just this spring I broke another toe on the other foot. Evidently having a horse land on a toe is not a good thing, even with riding boots on. Back to the oral greens 'drawing board', as well as about 80 capsules the first two days of Dr. Christopher's Complete Bone and Tissue formula, then about 25 to 30 after that each day.   Of course, copious amounts of Wounderful! Salve was applied.   As long as my pain was under control, I knew that I was giving my body enough herbs. If I started into pain again, I just simply upped the herbs (and made sure I wasn't doing too much on that foot!). The first three days I watched it run through about every color a bruise can do, and watched the toe reduce from double to normal size. Again, in four days, I was able to walk without a lot of pain, as long as I didn't try to walk up or down hill. Two weeks later, it was only a bit sore if I put tight shoes on. I know those are just small injuries (I've had some major ones), but their purpose is to show you the process. The body will heal every time if it gets what it needs, and it will do it much quicker than the 'average' situation would heal without herbal nutritional support.

I want to reemphasize that if you see any bone protruding or ready to protrude, or have a joint involved, you will need veterinary assistance. Don't forget to give cayenne to your animal (and to yourself) for shock avoidance. You can also pour some oil of garlic, with or without lavender essential oil blended in it, on a protruding area to help protect it from bacterial invasion. Keep the area clean without touching any tissue and the animal quiet while you await your vet. You will also need their help if you are unable to design or apply splinting to support the healing area.

Crushed Bones, Chips, Floaters

For crushed bones, regular breaks, sections of missing bone, chips, or floaters; you are going to treat these as tissue damage after you support the area with appropriate splinting. You don't want the bones to move while the body is building new bone cells to glue the areas together. If the bones move, they will just re-rip those brand new cells apart. I once had a human client with a broken foot who was under a doctor's care. She kept telling me the herbs weren't working very fast. During that same time she was packing boxes and cleaning her house in preparation to move instead of listening to her doctor to stay off of the foot and keep it elevated. She was pulling apart any attempt of the body to heal before it had a chance to harden those cells. Once she was convinced she was going to have to stay off of her foot, it healed rapidly. So please splint correctly for the situation to protect the area trying to heal. Large animals may have to be in a harness while the leg heals, making sure they can be just at barely standing height, but are not able to have pressure on the broken limb. The ideal situation would be to have access to a hoist and a warm water tank where (after a week to begin the healing process) the creature could carefully exercise in harness for two or three short periods of time per day, in the water without having to bear weight on the leg. The gentle water resistance will help the area to regain strength. The damaged bone will always try to repair back to its DNA body blueprint, if you keep the pressure off of it and give it the nourishment it needs to repair itself.

Chips and floaters will be dissolved by the body, or even moved out through the skin. Gaps will be filled in by new bone in the correct places, and crushed bone will regain its normal size and shape – even if it's been damaged without correct healing for a few years. Don't allow crushed legs to be amputated. Once it's gone, it can't be healed by the body. Bones that have healed together incorrectly will dissolve the incorrect welds and heal themselves correctly. It sounds sci-fi, but it is possible with correct herbal nourishment. Be ready to support that bone or joint with splinting when the inner weld dissolves. You may need a veterinarian to help you build a new splint to support the bone in the correct position while it starts to put itself back together correctly. Don't guess here. Hire your veterinarian, who is an anatomy specialist, to help you get it right.

Herbal fomentations are bliss to those experiencing bone damage. My husband used to really be able to relax when I made strong herb teas containing fresh comfrey leaves and freshly grated ginger root and apply them quite warm over his break. His doctor put him in a removable boot splint for me after surgery, so that we could keep access to the leg for herb work. Thank-you Dr. Bloom! Other herbs I like to use orally, in salves and in hot foot soaks for broken foot/ankle/fetlock issues are kelp, comfrey leaf and root, white oak bark, shavegrass (horsetail), lavender, fresh aloe gel (not orally), drinkable aloe juice, dandelion leaf, stinging nettle, slippery elm bark, and red raspberry leaf to name a few mineral rich plants. You can also use carrots, carrot juice, and gently warm raw carrot juice to a bit warmer than body temperature and poultice or do a fomentation or foot soak with that. Keep old towels and sheets around, as the carrot will stain. Marshmallow root powder is a great herb to mix in for a mineral resource and for its powerful anti-inflammatory power. I really like ginger and rosemary for stimulating herbs to mix with bone blends. The ginger will also relax the nervous system while it moves circulation, especially in the limbs, neck, and head areas. Try to keep your patient's movement somewhat limited, so they don't bounce around and increase their injury. Remember to use caution around stock large enough to crush you if they lose their balance and fall or step on you. Nervous system herbs are listed in that chapter to help you encourage your creature to relax and be quieter.

Joint damage

Please have your veterinarian help assess if there is any damage to a joint that may need pinning. A break in the joint area that compromises the strength of the area may not be visible at first, but may slip out of place without pin support. Joints that are obviously out of place call for a diagnosis to see if they are broken or dislocated. Your vet can help you get the area stabilized in both situations; then you can take over with herbal support, as in the Broken Bones section. I would most certainly want to include ginger as one of the herbs to encourage circulation to the areas. Salves containing cayenne or ginger can also be used in or near the area and below the damaged area to draw circulation through the entire limb.

Joints may require some physical therapy once they are deemed stable by the vet or your creature has healed long enough (2 ½ week minimum, but it can be longer- use your educated judgment and don't get in a hurry here) to start safely using it some. In this case, the leg can be carefully massaged and stretched and carefully bent to start regaining range of motion. Again, don't get in a hurry. It will take time to get full range of motion back, which you don't want until the joint is fully rehealed by the body. Remember to eliminate the bone robbing foods from the diet when you are trying to help the body repair bone or tissue.

Splints in Horses and Bucked Shins

Horses can get shin splints too. They can be caused by a young horse cavorting too hard in the pasture, or too much work stress on the bone. You will find a calcium weld bump that puts itself between the cannon and shin bones, usually on the front legs. Because a horse can never totally rest their front legs unless they are lying down, those legs seldom are relieved of stress, so the welds tend to be persistent.

Bucked shins are actually dorsal bone stress fractures. This is more common in hard worked horses, such as racehorses, which are already in training long before their bones are ready for such a task (or their knees, which aren't finished fusing until sometime after their third REAL birthday).

In both of these situations, you will want to work with them as in the Broken Bones section of this chapter including giving oral nutrition and salves on the area. They can heal with persistence, but give it some time due to the amount of weight, thus stress on a horse leg. In horses that have these and in young stock, remember to support their front legs with appropriate wraps to help support the leg, along with bone building herbs and foods during these events and ages.

Teeth Loose, Infected, Quidding or Sharps

For loose teeth after any gum infection is dealt with, wound support herbs can be used and you may be delightfully surprised at what the body may do with them. That's a much better solution than having to have teeth pulled. I would feed oral herbs and well as apply salves to the face area nearest the problem areas. I've said this several times, but replace mineral robbing processed and sugar feeds for whole herb and plant nutrition mentioned in other parts of this chapter. In dogs and cats, you will want to switch them to a raw whole foods diet. Don't forget some fruit, vegetables and herb mixes for additional support.

Infected teeth should be handled as in the Immune system chapter in the Bacteria section.

Quidding or sharps are terms given to plant eating animals that wear their molars unevenly, causing sharp edges (sharps) that poke and cut inside of the cheeks. This causes pain and can cause secondary infection in any damaged tissue including abscessing. If you see your animal dropping feed as it chews (quidding), you might suspect this issue. Also check their teeth for this if you have an animal that is not holding weight well. If you can safely feel inside of the mouth by putting a speculum in and feeling the outside edges of the teeth; you can try. Do use a speculum, so you don't get bitten. When it comes to checking horses, I let my vet do that. They are much more skilled at dodging molars. I don't need to have an herb story on a crushed finger! Neither do you. I have had to have goats and horses 'floated' or filed by veterinarians. Mini horse floats will sometimes fit in goat mouths. I have also picked up a small wood file from the hardware store for my vet to use. After the teeth are repaired, carefully syringing some drinkable aloe along the sides of the mouth, or olive or flax oils mixed with 2 drops of lavender essential oil, can be very soothing to them. Then continue with bone and tissue repair herbs, including using a salve on the cheek exteriors two to three times per day for at least a week to speed up tissue healing by the body.

Uric acid buildup or Gout

This really is a kidney problem that is showing up in other parts of the body, usually the joints. But I'll include it here because when people think of gout they think of the joints and not the kidneys. It is more common in meat eating creatures. If their kidneys are not functioning well, or their animal protein consumption gets ahead of the kidney's ability to process it, then uric acid will back up into other parts of the body causing inflammation in the joints. I have witnessed people with this very painful condition. Kidney support would include the addition of: distilled water, raw apple cider vinegar, cherry juice and cherries, ginger, cayenne, marshmallow root (for inflammation), flax seed (for inflammation), rosehips, lemon, uva ursi, dandelion, juniper berries, nettle and boneset for a few.

Now take a deep breath and let it out slow. This has been a lot of information on a very complicated creation- your creature's body. You are to be commended for reading through this book and for your wanting to have a home where creatures will be blessed and loved on. I trust that you found something helpful in here to better the life of you and your creature as you take care of them for Our Good Shepherd.

May our Lord God forever give you guidance and strength and passion!

Many abundant blessings,

Kat

Adonai will always guide you; He will satisfy your needs in the desert, He will renew the strength in your limbs; so that you will be like a watered garden, like a spring whose water never fails. You will rebuild the ancient ruins, raise foundations from ages past, and be called "Repairer of broken walls, Restorer of streets to live in." Isaiah (Yesha'Yahu) 58:11-12. The Complete Jewish Bible

Appendix

9th Amendment Rights

Consider claiming your 9th Amendment Rights. I have a book listed in the recommended reading list which can educate you more on this topic. Certainly you can and should also consult an attorney. Kat and her husband have claimed their 9th Amendment Rights back to the date of their 18th birthday to educate and provide services in any alternative field that is not expressly excluded by law. They have also claimed their rights to provide products that are not expressly excluded by law. You may want to consider your rights to choose any service or product that you desire. This in no way construes any legal advice. For that you do need to consult an attorney.

Classification, Linear Appraisal, Evaluation

Consider gaining permission to attend a classification, evaluation, or linear appraisal type of workshop or session where animals are evaluated according to their conformation standards by some of the highest trained individuals in that species. You will learn more than numbers. You will learn why a specific trait needs to be that way to contribute to the usefulness and longevity of the animal or how a trait can create future problems. My herd is appraised nearly every year, and I always learn more! Before you attend, ask how you can help and if you can help provide healthy refreshments. You will be better received and may be asked to attend again in the future. Be sure to not interrupt the process. It can be a long, tired day for the herd owner followed by sometimes days of clipping or other prep work to be ready. It can also be a long hard day for the scorer. They may be on a heavy travel schedule or recently out of their time zone, so try not to burden them with questions. If you are attending someone else's session then save those for after the appraisal day unless they specifically ask you if you have a question.

The Accessible Pet, Equine and Livestock Herbal

Links, Books and Resources of Interest

Here is a nice book list to get you started. Even in this age of internet I am still a book person (with a mug of herb tea of course)! If you would like to purchase books via our Amazon link on our website, then we will also get credit for those purchases to help us fund additional educational projects for you. You also may check our website to see which books we are carrying.

20,000 Secrets of Tea, Victoria Zak

Back to Eden, Jethro Kloss

The China Study, T. Colin Campbell, PhD & Thomas M. Campbell ll MD

The Complete Book of Essential Oils & Aromatherapy, Valerie Ann Worwood

The Complete Herbal for Farm and Stable, Juliette Bairacli-Levy

Doctor Mom, Sandra Ellis

Eat to Live, Joel Fuhrman, MD

Goat Medicine, Mary C. Smith, et al.

The Goat Keepers Veterinary Handbook, Peter Dunn

The Grape Cure, Johanna Brandt MD

The Green Pharmacy, James Duke, PhD

The Green Pharmacy Guide to Healing Foods, James Duke, PhD

Health through God's Pharmacy, Maria Treben (translated from German)

How to be Your Own Vet (Sometimes), Ruth B. James (for equines)

Make an Informed Vaccine Decision, Mayer Eisenstein, MD, JD, MPH et al.

Peterson Field Guides (the medicinal herb ones), various authors

School of Natural Healing, Dr. John R. Christopher

Veterinary Parasitology Reference Manual, William J. Foreyt PhD,

Washington State University, Pullman, 1997 (fourth edition)

This book is quite complete. It covers feline, canine, bovine, caprine, ovine, porcine, ratites, camelids, equine, poultry, reptiles, marine mammals and wildlife. If your veterinarian doesn't have one of these consider getting another for them for a gift!

The Wheatgrass Book, Ann Wigmore

Your Body's Many Cries for Water, Dr. Batmaghlidj

Also watch for herb books that have been translated into or written into English from other languages. They tend to be excellent.

Consulting

Kat Drovdahl, MH et al. is available for consultations on your or your creature's situation. She absolutely will NOT DIAGNOSE and per the FDA will not treat, cure, diagnose, or prevent any disease. She will educate you on the traditional approaches she would use for body support if her, her husband or her creature were experiencing the same situation. firmeadowllc.com For an assessment (not a diagnosis) consider iridology to show what systems are off. It will not tell us why, but it will tell us what system or organ isn't functioning up to par. In humans also consider reflexology. For a diagnosis please see your doctor or veterinarian.

Internet Links

Please note that these links are as of the time this book is published. Companies and links can change over time. In that case you might try Googling them or looking for updated versions of this book should we be blessed to be able to do revised updates.

The Accessible Pet, Equine and Livestock Herbal

EMF Shields

EMF Shields help change your exposure to electromagnetic frequency activity from cell phones, computers, appliances, electronics, etcetera. There are many reports now due to the possible contribution of these conveniences to the increase in some cancers, many maladies, and DNA damage. Do more research if this topic interests you. More information is listed in the Nervous System chapter. You can obtain scientifically developed and tested shields through firmeadowllc.com .

Essential Oils

Fir Meadow LLC   firmeadowllc.com

Swiss Aromatics OriginalSwissAromatics.com

Dairy Goats   firmeadowllc.com

Fir Meadow LLC dairy goats are whole herb raised and tested CAE Negative. They succeed on a national level for milk, show and linear appraisal. We sell youth project goats, open show stock, and homestead goats. Baby goats can be air shipped at buyer expense in the United States before they reach about 55 pounds. We currently have lamanchas and one toggenburg. We take non-refundable deposits on future kid crops year round. My website also carries classified ads on whole herb raised livestock and pets to give a resource place for people to search for pets and stock from like minded sources.

Herbs/herb products

Fir Meadow LLC (firmeadowllc.com) carries Dr. Christopher human products as well as a complete line of animal products. All Master Herbalist formulated, no filler, efficacious herb quality.

Iridology Photography and Reports

Human, equine, pet and livestock iridology by Kat Drovdahl DipHIr, CEIT. See our website at firmeadowllc.com for details or to email questions. This is a WONDERFUL tool to assess levels of wellness in tissues and organs of the body. I am simply amazed by what we can see with every iris and sclera that I view. Then use this book to help support systems that need support after you receive your report. For affordable and portable Iridology cameras see milesresearch.com Mention my name and you may receive a discount. This is the portable equipment that I use- it is light and small enough for a lady to pack around. I also do video work with this equipment.

Azure Standard

azurestandard.com is a great resource for health food store types of items. They do monthly and bi monthly drops in over 1/3 of the United States as of this writing and of course will UPS items. They do expand their drop deliveries from time to time so recheck their website if they don't come to your area now. I relied on them heavily when I used to live in a very rural area.

Horizon Herbs

horizonseeds.com I love the variety of traditional wellness herb seeds from many parts of the world. They may be the best resource in the world. They also propagate some plants and some of those can also be shipped. Tell them I sent you if you like.

Soap

Handmade skin nourishing goat milk soap with real essential oils. http://knhgoats.tripod.com Use for you, your creatures and your horse leather cleaning jobs. This is the only soap my husband will use. She also carries soap making supplies and gift baskets for your gift needs. If the website changes in the future do a search for KNH Ranch or Heather Janke or email us and we'll forward you to her.

Supplies for Herb Product Making

Supplies for making your own herb products can be found at Fir Meadow LLC as well as health food stores and other websites. If you don't see it, ask us and we'll see if we can accommodate you.

Schools

The School of Natural Healing - see the link to them from our website: firmeadowllc.com   If you access them through our link we will get credit if you do decide to sign up for a course and you will get the discount that they are offering at the time. This is where Kat obtained much of her formal herbal education.

Watch for future educational works in book and DVD format by Kat and for school development for livestock and pet herbalism on the firmeadowllc.com website.

Vitamix blenders

Kat just loves these hardworking blenders for working with herbs, drenches, smoothies, dressings, sauces, hummus, guacamole, salsas, coleslaws, raw heated soups, fresh frozen sorbets and much more. We use ours every day! You can link on from her business website at firmeadowllc.com if you like. This will give you free US or Canada shipping and a referral to me.

Water Distillers

www.waterdistiller.com has economically priced, stainless steel jacketed distillers with good customer service. There are several models and sizes to choose from.

First Aid

Here is a list of first aid herbs and products to consider keeping on hand for body support… Traditional uses listed. All product names are trademarked property of Fir Meadow LLC.

Cayenne- powdered and tincture: any emergency including heart, stroke, bleeding, shock and hypothermia.

ClostridEaze: support for clostridium/enterotoxemia issues.

DBug salve: support for poisonous and/or irritating bites and stings.

DCongest salve: support for lungs, congested udders, swellings, joint discomfort.

KetoMix: support for the body undergoing ketosis or pregnancy toxemia issues.

Kidney Bladder Stones: support in kidney stones & urinary calculi and for nourishment of the affected organs.

DTox herb mix: support in some plant poisonings.

DVenom: support in poisonous bites and stings.

Essential oil- Eucalyptus globulus: respiratory, pain support.

Essential oil- Lavender: stress, inflammation, injury, infection   support.

Essential oil- Peppermint: circulation, digestive, bloat, infection, pain support.

Fresh Start: liver and kidney support.

Heart Support: heart support, circulatory support, infection.

HerBiotic: infection, illness & gangrene support.

The Accessible Pet, Equine and Livestock Herbal

HerBamine: pain and inflammation support.

Ketomix: ketosis & pregnancy toxemia support.

Lobelia inflata: seizures, stress, bound up musculature.

ReBuilld salve: tissue and spinal column support.

Udder Blast infusion: mammary infection support, external infection support.

Wounderful! salve: tissue and bone support, poison oak support.

Measurements

5 ml/cc equals one teaspoon

15 ml/cc equals one tablespoon

30 ml/cc equals two tablespoons or one ounce of liquid

7 tablespoons per ounce of most powdered herbs

21 teaspoons per ounce of most powdered herbs

Small herb parts (cut and sifted)- double the powder dose.

Recipe Reminders

Essential oil blends for topical use. I use an average of 5 drops per teaspoon of olive oil for the blend. Weaker or younger animals or very strong essential oils may be from zero to three drops depending on the situation. This is just a starting point. Seek a consultation from an experienced aromatherapy counselor if you need more guidance for your situation.

Herb Balls. I take 8 or 16 doses of powdered herb blend and mix with just enough black strap molasses to stick the powder together. Then I divide the dough by the number of doses I put in, say 8 in this case. I roll those into balls, then roll them in cinnamon or slippery elm bark powder and store in a container in the refrigerator for up to one week. They can be frozen for longer storage. There will be some loss of quality when you freeze them, so consider double dosing if you do that.

Homemade Electrolytes. I use fresh juiced grapefruit juice. Remember to not use that for creatures on heart medication.

Honey for Bees. Gently heat their own raw organic honey in a double boiler with herbs that you select for their nourishment, cool and serve. 1 teaspoon of dry powdered herb will be plenty for one pint of honey to start with. You can slowly adjust upward if you feel led to do that.

Honey Infusions are fun. I like adding them to my winter tea or feeding them by the spoonful. I take a clean quart canning jar and stuff it full of soft spring needles of pine (not ponderosa), coastal redwood, or fir and then fill the jar with raw honey. Then I label it with a permanent marker and set it on a rock in my herb garden. I also put a note in my calendar for two months later that it is finished, in case the ink bleeds off. Then I gently warm it in a double boiler and strain it while it is warm into fresh jars. This is a nice antioxidant treat and makes great holyday gifts.

Horse, Livestock, and Creature Chow. Please see the end of chapter 3 for several recipes.

Oil of Garlic. Crush or press several cloves of garlic (I like four to six for home use), place in a pint canning jar and cover with olive oil to a height of about two to 2 ½ inches. Put a permeable fabric like a cotton cloth over the top with a rubber band to hold in place. You need to allow moisture from the garlic the opportunity to evaporate. Stir or swirl daily and keep out of direct light.

Rejuvelac for a natual probiotic. In a quart canning jar with distilled water soak 1 cup of any grain (rye, barley, emmer, millet, etc.) wheat being the first choice for many. Strain and rinse the wheat for day one. Then refill with distilled and let the water sit for two days. It should be a bit like 'pond water'. This is what you use. You can get three batches from the same grain (there is no need to toss out the new day one water). Also consider raw apple cider vinegar, raw honey and garlic for excellent probiotic sources.

The Accessible Pet, Equine and Livestock Herbal

Stall/Bedding Freshener.   Twelve to fifteen drops of essential oil mixed with one cup of baking soda.   Lavender is my favorite for a number of reasons.   Rosemary, grapefruit, lemon, and peppermint are also good choices.

Turbo Carrot Juice. I use 4 to 6 carrots, a 1 inch chunk of ginger and two to four garlic cloves for a 100 to 200 pound creature.   One half to one medium tangy apple.

Turbo Onion Poultice.   I heat the oven to 225 degrees Fahrenheit and chop up part of a large juicey white onion, 1 tbsp olive oil. I bake that covered for 20 minutes, then add, some respiratory chapter herbs, a large pinch of cayenne, one clove of pressed garlic, and 2 drops of Eucalyptus globulus essential oil.   I add a bit more olive oil, toss well, and apply for at least three hours. I use this for a 35 pound to 100 pound animal. Adjust up or down for larger or smaller creatures.

Vaginal/rectal boluses.   Mix one oral dose of herbs with some gently heated coconut oil and mix to pie dough consistency. Shape into a small finger like shape and refrigerate. Count out several doses at a time to make several to keep in the fridge. Gently smooth any edges with warm hands before inserting one or two.

Weak animal juice. 1 tangy apple, 4 carrots, and ½ teaspoon of wheat grass powder, slippery elm, red raspberry and or nettle powder, God's Greens, or Better Daze and carefully drench. Extremely weak animals can receive this at body temperature via enema. Elevate the hips to keep it in longer. This is for a 100 to 200 pound creature. Adjust the dosage up or down for smaller or larger animals.

Stories

I love hearing how herbs have supported a person or their beloved animals. With literally thousands of herbs and thousands of uses, we all can learn more from each other! Feel free to share those with me, if you would like to. Please note if we can have permission to share your story with others. I am only interested in stories that adhere to the foundations taught in this book, for the long term best interests of the creature or human involved.

Stories can be submitted to: PO Box 1089, Gold Hill, OR 97525 They can also be submitted by email via the firmeadowllc.com website email link.

Watch for future book, DVD, classes, and other projects by Kat if that interests you. Watching the website yourself or via a friend is the best way to stay abreast of these resources and where to obtain them. I will not be able to personally respond to contacts seeking updates due to the volume of contacts.

Your creatures or feed can be listed on our website for an annual fee as a resource to others of chemically free raised creatures, feed, hay and produce. See the website at www.firmeadowllc.com to find a listing of like minded resources. If your creature category is not yet there, I will make one for you. If you use this to find something, please let them know you found them through our website.

Abbreviated Index – significant sections are underlined

Notes

Made in the USA
Columbia, SC
10 February 2020